The Usborne 2nd Book of KnowHow

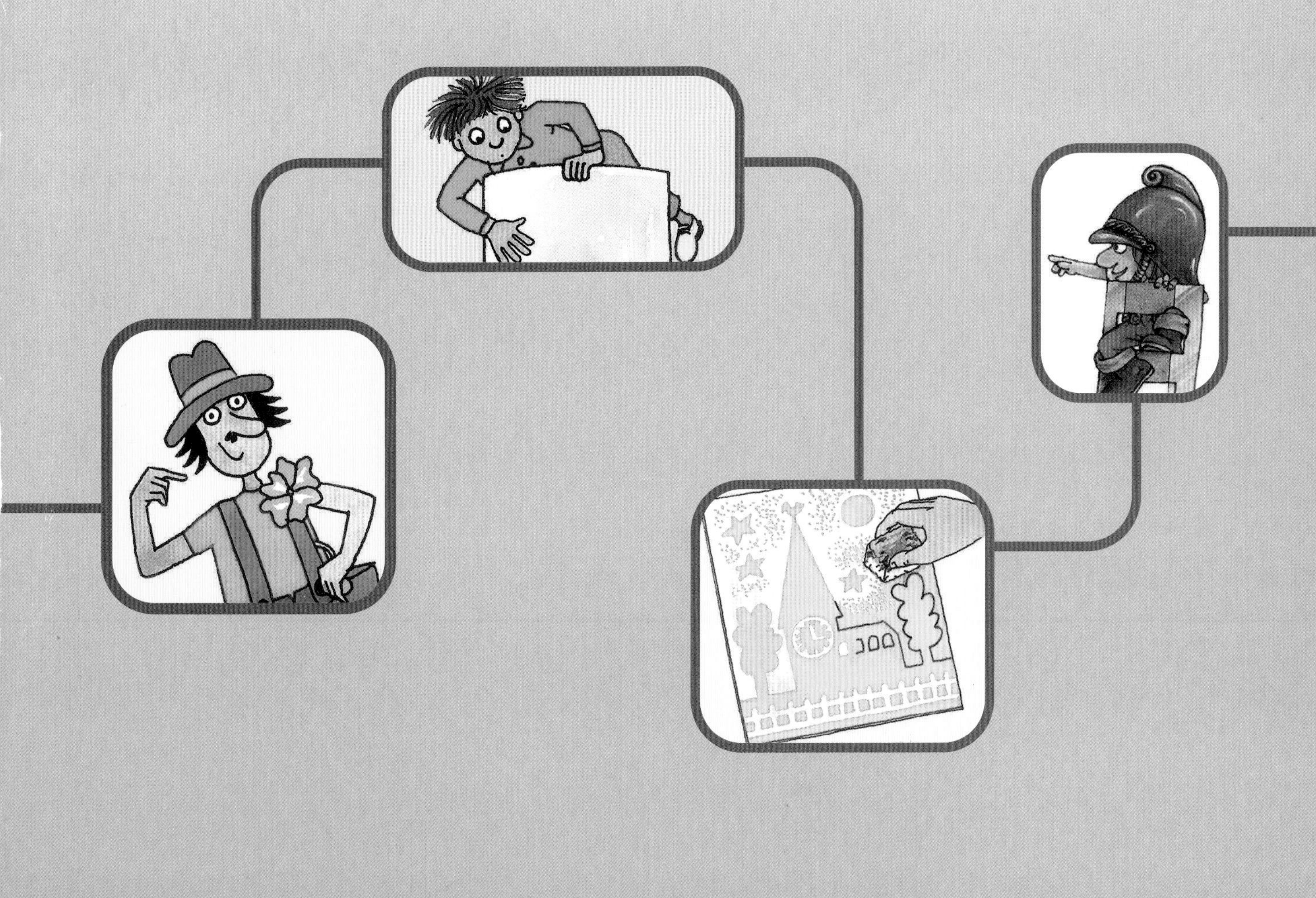

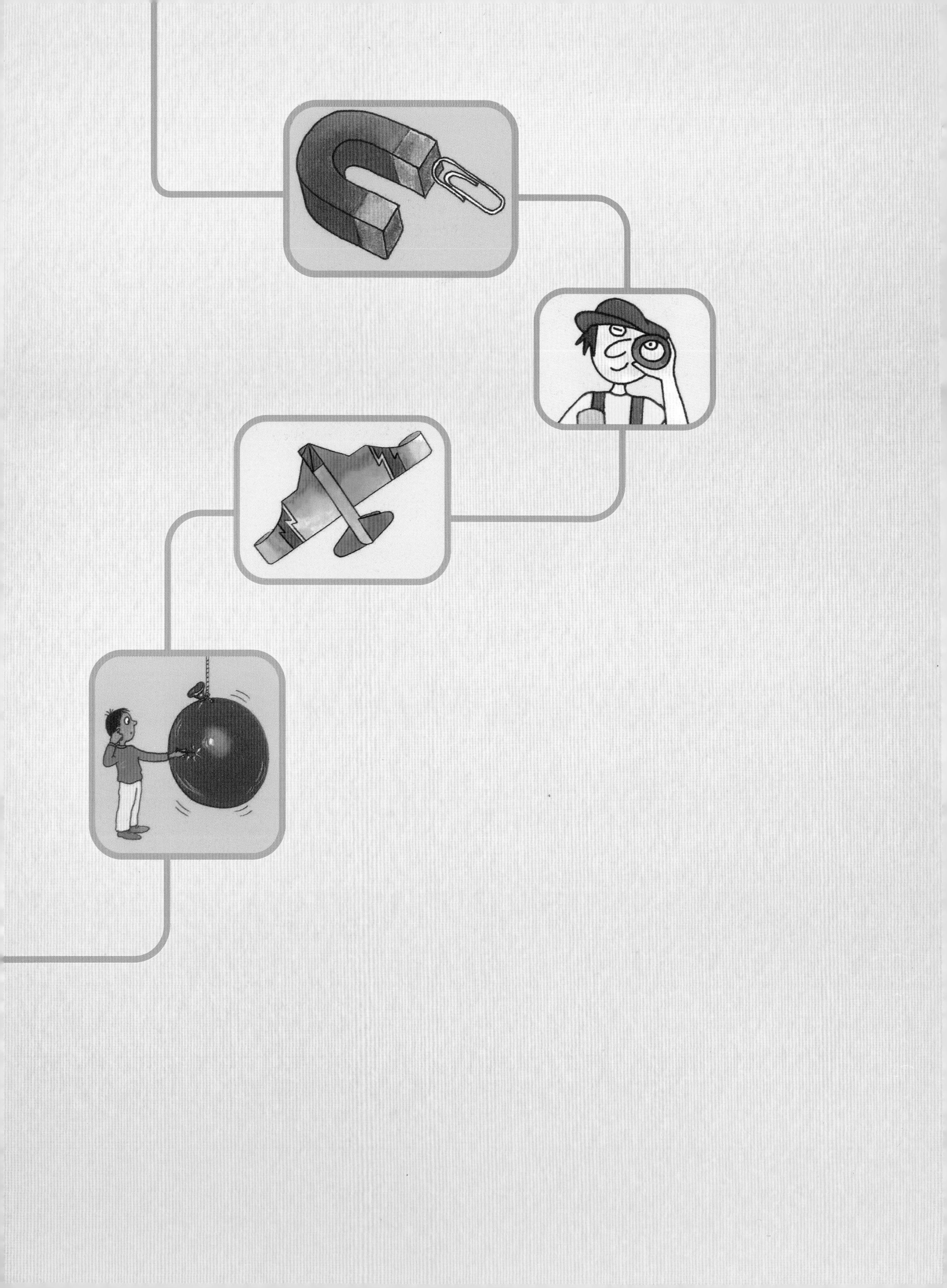

The Usborne 2nd Book of KnowHow

Heather Amery, Judy Hindley, Ian Adair,
Anne Civardi, Annabelle Curtis,
Angela Littler and Mary Jane McNeil

Illustrated by Colin King,
Neil Ross, Malcolm English,
Zena Flax and Pierre Davies

Designed by John Jamieson,
Sally Burrough, Jim Laidlaw, David Armitage,
Patricia Lee and Mike Olley

Edited by Struan Reid

Contents

Jokes & tricks

Matchbox magic

SMALL CHANGE

Take the tray out of the box. Cut a slit in the bottom of one end of the tray, wide enough for a coin.

(a) Hold a big coin on the tray. (b) Then push the tray into the cover so the coin is held inside.

Show someone that the box is empty and ask them to drop in a small coin.

Tilt the box so the small coin slides out of the slit in the tray and into your hand.

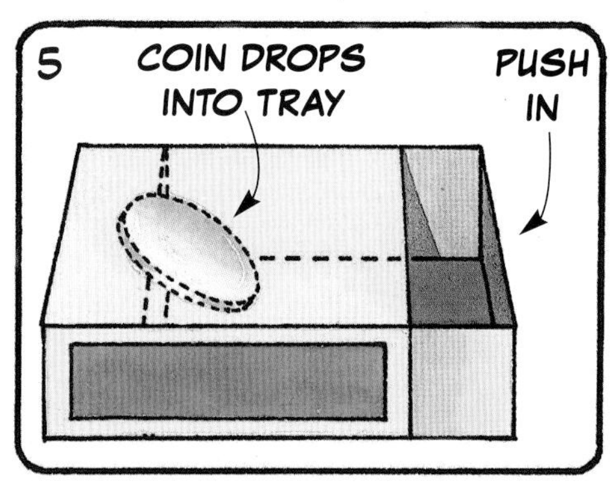

Push in the tray. The big coin drops into the tray. Hide the small coin in your hand.

Say some magic words. Open the matchbox again and tip out the big coin into your hand.

OBEDIENT MATCHBOX

Hold the string with the box loosely. The box will slide slowly down. To stop the box, pull the string tight.

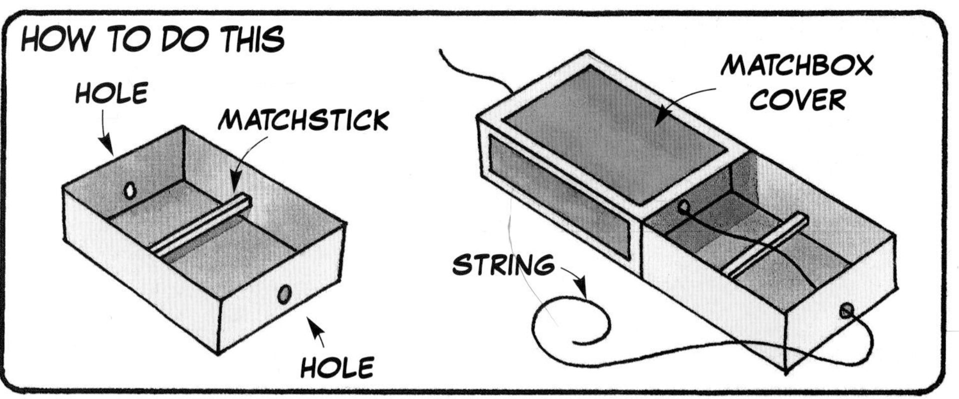

Take the tray out of a matchbox. Make a hole in each end of the tray. Break one end off a matchstick so it just fits into the tray. Jam it into the tray.

Push a piece of string through one hole, over the matchstick and out through the other hole. Slide on the cover.

What's a good place for water skiing? A sloping lake!

MORE MATCHES

For this you need a box of safety matches which looks exactly the same on both sides of the box.

As you do the trick, hold your hand over the box so that no one can see the other side.

Close the box and secretly turn it over in your hand. Do not shake it or the matches will rattle.

Take the tray out of the box. Cut out the bottom very neatly. Pull off any bits of paper.

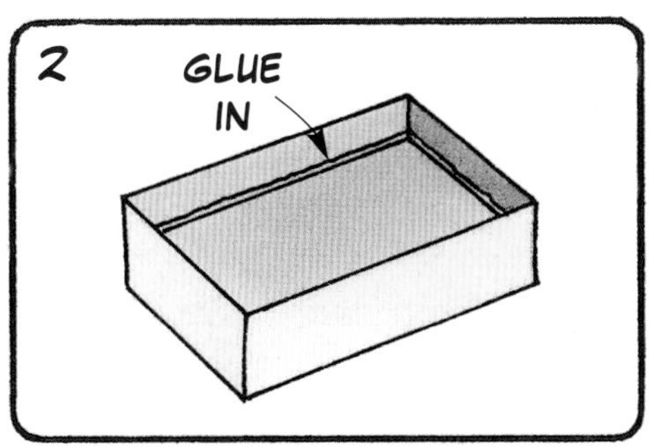

Push the bottom half-way up into the tray. Glue it all the way around. Allow the glue to dry.

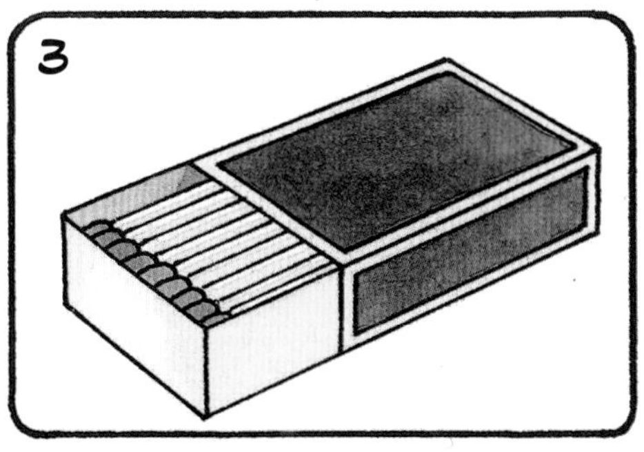

Fill one side of the box with matches. Turn the box over and fill up the other side.

RED TO BLUE

You can use this matchbox to do other tricks. Here is a simple one. You can probably think of some of your own to do.

Remember never to let anyone look very closely at the box, or they'll see how you do the tricks.

Before you start, put a piece of blue paper in one side of the box. Turn the box over. Show that it is empty. Put in some red paper.

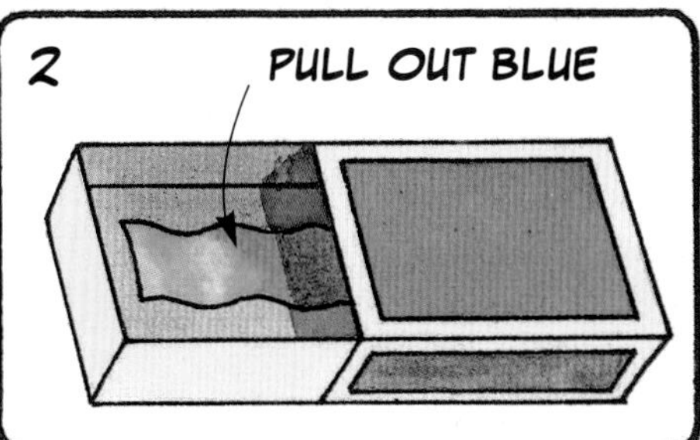

Close the box and secretly turn it over, saying the magic words. Open the box and the red paper has turned blue.

RATTLING BOXES

THE SECRET

You need three boxes of safety matches – one full box, a half-full one and an empty one. Jam extra matches into the full one so it doesn't rattle.

Put the half-full box up your left sleeve and hold it there with an elastic band around your arm. When you shake the empty box, the box up your sleeve rattles. When you shake the full box, hold it in your right hand or the one up your sleeve will rattle.

How do fish get to school? By octopus!

Jack-in-the-tube

Push down the head of this jack-in-the-tube and leave it to pop up again. If it takes a long time to jump, tap it very gently on the end.

YOU WILL NEED

- 3 small cardboard tubes
- a ping pong ball
- 5 long, thin rubber bands
- 2 long, big-headed pins
- sticky tape and scissors
- thin paper and paints

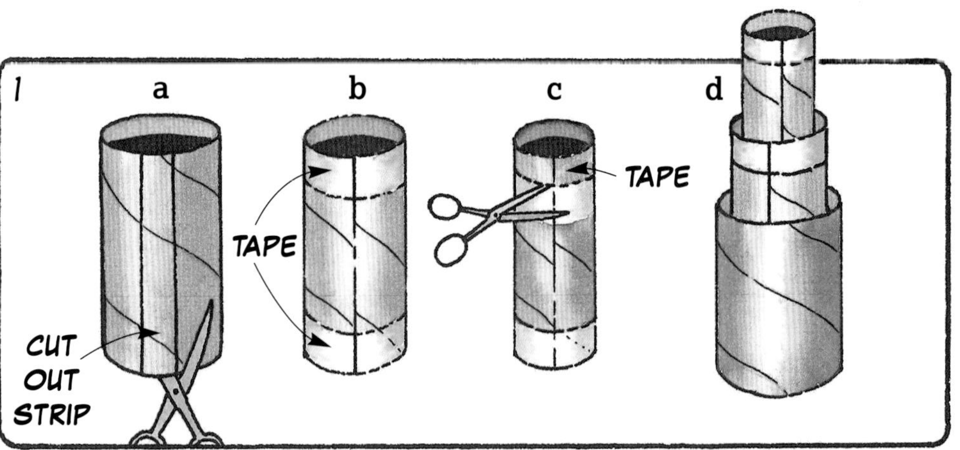

(a) Cut a strip, about 1cm (½in) wide, out of a cardboard tube. (b) Hold the cut edges together and stick them with tape.

Cut a strip, about 2cm (1in) wide, out of a second tube. Stick it with tape. (c) Cut 2cm (1in) off the top. (d) Put the three tubes together, so they slide easily inside each other.

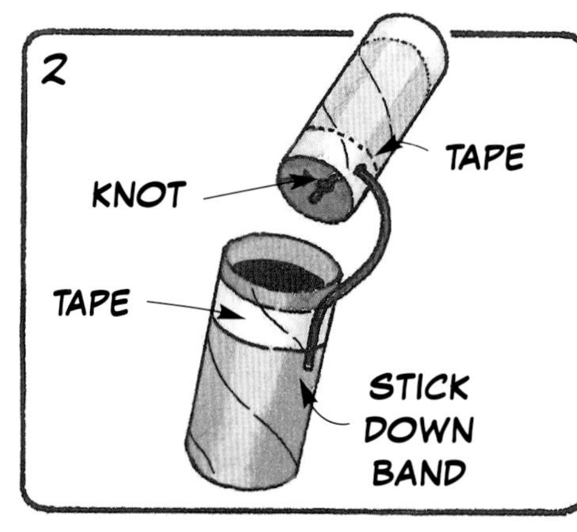

Make a hole in one side of the smallest tube. Cut a rubber band in half. Push one end through the hole and tie a knot. Tape the other end to the second tube.

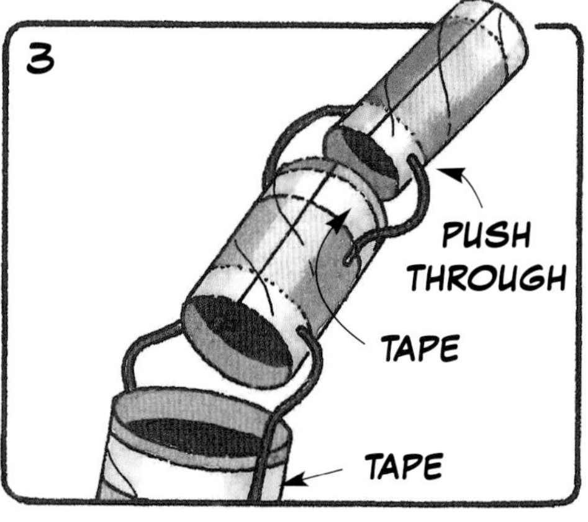

Join the second tube to the third tube in the same way. Now join the other sides of each tube with rubber bands. The tubes should be about 2cm (1in) apart.

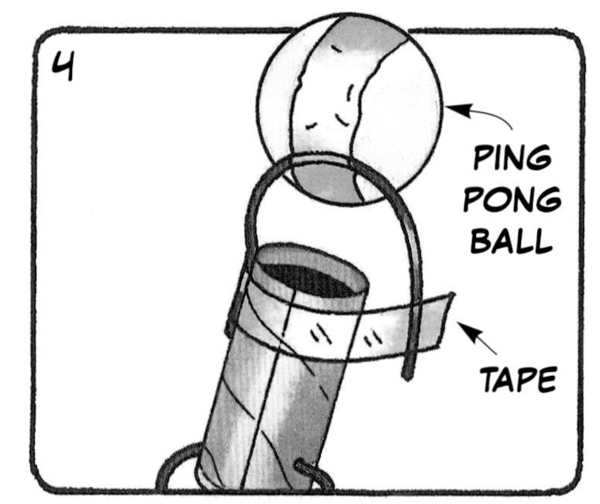

Cut another rubber band in half. Tape it to the top of the smallest tube. Then tape the ping pong ball to the rubber band.

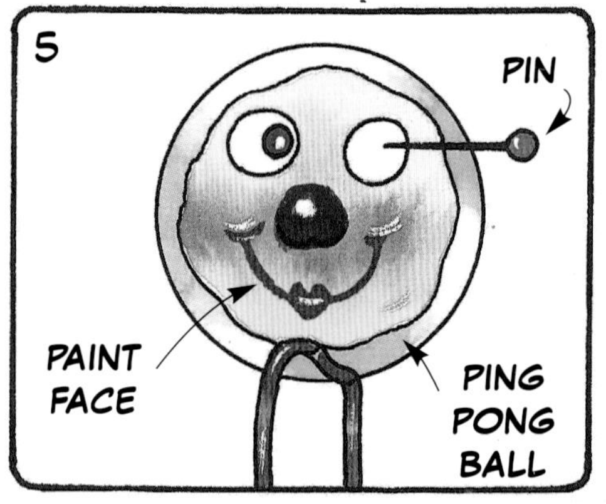

Push pins into the ping pong ball for the eyes. Paint or draw in the face. Paint the tubes or cover them with bright paper.

Man: Hey, you're not allowed to fish in that river.
Boy: I'm not fishing. I'm teaching my pet worm to swim!

Squirting flower

Put this flower in your button hole. When someone is close enough, squeeze the tube to make it squirt water.

YOU WILL NEED

- an empty plastic tube with a screw-on top, such as an old hand cream tube
- a plastic drinking straw
- a bright plastic bag
- a paper clip, scissors
- waterproof glue
- thin thread

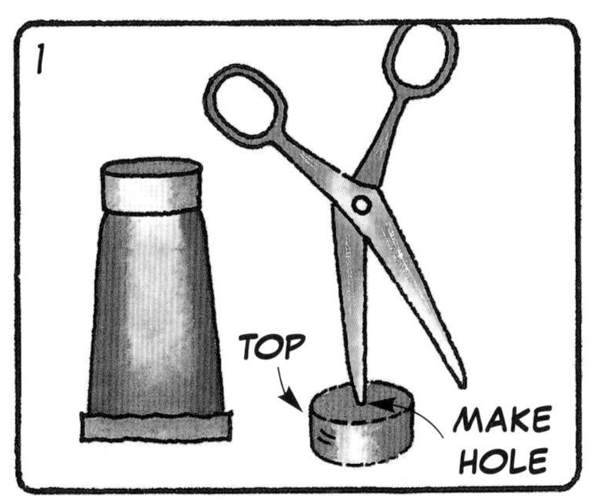

Take the top off the plastic tube. Make a small hole in the top with scissors, like this.

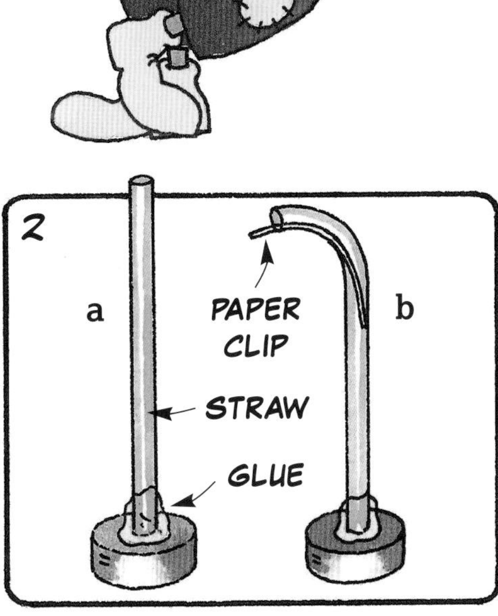

(a) Push one end of a plastic straw into the hole. Glue it to the top. Straighten out a paper clip.
(b) Bend over one end and push it into the top of the straw.

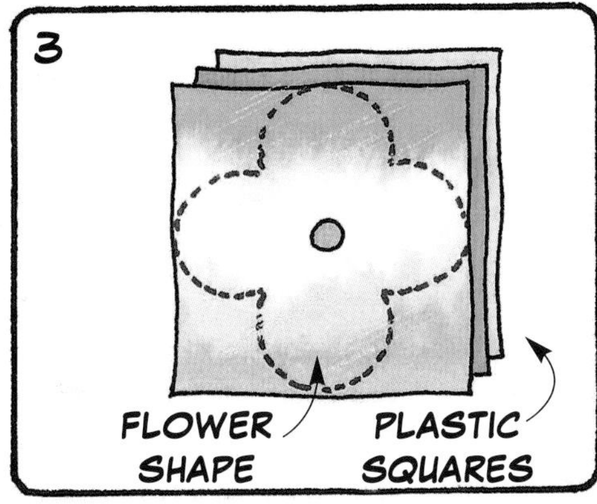

Cut three squares from a plastic bag. Put them together and cut out a flower petal shape. Cut a small hole in the middle of each shape.

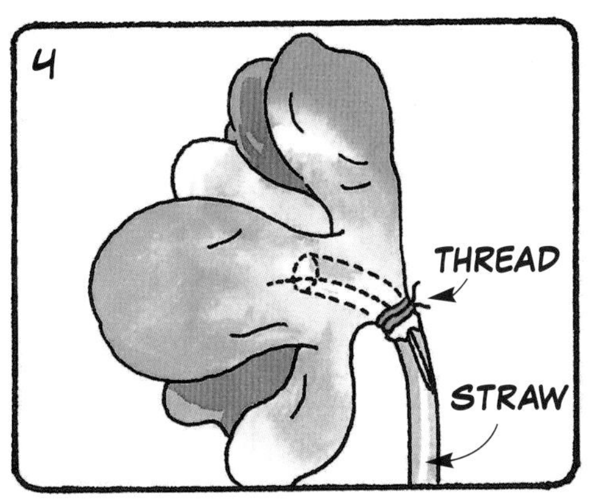

Push the top of the straw through the holes in the flowers. Tie them to the straw. Pour water into the tube and screw on the top.

SCENT BOTTLE

Make about six small holes in the bottom of an empty plastic bottle with one blade of the scissors, like this.

Fill the bottle to the top with water, and screw on the lid very quickly. If you hold the bottle upright, no water will come out. But when someone takes off the lid, just watch . . .

What was purple and tried to conquer the world? Alexander the Grape!

Puzzlers

MAGIC SEESAW

Set up this seesaw and make it go up and down as many times as you like. Be careful not to touch the cups as you do it.

YOU WILL NEED

- a strong ruler or flat piece of wood about 35cm (14in) long
- 2 empty yoghurt pots or paper cups
- a matchbox
- water

Place the middle of the ruler on the matchbox, like this. Put a pot or cup on each one. Make sure they balance each other exactly.

HOW IT LOOKS

THE SECRET

When you dip your finger into the water in a cup, the seesaw goes down. Anyone can do this. When you put your finger in an empty cup, bend down very close to it and pretend to try very hard. Then groan and sigh a little as if it is difficult. When you groan, blow gently into the cup and it will go down. Then groan and blow gently into the other cup. Make sure you don't touch the cups.

SPOOKY STRAWS

Cut a straw in half. Put the pieces down. When you put a finger between them and say the magic words, they move apart. When you speak, blow gently at the same time down your finger.

LINKING CLIPS

Glue two matching envelopes back to back. Link up seven paper clips and drop them into one of the envelopes. Close the flaps on both envelopes.

Open the empty envelope. Drop in seven clips and close the flap. Secretly turn the envelopes over. Open the flap and tip out the linked clips.

If a buttercup is yellow, what shade is a hiccup? Burple!

PAPER CHASE

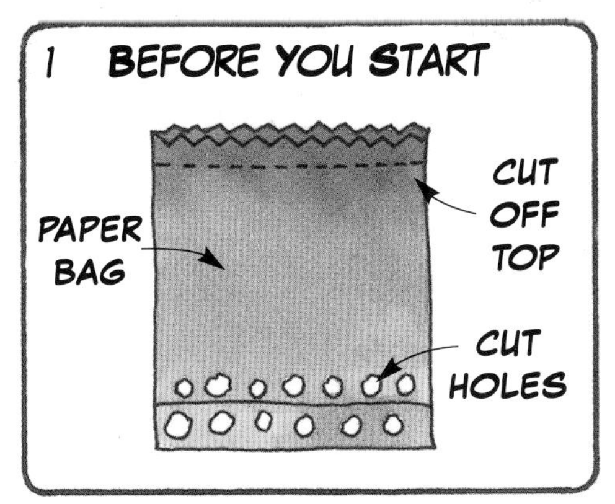

Find two small paper bags which look the same. Cut 1cm (½in) off the top of one bag. Cut holes in the bottom of the bag, to let air through when you blow in it.

Cut up lots of pieces of bright paper. Put all the pieces into the second paper bag, the one without the holes in it.

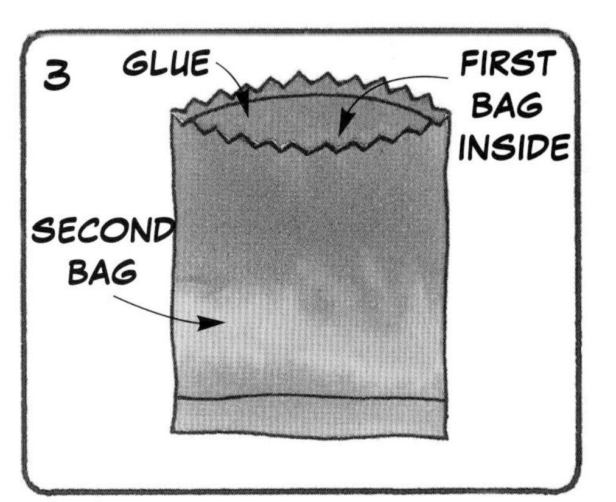

Then push this bag into the one with holes. Glue the edges of the bags together at the top. The inside bag should be smooth. Now crumple up the bags.

Tie a knot in a corner of a hanky. (a) Hide the knot in one hand. (b) Flip the hanky upwards, twice. (c) The third time, drop the knot and grab the other end.

What are the best things to put into a fruit pie? Your teeth!

Creepies and crawlies

CLIMBING SPIDER

This monster spider climbs down its thread and up again. Hang it up in a dimly-lit room and no one will notice how you work it. The nastier it looks the bigger the horrible surprise.

YOU WILL NEED

- 6 pipe cleaners
- cotton balls
- 2 small buttons and 2 pins
- thin black thread
- a paper clip
- glue and black paint

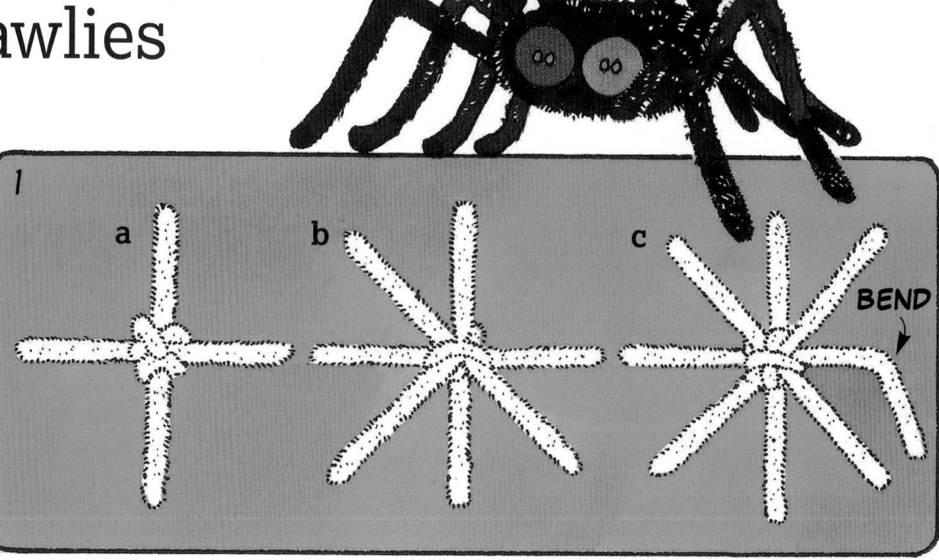

(a) Put two pipe cleaners across each other, like this. Wind a third one around them. (b) Join on a fourth cleaner with another one.

(c) Now put on the last pipe cleaner and fasten it on to make the eight legs of the spider. Bend over all the legs.

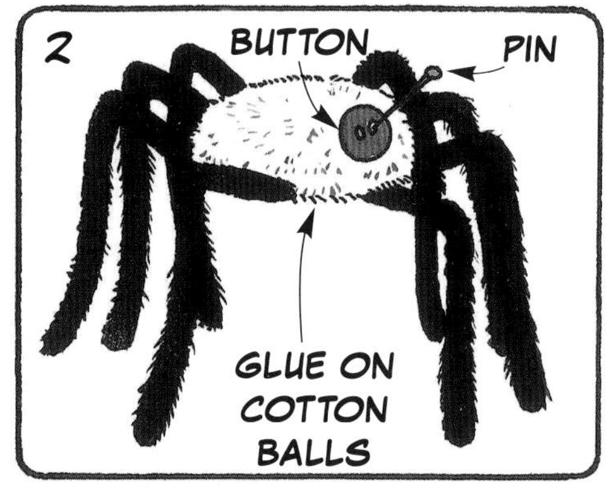

Glue cotton balls to the middle of the legs to make the body. Paint the whole thing black. Pin on two bright buttons to make the eyes.

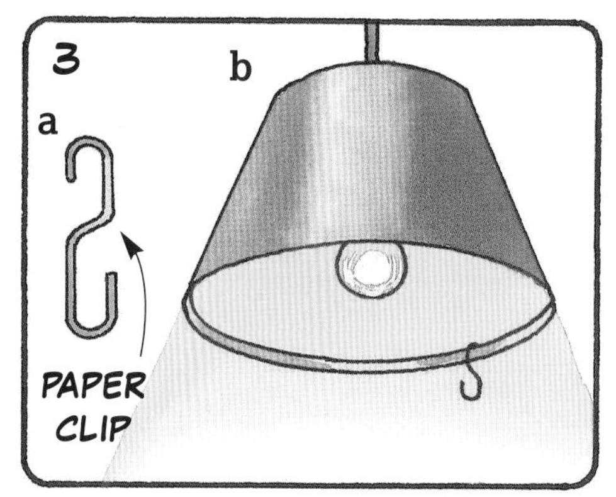

(a) Bend a paper clip, like this, to make a loop at each end. (b) Hook one end onto the inside of the frame of a lampshade, like this.

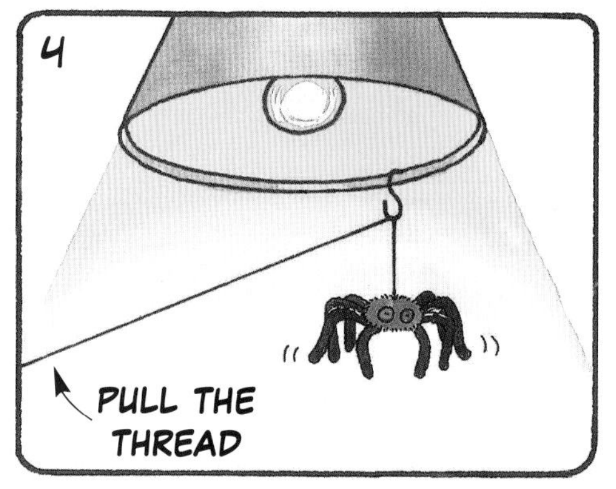

Tie a long piece of thread to the top of the spider. Hook the thread over the clip. Pull the thread to make the spider go up and down.

CREEPY CRAWLIES

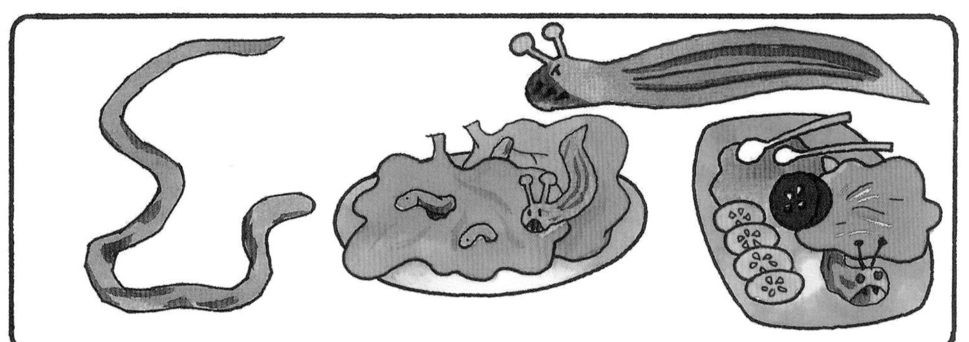

You can make lots of creepy crawlies out of model clay. You could roll out a pink bit to make a worm, or make a brown slug.

If you place them on a lettuce leaf or in a plate of salad, these nasties will look quite real and will put anyone off their food.

Cut a pipe cleaner in four pieces to make caterpillars. Paint them in yellow and green stripes and bend them in wriggly shapes.

How do you know when it's raining cats and dogs? When you step in a poodle!

FLYING BAT

This bat flies across a room at great speed. Make it look as horrible as you can. It will look best in a fairly dark room.

YOU WILL NEED

- a sheet of stiff black paper, or white paper and black paint
- black paper, 8cm (3in) long and 4cm (1½in) wide
- 2 pipe cleaners, a curtain ring
- very thin nylon string or fishing line, about 8m (26ft) long
- glue, sticky tape and scissors

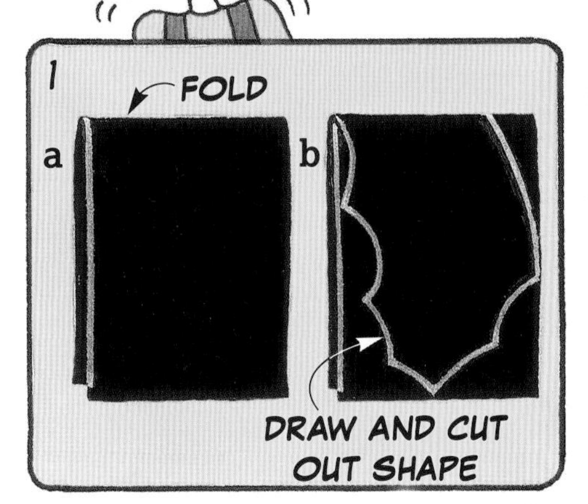

(a) Fold the sheet of paper in half. (b) Draw the shape of a bat's wing on one side. Cut out the shape but don't cut along the folded edge. Open out the paper.

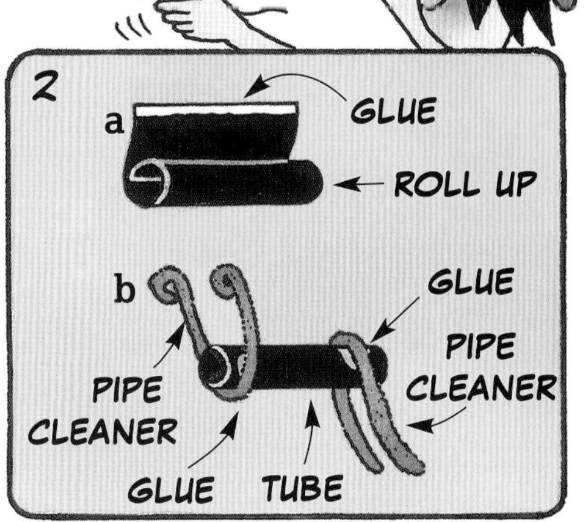

Roll up the small piece of paper into a tube. (a) Glue the edge. (b) Bend a pipe cleaner around one end for the eyes and one at the other end for legs. Glue them on.

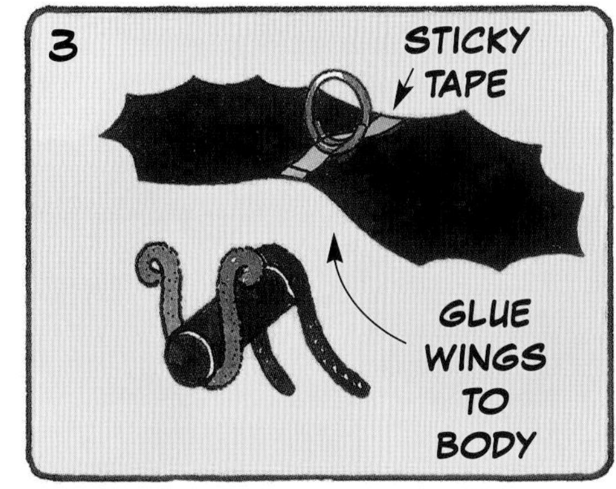

Stick the curtain ring upright to the middle of the wings. Glue the wings to the body. Paint the pipe cleaners black and bend them.

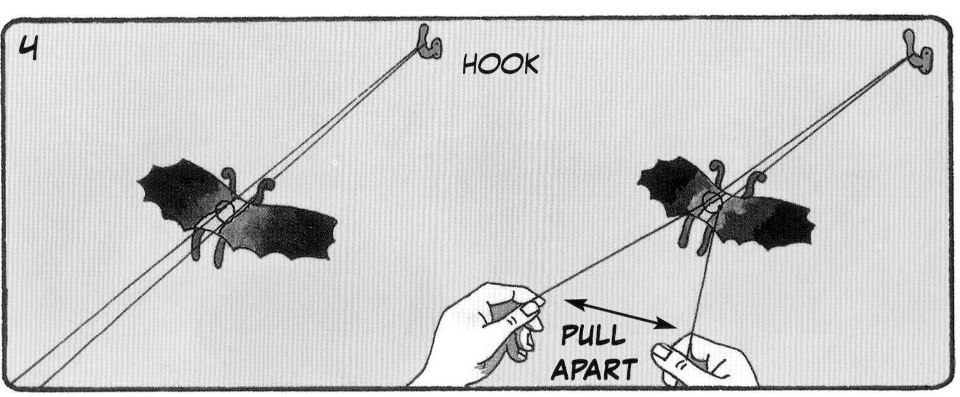

Hook the middle of the string onto a door hook, fairly high up. Slide the ends of the string through the ring on the bat.

Hold one end of one string in each hand. Slide the bat close to your hands. Pull the strings apart. The bat will fly along them.

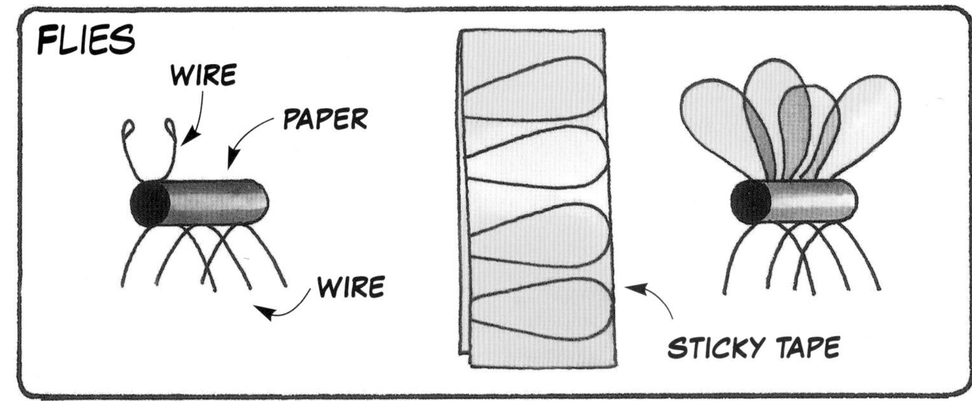

Make a roll of paper and glue the edges together. Cut three pieces of thin wire. Glue them on to make legs. Paint the paper black.

Fold over a piece of sticky tape so the sticky sides are stuck together. Cut out four oval shapes and glue them on as the fly's wings.

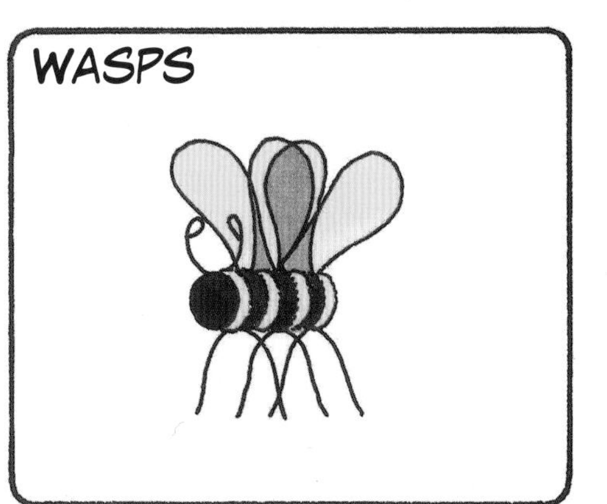

For a wasp, make another fly and wind a pipe cleaner around the body. Paint it in yellow and black stripes, then glue on the wings.

Did you hear about the monster with eight arms? He said they came in handy!

Amazing water tricks

TRICKY TUMBLERS

Playing with water is good fun, but be careful where you do these tricks. Hold the glass over a big, empty bowl or put a deep tray on top of a table.

Use a thick drinking glass which will not break easily or, better still, an unbreakable one.

When you do these tricks, turn the glass over as quickly as you can. You will have to rehearse them a few times first.

Put a piece of thin cloth over a glass. Let it flop over loosely. Pour in some water, through the cloth, until the glass is full.

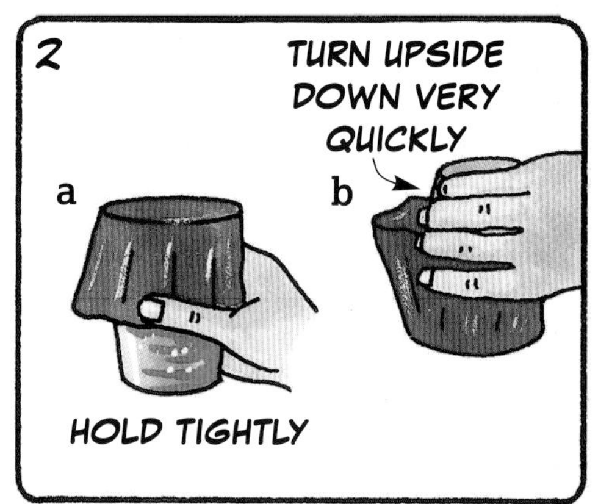

Stretch the cloth over the glass. Hold it down with one hand. Turn the glass upside down. Hold it straight and the water will stay in.

Fill up a glass with water, almost to the top. Place a piece of stiff, thick paper over the top of the glass. Hold the paper down with one hand.

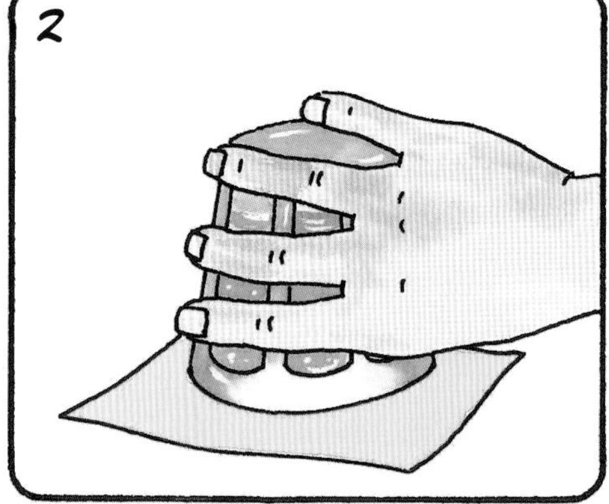

Hold the glass with the other hand and turn it over quickly. Take away the hand holding the paper. The paper will stick to the glass and keep the water in.

Put an empty glass down on a sheet of stiff, clear plastic. Draw around the glass with a ball point pen. Then cut along the line with scissors to cut out a circle.

Hide the plastic circle under the paper. Fill up the glass. Hold the circle under the paper and put it on the top of the glass.

Make sure the circle is exactly over the top of the glass. Hold the paper down with one hand and turn the glass over with the other.

Peel the paper off very slowly and carefully. The plastic circle will stick and hold the water in. This will look like magic.

When is it bad luck to be followed by a black cat? When you're a mouse!

CHANGING SHADES

This trick will really puzzle people, but don't let them come too close when you do it. Try it out first so you get it just right.

You will need a glass with lines or ridges on it, a small square scarf or bright handkerchief, and some pieces of stiff, shaded plastic or acetate. If you can find lots of different shades, you can make the trick last much longer.

HOW IT LOOKS

1. Hold up a glass full of green water. Drop a bright scarf or handkerchief over it.

2. Lift off the scarf and the water has changed to orange. Cover the glass and change it again.

Cut out pieces of shaded plastic so that they just fit tightly inside the glass. Cut about 1cm (½in) off the top. Each piece should slide in and out easily but stay upright.

Make a small hole in the top of each plastic shape. Tie a short piece of nylon line or thin white thread to each shape.

Push all the shapes into the glass so they stand upright. Hang the strings over one side, towards you. Pour in enough water to fill the glass nearly to the top.

Hold up the glass. Make sure the shapes are flat towards the people watching, or they'll show. Drop the scarf over the glass.

Pick up a thread through the scarf and lift it up. Hide the shape in the scarf. Cover the glass again and take out another shape.

When you have taken out all the shapes, drink the water to show it is real. Or make the trick longer by putting back the shapes.

What do you get if you cross a hen with a guitar? A chicken that plucks itself!

Disappearing balls

This is a very good trick. People can stand quite close without seeing how you do it. Follow the instructions carefully and do the trick several times in secret so that you get it right.

Before you start, crumple up four pieces of tissue paper into balls.

You also need two saucers.

When you do the trick, hold the saucers upside down, with your thumbs on top and fingers underneath. Pick up the paper balls between your fingers so they are hidden under the saucer. Don't turn the saucers over during the trick.

SAUCER UPSIDE DOWN

BALL BETWEEN FINGERS

1. Put the four balls on the table in a square, like this. They should be about 20cm (8in) apart. Pick up the two saucers with your thumbs on top and fingers underneath.

2. Cover two balls with saucers, then two more several times. The last time, secretly pick up ball 1 in your right hand. Slide the left saucer over the empty place. Put the right saucer over ball 2 and drop ball 1.

3. Leave both saucers on the table and pick up ball 3 in your left hand. Pass it carefully over to your right hand.

4. Pretend to push ball 3 up through the table. Knock the underside of the table, pretending it is solid and hard to get through. Secretly hide the ball in your right hand.

5. Pick up the saucer in your left hand to show the two balls underneath it. Then pass the saucer to your right hand, which is hiding ball 3.

6. Put the saucer in your right hand over the two balls and drop ball 3 beside them. Now pick up ball 4.

7. Pretend to push ball 4 up. Hide it in your right hand. Lift the saucer with your left hand to show three balls. Pass the saucer to your right hand. Put it over the three balls and drop ball 4 beside them.

8. Put your hand under the table. Pretend to move ball 4 from the empty saucer and push it under the other one. Lift the saucer to show the four balls. Lift the other saucer to show nothing is under it.

How does a sparrow with engine failure land safely? By sparrowchute!

NIGHT PINGER

This is a good trick to do at night. Put the pinger in a cupboard in a bedroom or under a bed. It will go on working for a very long time. As the peas absorb the hot water, they grow bigger. They push out of the cup and drop onto the tray.

YOU WILL NEED

- 2 plastic cups or pots
- a tin tray or big baking tray
- a big cardboard box
- dried peas or beans
- glue

Glue the cups, end to end, like this. Fill the top cup with as many dried peas as you can push in.

Put the tray in the cardboard box. Stand the cups on the tray. Pour hot water into the top cup. Close the box and wait for the peas to start pinging onto the tray.

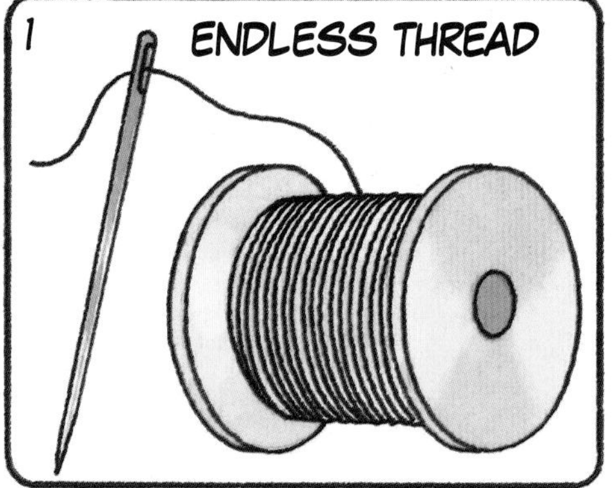

Push the end of the thread on a reel of brightly shaded cotton through the eye of a big needle.

Push the needle through the sleeve of your shirt from the inside. Pull off the needle, leaving some thread outside.

When someone says 'You've got a thread' and pulls it, the thread gets longer. Make sure the reel can unwind but stay hidden.

CARDBOARD FLAPPER

Pass the flapper to a friend or send it in an envelope through the post.

YOU WILL NEED

- a big paper clip or piece of strong, bendy wire, about 12cm (4½in) long
- a rubber band, sticky tape
- cardboard, 12cm (4½in) long and 8cm (3¼in) wide
- a small square of thick cardboard

Bend the paper clip or wire into this shape. Bend over the two ends. Hook the rubber band across the top.

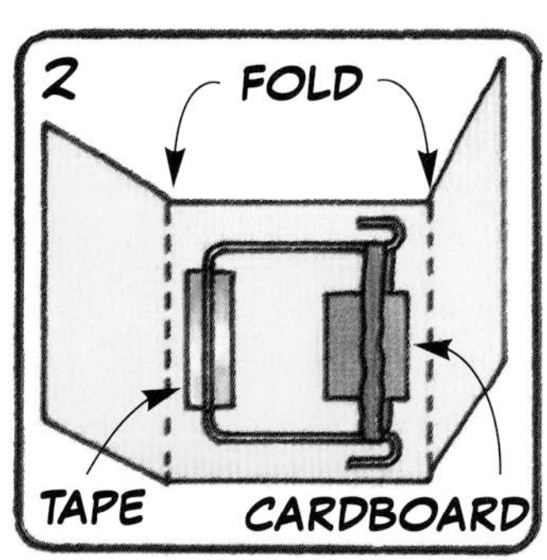

Fold the cardboard in three. Stick one side of the clip to the middle fold. Slide the cardboard square between the band.

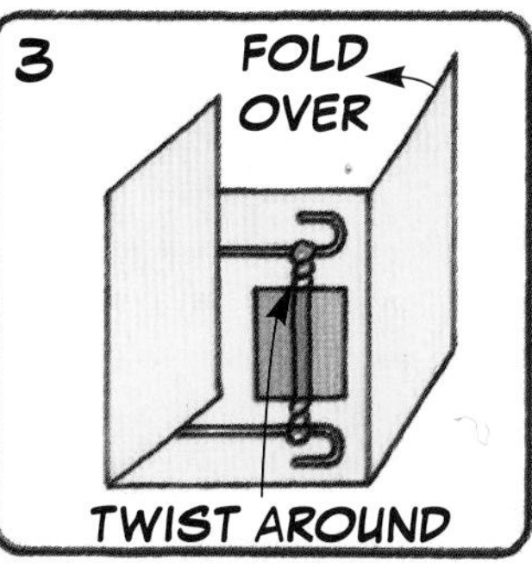

Wind the cardboard square 20 times. Fold over the two flaps of the cardboard strip to stop the square from unwinding.

What do you get if you cross a mink with a kangaroo? A fur coat with big pockets!

Magic balls

You will need to try out this trick quite a lot first, or people may see how you do it.

You'll need clear nylon thread, or strong thin black or brown thread, and a cardboard box.

If the box is thin cardboard, tear it up at the end to prove there are no balls in it.

Stick some thin, strong thread to a ping pong ball. Tie the other end to a safety pin. Put the safety pin in the hem of a big handkerchief.

(a) Hold up the hanky with the ball toward you. (b) Fold it in half. (c) Tip the ball into the box. (d) Let the hanky fall on the box.

(e) Pick up the two corners nearest you so the ball faces you. You can tip out the ball lots of times. Show the box is empty.

What do you do to a blue banana? Cheer it up!

Magic tubes

Lots of things can appear out of these magic tubes. Pull a tube down when you are taking one off. Push it up from the bottom when you are putting it on again.

YOU WILL NEED

- a small tin can without a lid
- 2 sheets of thin cardboard or thick paper, big enough to roll around the can
- a paper clip and sticky tape
- bright ribbons or long strips of thin, shaded paper

1
CAN
TAPE
CARDBOARD

Put the can down on a sheet of cardboard or paper. Roll the sheet loosely around the can to make a tube. Stick the edge with tape, as you can see above.

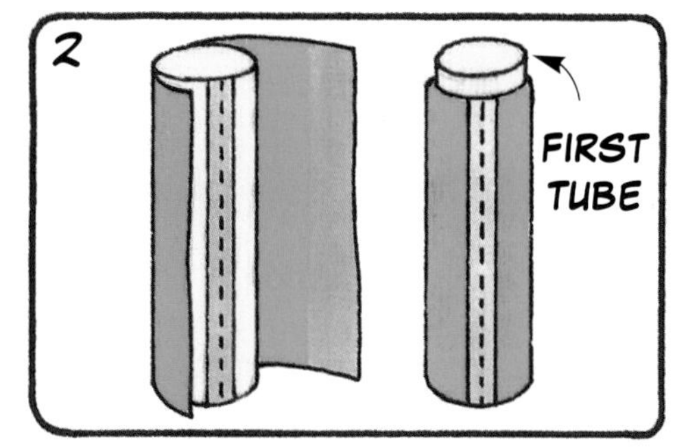

Roll up the tube in the second sheet of cardboard to make another tube. Stick the edge with tape. The first tube should slide easily inside the second one.

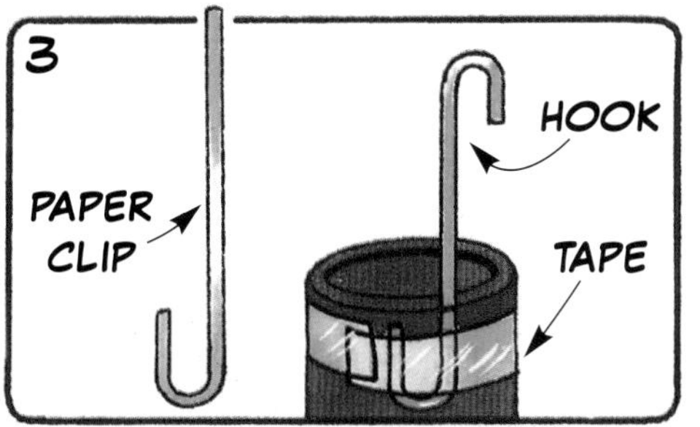

Straighten one end of a paper clip. Stick the loop end to the top of a can with tape. Bend over the straight end to make a small hook.

4
RIBBONS

Slide the first tube into the second one. Put the can into the top. The clip must hook over the top. Fill the can with ribbons.

THE SECRET

Keep the hook toward you. Hold the outside tube and slide the inside one down. Show that it is empty. Now slide it up inside the outside tube. Hold the inside tube at the top and slide the outside one down. Show that it is empty. Slide it on again from the bottom. Hold both tubes in one hand and pull the ribbons out of the tin.

HOW IT LOOKS

What did the hungry computer eat? Chips, one byte at a time!

Table tricks

Here are some good tricks you can play while you are sitting at a table having a meal.

FOR THE TABLE NAPKIN CREEPY YOU WILL NEED

- an empty cotton reel
- a candle
- a table knife
- a strong rubber band
- a thin stick, 10cm (4in) long
- a small paper table napkin
- scissors, matchstick, sticky tape

Push the band through the reel. Push a piece of matchstick through the loop at one end. Stick the matchstick to the reel.

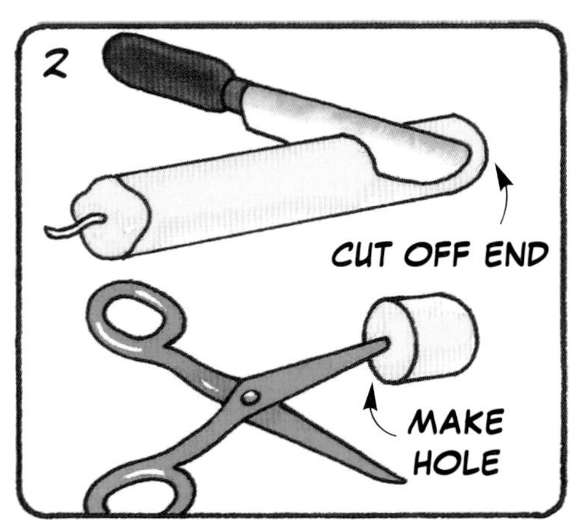

Cut a ring, about 1cm (½in) wide, off the end of a candle with a table knife. Make a hole through the middle with scissors.

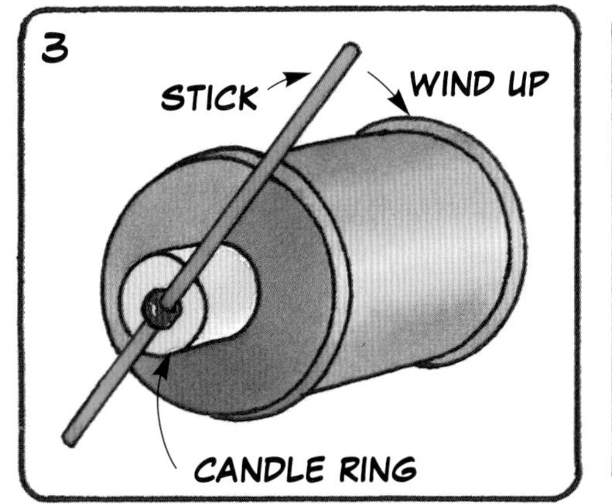

Push the free end of the rubber band through the candle ring. Push the stick through the loop. Wind the stick around 20 times.

Put the cotton reel on the table when no one is looking. Drop a small table napkin over it. Leave it to creep along very slowly.

Cut a circle, about the size of a saucer, out of very thin black cloth. Snip the edges all the way around. Put it over the cotton reel.

Cut several squares from a white sponge. Mix them in with sugar lumps. They'll float in tea or coffee.

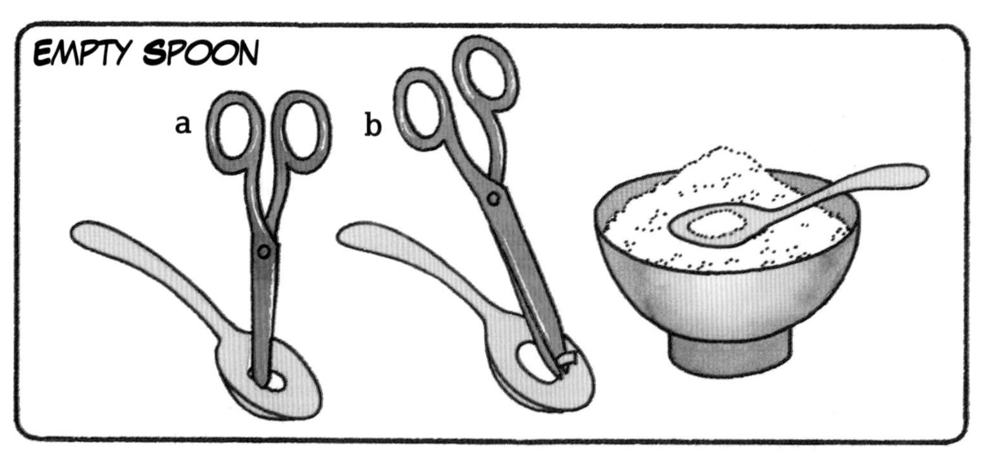

(a) Make a hole in the bowl of a plastic spoon. (b) Cut out a big hole as neatly as you can.

Place the spoon in a sugar bowl. Anyone trying to spoon up sugar will get a surprise.

How do skeletons call their friends? On the telephone! (printed upside down)

Print, paint & paper

Glue and glitter prints

YOU WILL NEED

- tubes of different shaded glitter
- glue or paste
- scissors
- sheets of paper
- a paint brush
- thin card
- old newspaper
- leaves and ferns

FERN AND GLUE PRINT

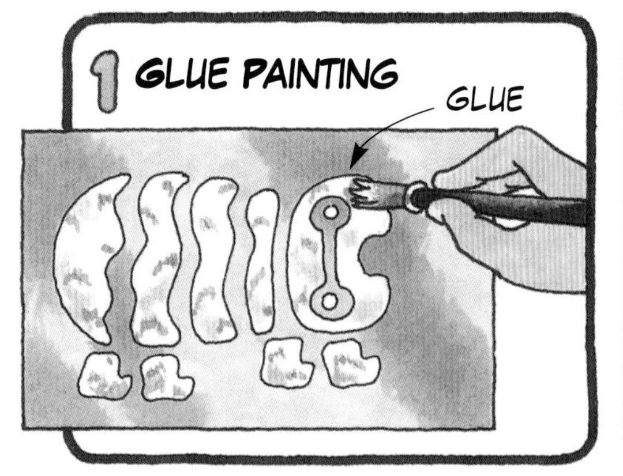

Draw a shape, perhaps an elephant or a monster, on a piece of paper. Paint glue over the parts you want glittered, either all over or in stripes or dots.

The glitter comes in tubes or tubs. Sprinkle one shade of glitter over the glue shape, making sure that it is well covered. Leave it to stick for a few seconds.

Cut a shape out of cardboard. Paint one side with glue and press it, glue side down, onto some paper. Lift the shape up quickly so it doesn't have time to stick.

Sprinkle some glitter on to the paper and then shake it off gently. Do this lots of times until you have a row of glue prints, like the example you can see above.

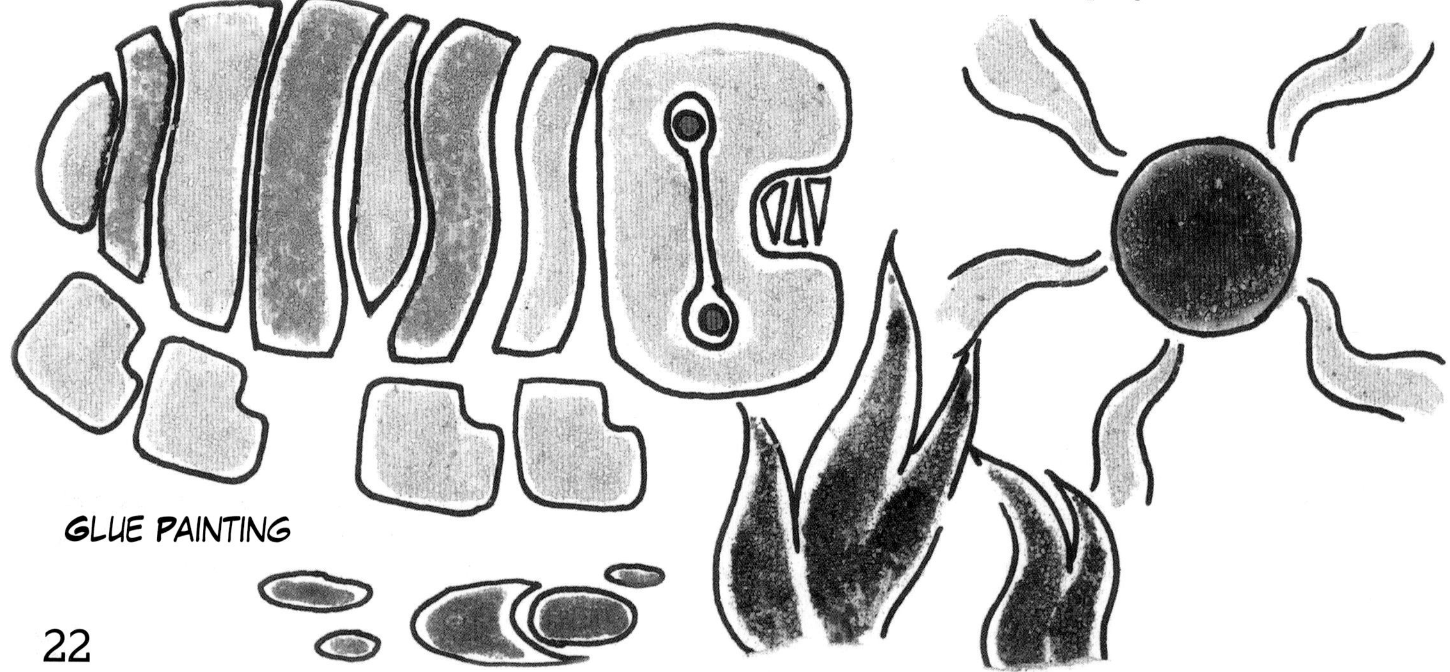

GLUE PAINTING

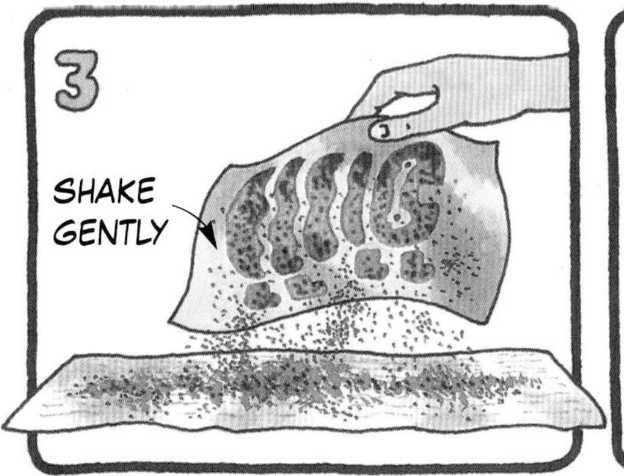

Pick up the paper and shake it gently over some newspaper. You will find that a lot of the glitter will stick to the glue and leave a brightly shaded shape.

If you want to put another shade on the glue shape, paint the unshaded parts with glue and sprinkle on a different glitter. Now shake it off gently.

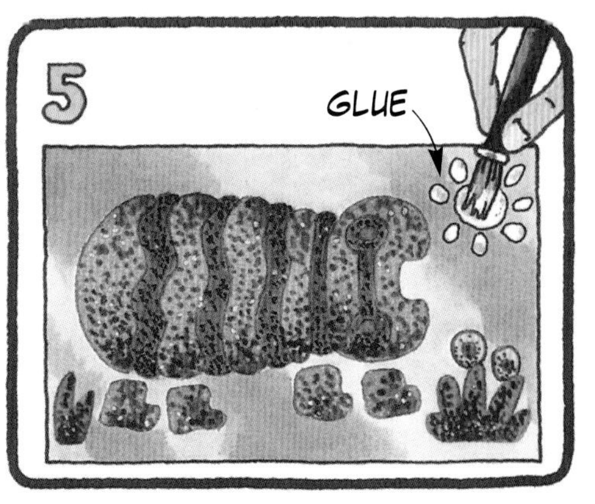

Decorate the picture by painting more shapes with glue and sprinkle on different glitter, one at a time. You can use the glitter left on the newspaper again.

LEAF AND GLUE PRINT

LEAF AND GLUE PRINTS

Use leaves to make prints. Cover one side of the leaf with glue, press it on paper, lift it off and sprinkle glitter over the glue print.

HOME-MADE MIXES

Try using kitchen powders like cocoa, instant coffee and paprika instead of glitter. Mix them with sugar, sand or sawdust.

Roller prints

YOU WILL NEED

- card tube about 7cm (2¾in) long
- a small piece of cardboard
- two pencils
- a sheet of foam sponge
- strong glue
- a knitting needle
- an empty cotton reel
- some model clay
- poster paint
- an old baking tray
- sheets of paper
- scissors

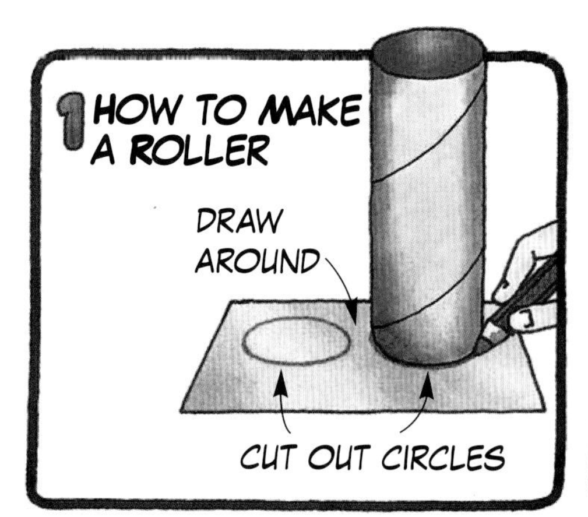

Draw two circles on some cardboard, using the end of the card tube as a guide, like this. Cut out the circles carefully with a pair of scissors.

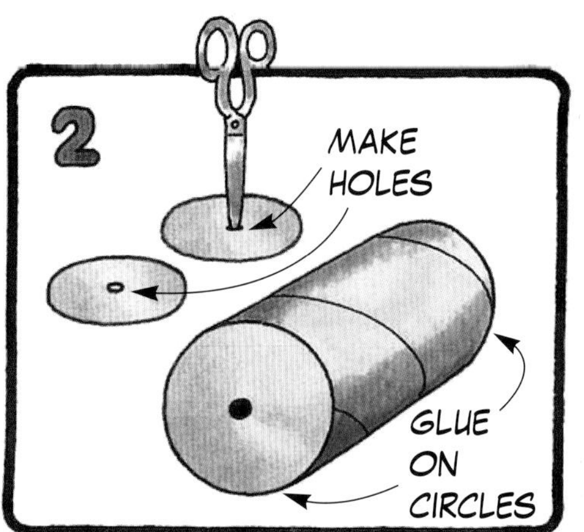

Make a hole in the middle of each cardboard circle with scissors, like this. Glue the circles to the two ends of the tube with strong glue and leave the glue to dry.

Cut some sponge the same length as the tube. Put the tube on the sponge and roll it up until it covers the tube. Then cut off the excess.

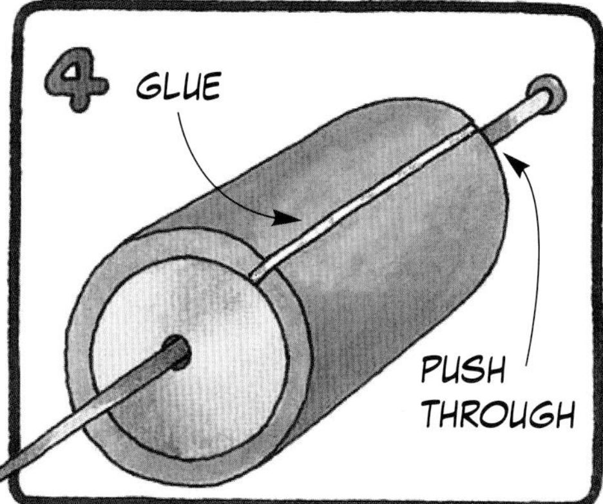

Roll the sponge around the tube and glue the edges together. Don't glue the sponge to the tube. Push a knitting needle through the tube.

Spread some paint on an old baking tray. Roll the paint out with your new roller until the sponge is evenly coated with paint.

Place some paper on top of newspaper and roll the roller across the paper. Use the roller for part of a picture like the sky.

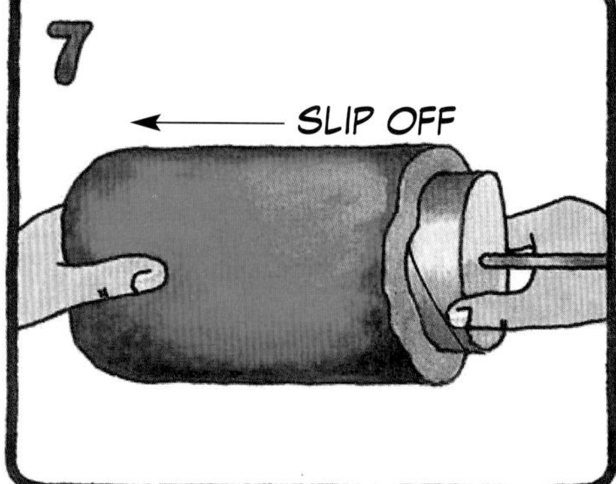

To clean the sponge, carefully slip it off the cardboard tube and wash the paint off with soap and water. Dry it and then slide it back on.

You can print lots of different patterns by cutting shapes out of the sponge on the roller with scissors, like this.

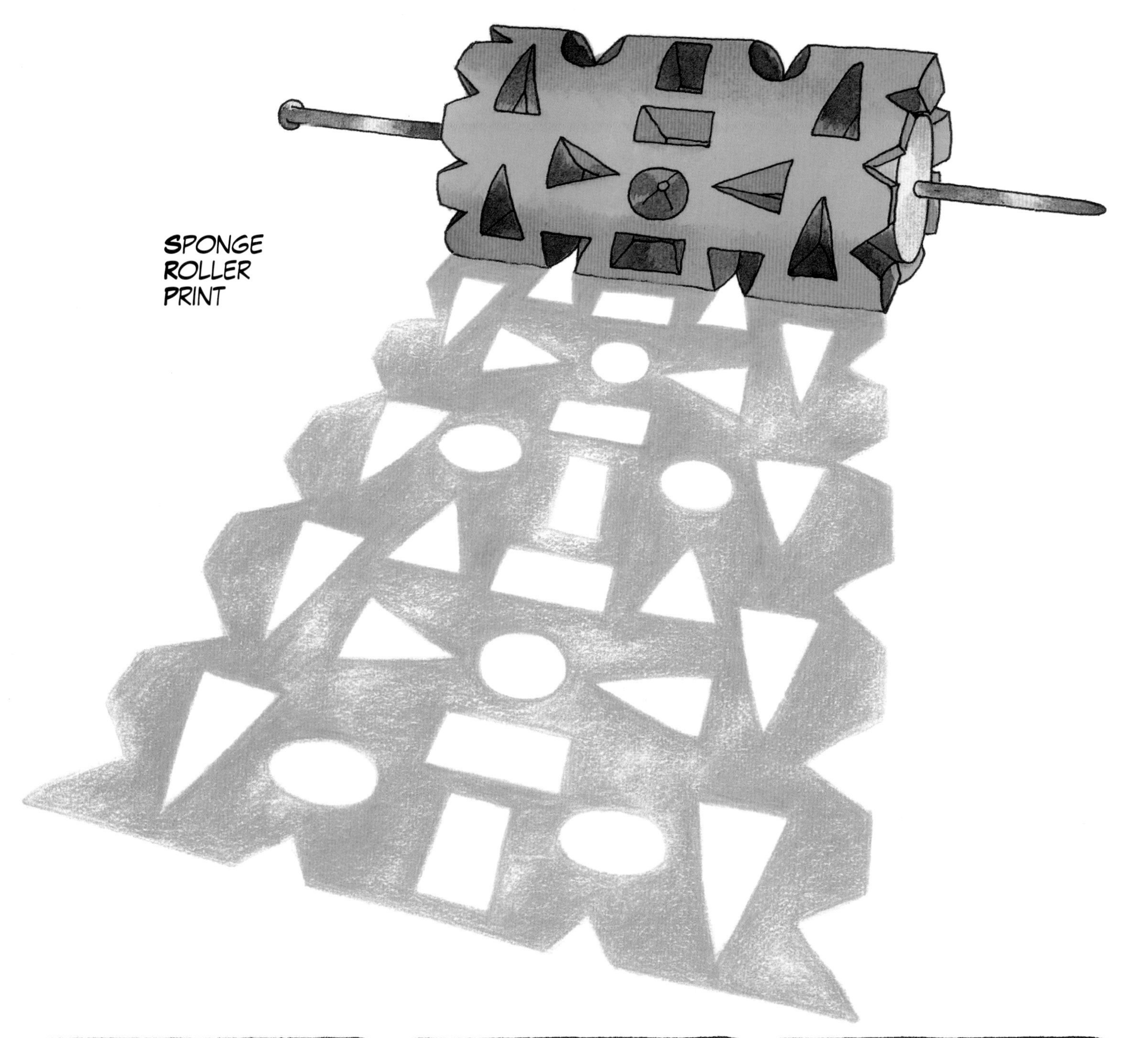

For a smaller roller, cover an empty cotton reel with a layer of model clay. Push a pencil through the holes in the reel.

Press different shapes into the model clay, using either end of a pencil. Press hard to make deep marks in the clay.

Roll the cotton reel in paint and push it across the paper. Before using another shade of paint, wash the first paint off.

Printing a cartoon

Cut out this cardboard cartoon man and you can print a whole story with one block. You will need a piece of thick expanded polystyrene. This is often used as packing for office equipment and cameras, so try asking in a store if they have any to spare.

When you have made one printing block, you can add more pieces. You could give the man a stick or an umbrella to carry.

Mix lots of thick but runny paint on a plate. If the card pieces of the cartoon stick to the paint, stir in more water with a brush.

YOU WILL NEED

- expanded polystyrene, about 3cm (1¼in) thick
- thick cardboard, or two thin pieces stuck together
- some pins
- thick poster paint
- a plate or old baking tray
- sheets of paper
- old newspaper
- a paint brush
- scissors

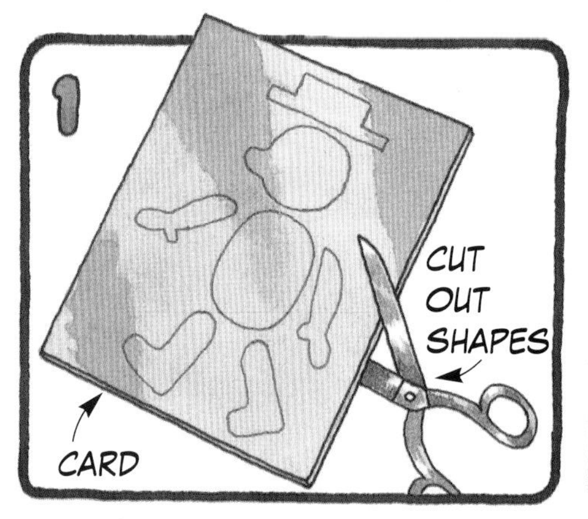

Draw the shape of a cartoon man on a piece of thick cardboard. Cut out the shape in pieces so that the arms, legs, head, body and hat are in separate pieces.

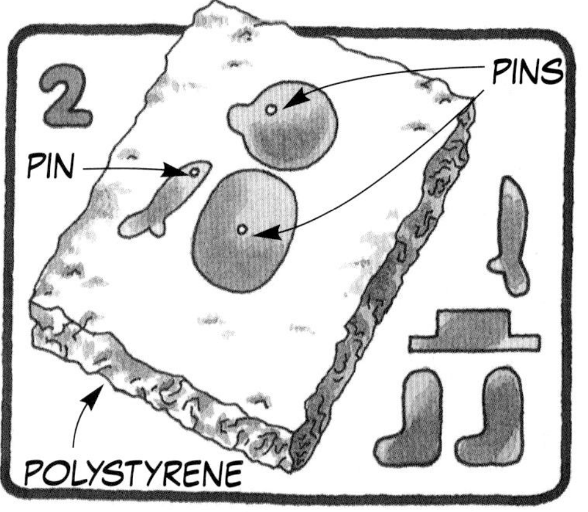

Push a pin through the body and into the polystyrene block. Pin on the arms, legs and head close to the body. Pin the hat near the top of the man's head.

Put some thick poster paint on the plate. Dip the cardboard shape in the paint, making sure it is well covered with paint.

Press the polystyrene block, paint side down, on a piece of scrap paper. When it looks good, print the shape on clean paper.

When you have printed the man standing, try moving his legs apart to make him walk or step forward. Then make a print.

To make him look as if he's running, move his legs farther apart and tilt his body forward. Then print him again.

To make the man go the other way, take his legs and head off the block. Pull out the pins, turn the shapes over and pin them again.

Charlie Card

When you have made a cartoon block, you can print as many pictures as you like, changing the man a little for each print. Try printing a dog by cutting out a body, four legs, a head and tail. Pin them onto a separate block.

When you have made lots of prints, draw or paint in a path, trees, houses and other things. Make up a story to go with the pictures. We have started a story about Charlie Card and his dog, Mr. McGreedy, and have left it for you to write an ending.

One day Charlie Card takes his dog, Mr. McGreedy, for a walk. Mr. McGreedy lags along behind and thinks the walk is very boring.

Suddenly a great gust of wind blows Charlie Card's hat off. Mr. McGreedy watches it whirl away down the road.

Mr. McGreedy thinks this is much more fun, and he chases after the hat. Charlie Card runs after Mr. McGreedy and the hat.

Charlie Card watches the hat so closely that he doesn't see a stone in the road. He trips over it and falls flat on his face.

Slowly Charlie Card gets up. He is wet and muddy and his toe hurts. He wishes he had stayed in his warm and cosy house.

He brushes himself down and starts to run after his hat again, and Mr. McGreedy who is a long way away. Now it begins to rain.

Charlie Card has now almost caught up with Mr. McGreedy when they both arrive at the bank of a wide river.

Mr. McGreedy is watching the hat and falls into the river. Charlie Card manages to grab his tail. Now write the end of the story.

Monoprints

These prints are called monoprints because you can never make two prints exactly the same.

Before you start, cut out a window mount. This holds the paper just above the paint and makes prints with tidy edges. The paint for monoprints must be sticky and not too wet. If a print has splodges on it, leave the paint on the tray to dry a little before trying again.

If there is too little paint on a print, add a few drops of water to the paint and mix it with a brush.

YOU WILL NEED

- poster paint or block printing paint
- an old baking tray or old mirror
- a sponge roller (see page 24)
- thin cardboard for a window mount
- a ruler and a pencil
- sheets of paper
- a paint brush

Cut some card to fit on the tray or mirror. Put a ruler on one edge of the card and draw a line, like this. Draw lines along the other sides. Cut along the lines.

Spread some sticky paint with a sponge roller over the tray or mirror. Put the card mount on the paint. The paint should fill the inside of the mount.

Place a sheet of paper over the mount. As you do this, hold the paper down very gently at one corner, like this. Now draw a shape on the paper.

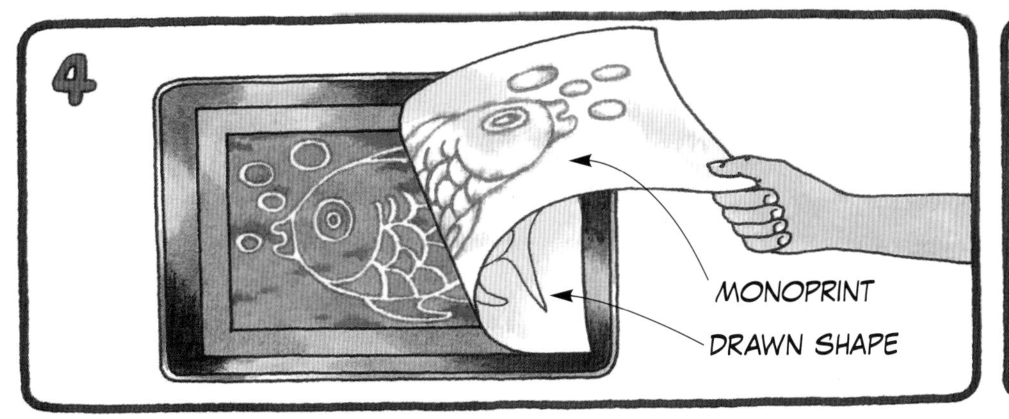

Lift up one corner of the paper and peel it off the paint. You now have a monoprint on the other side of the piece of paper.

When you are drawing a picture, remember that the monoprint will be the other way around.

Before the paint dries on the tray or mirror, put a new sheet of paper on it and rub it all over with your hand. The print you make like this is called a negative print.

Make a monoprint using one shade and let it dry. Wash the paint off the tray or mirror and spread on a different shade. Put the mount over the paint again.

Put the print down on the second shade, paint side down. Draw in more of the picture. Lift up the paper and let it dry. Now do the same with a third shade.

To create different tones in the paint, put a sheet of paper on the paint and press it lightly with your fingers. Or drag a comb across the paper to make wriggly lines.

Cut or tear different shapes out of paper and arrange them on the paint. Put a sheet of paper over the shapes and then gently press down on the paper.

Lift up the paper. Pick the paper shapes off the paint carefully, like this. Put a new piece of paper on the paint and rub your hand over it to make a negative print.

For a scrape print, scrape a shape or pattern in the paint with the handle of a paint brush. Place a piece of paper over the paint and then rub all over it to make a print.

Paste and paint pictures

Try making these bright paste and paint patterns and pictures. Take a print of each one to make another picture. They will all be rough and bumpy.

YOU WILL NEED

- white or shaded cardboard or thick paper
- thick paste
- poster paint
- sheets of paper
- a paint brush

1 PASTE AND PAINT PATTERNS

Brush stripes of thick paste on to a piece of white or brightly shaded cardboard or thick paper. Brush thick poster paint over the paste.

2

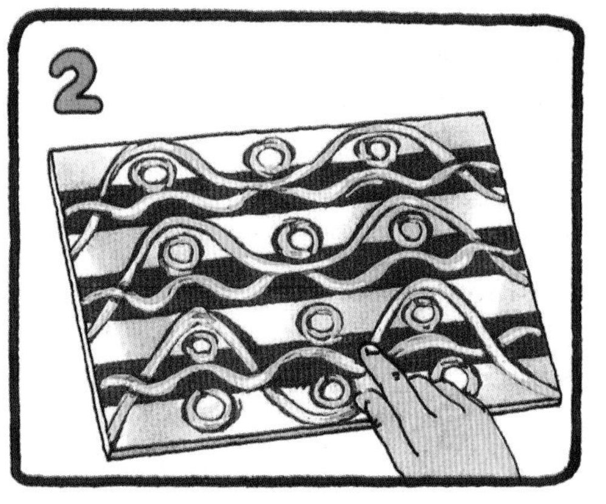

Slide your fingertips through the paint to make different patterns. If you make a mistake, brush over the pattern and start again.

1 PASTE AND PAINT PRINTS

Spread some paste on cardboard in an animal or flower shape. Brush paint over the paste. Add details by sliding your fingers and brush handle through the paint.

2

To make a print of your picture, lay a sheet of paper on the cardboard, being careful not to smudge the paint.

Rub all over the paper very gently with the side of your hand. Then pick up a corner of the paper and peel it off the cardboard.

Wash-off pictures

When you have made a wash-off picture, the paper will be wet. To stop it from drying in wrinkles, stretch it before you start.

To do this, gently rub a sheet of paper with a clean sponge dipped in water. Stick the edges to a board with masking tape. Allow it to dry and gently remove the tape.

YOU WILL NEED

- white poster paint, black Indian ink or bright waterproof ink
- thick paper
- pencil, paint brush, fine sponge

Draw a picture or a pattern on a sheet of thick paper. Brush white poster paint on the parts of the picture you want to be shaded.

To make light splodges, try dabbing white poster paint on the picture with a fine sponge. Leave the poster paint to dry completely.

Cover the paper and the white poster paint with a layer of black Indian ink or bright waterproof ink. Leave the ink to dry.

When the ink is dry, hold the picture under running water and rub the picture with your hand. Lay the paper down flat to dry.

Mixing shades

Red, blue and yellow, black and white paints can be mixed together to make all the shades of the rainbow. To make darker or lighter shades, add a little extra black or white.

YOU WILL NEED

- poster paint
- light shaded tissue paper
- glue
- white paper
- a string block, paint brush
- an old plate for mixing

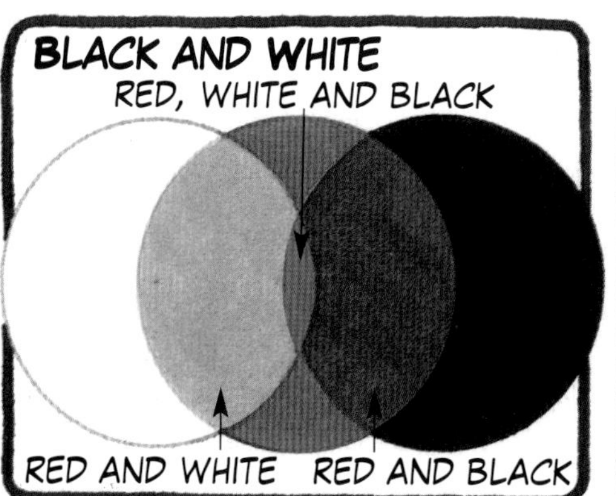

To make a shade lighter add white. White mixed with red makes pink. To make shades darker, add a little black. Red mixed with black will make dark red.

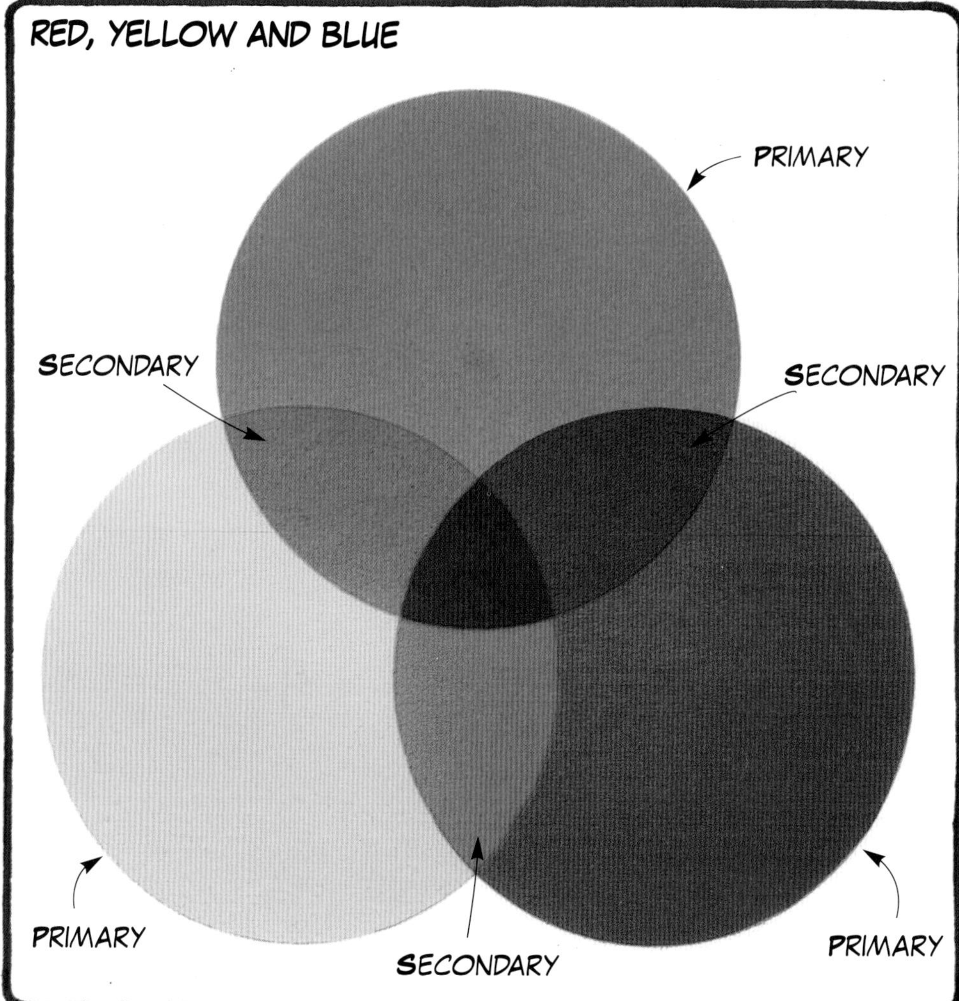

Red, yellow and blue are primary shades. Two primaries mixed together make a secondary one. Red and blue make purple, blue and yellow make green.

Yellow and red make orange. Purple, green and orange are secondary shades. When you mix two together, mix the lighter one first and then add the darker one.

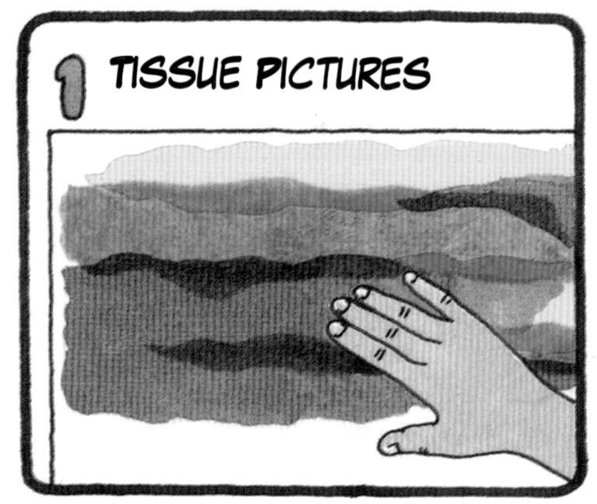

Tear sheets of light tissue paper into strips. Glue the strips on to some white card, overlapping the edges to make new shades.

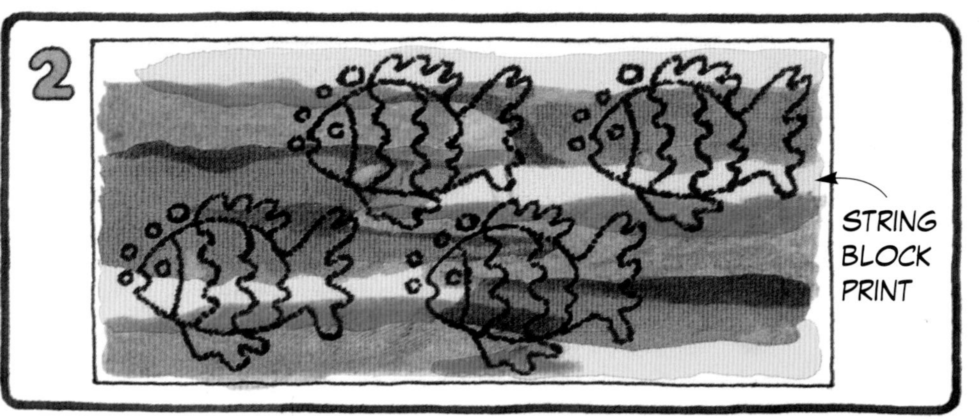

When the glue on the tissue paper is dry, use a string block and black paint to print shapes or patterns on it, like this.

You can make a string block by drawing a pattern onto a small wood block. Glue some string on the pattern and allow to dry.

Overprints

Instead of mixing paints before you use them, you can try printing one shade on top of another to make a new shade. To make pictures with neat edges, the cardboard shapes must be placed exactly on top of each other.

YOU WILL NEED

- pieces of thick cardboard
- poster paint or waterproof inks
- scissors, pencil, sheets of paper
- sticky tape loops. To make these, curl some tape, sticky side outside, into a loop and stick the ends together.

Draw a shape on thick cardboard and cut it out. Put the cut-out shape back on the cardboard, draw around it and cut out a second shape. Do this once again.

Stick one shape to a cardboard block with sticky tape loops. Brush ink or paint on the shape and make a print. Before you lift the block off, draw around it.

Draw around the shape on the cardboard. Pull the shape off. Cut pieces out of the second cardboard shape and press it on the block so that it fits inside the pencil marks.

To apply a second shade, fit the block inside the marks on the paper and print over the first shade. You can add more shades.

Mobiles

Gently blow on the mobile to make it move. The balance is so delicate that it will move with currents of air that you don't even notice.

Each hanging piece has a balance point and the arms of each move from side to side, as well as up and down. Once you see how the balance works, you can design new moving patterns.

YOU WILL NEED

- stiff wire or thin sticks
- button thread (strong thread)
- stiff paper and glue
- scissors and needle

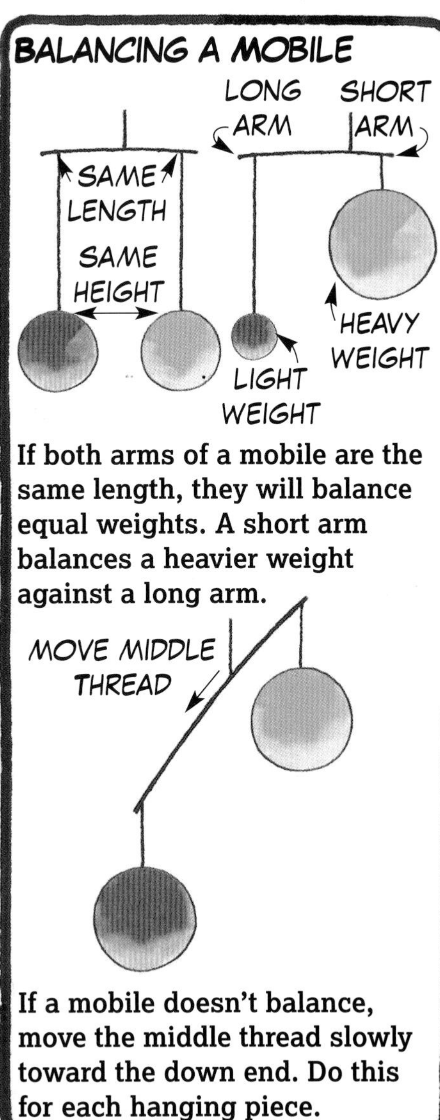

If both arms of a mobile are the same length, they will balance equal weights. A short arm balances a heavier weight against a long arm.

If a mobile doesn't balance, move the middle thread slowly toward the down end. Do this for each hanging piece.

Slot two paper circles together as shown. String the models together with needle and thread and hang from the wire.

You can repeat this to make lots more circles in different sizes. Lift the mobile by the top thread to balance it.

Lacy lanterns

To make these lacy lanterns, use the thinnest paper you can find.

Make the cuts very deep and as close together as possible. When you first make the lantern it will be shaped like a flying saucer. As it hangs, it will gradually open up.

YOU WILL NEED

- thin paper and scissors
- string and glue
- stiff paper for the base and top

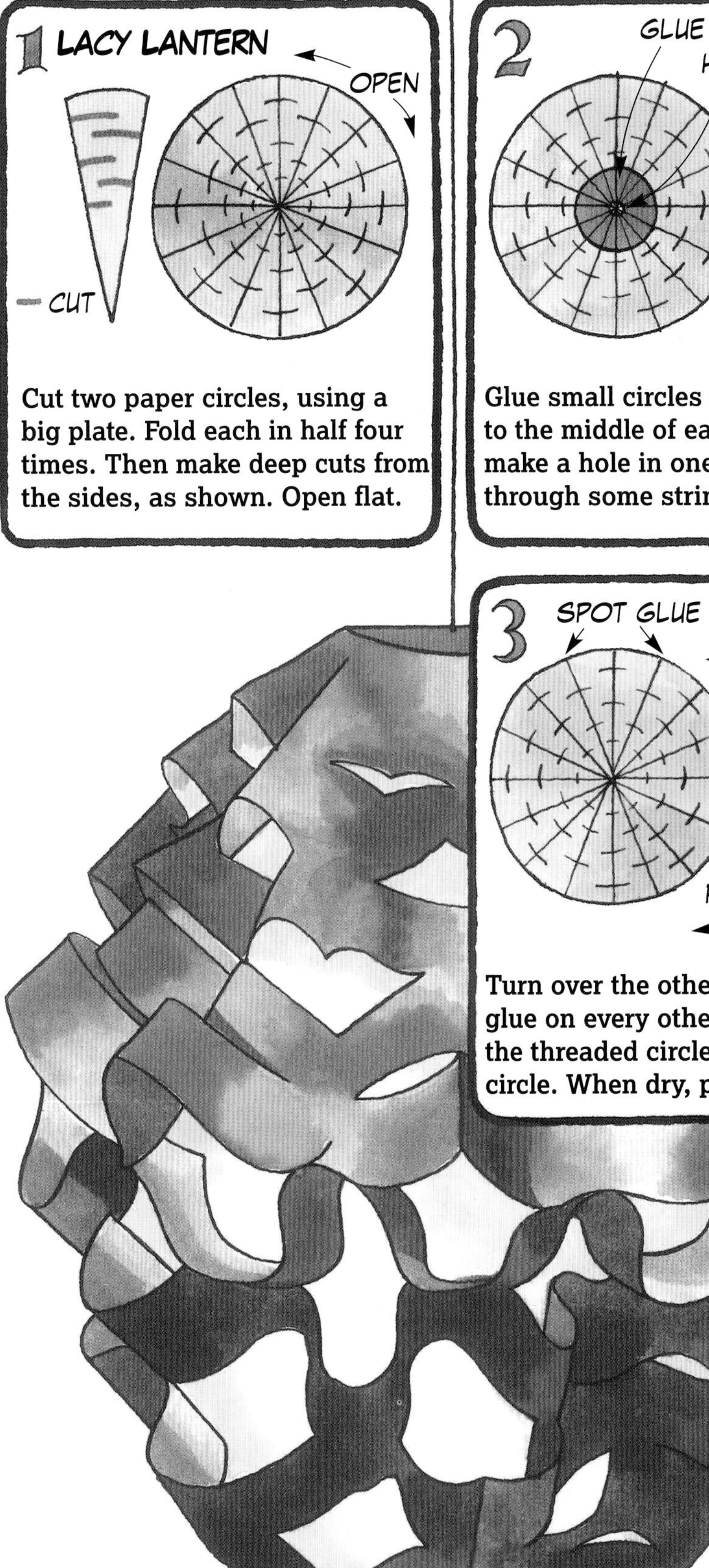

Cut two paper circles, using a big plate. Fold each in half four times. Then make deep cuts from the sides, as shown. Open flat.

2

GLUE

HOLE

Glue small circles of stiff paper to the middle of each. When dry, make a hole in one and thread through some string. Knot ends.

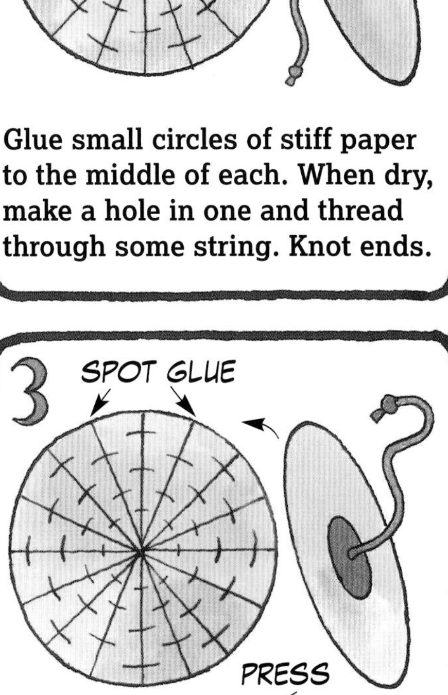

Turn over the other circle. Spot glue on every other fold. Press the threaded circle on the sticky circle. When dry, pull apart.

FLYING FISH MOBILE

It may help to hang your mobile from a coat-hanger. This one uses three balancing pieces. Make all the models first and lay the whole pattern flat on a table to fit it together.

Paper soldiers

YOU WILL NEED

- stiff paper
- ruler and scissors
- pencil and paints
- glue

Remember to use strong glue with a nozzle, so that you can dab spots of glue to add some details such as cut-out eyes. Use a pencil end if your fingertips get too sticky.

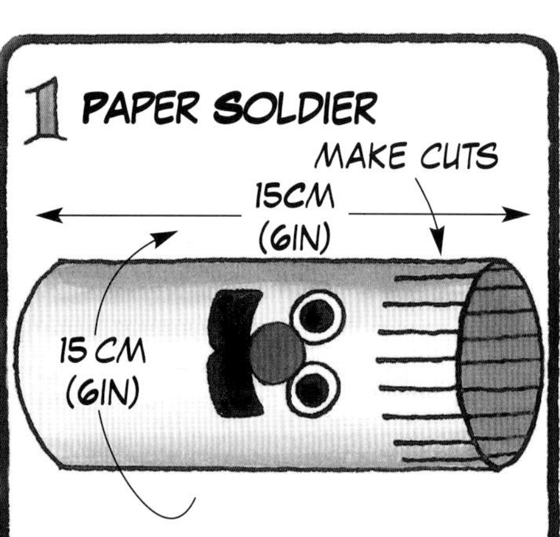

For the body, make a paper roll of these measurements. Make cuts at the top. Paint the face and glue on details like eyes.

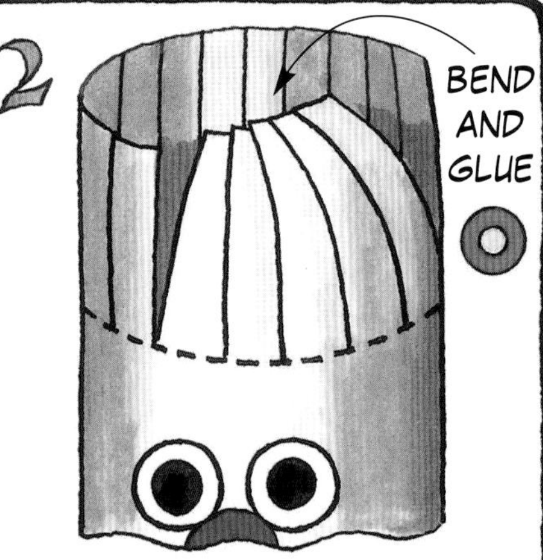

Dab glue on the top strips. Bend one on top of another to make a dome shape.

Hold the paper in one hand. With the other hand, hold the paper tightly between thumb and closed scissors. Pull away with a quick, sharp movement.

To glue a roll, press the inside of the join with a pencil, as shown. Use a pencil whenever you can't reach inside.

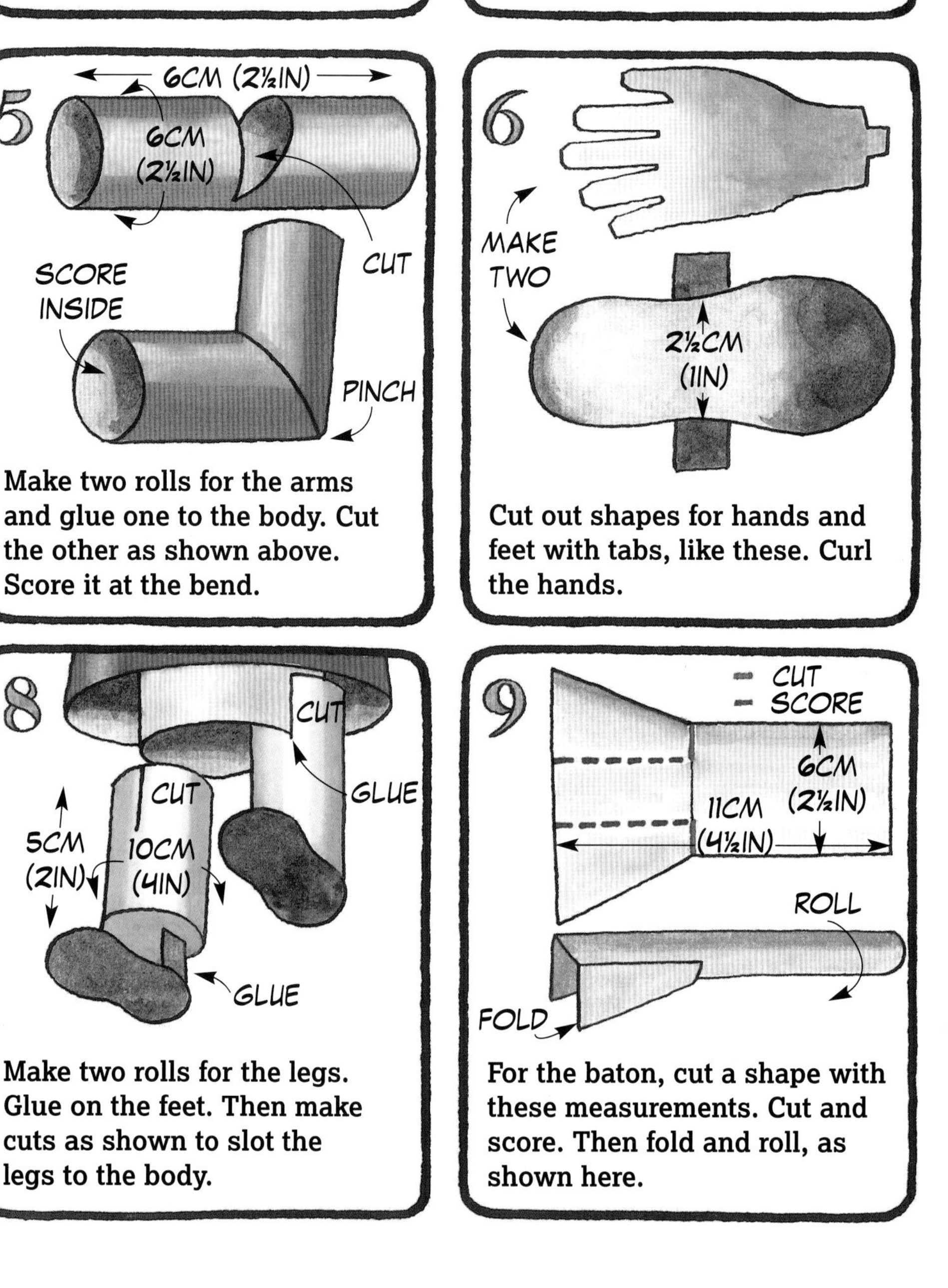

Make two rolls for the arms and glue one to the body. Cut the other as shown above. Score it at the bend.

Cut out shapes for hands and feet with tabs, like these. Curl the hands.

Make two rolls for the legs. Glue on the feet. Then make cuts as shown to slot the legs to the body.

For the baton, cut a shape with these measurements. Cut and score. Then fold and roll, as shown here.

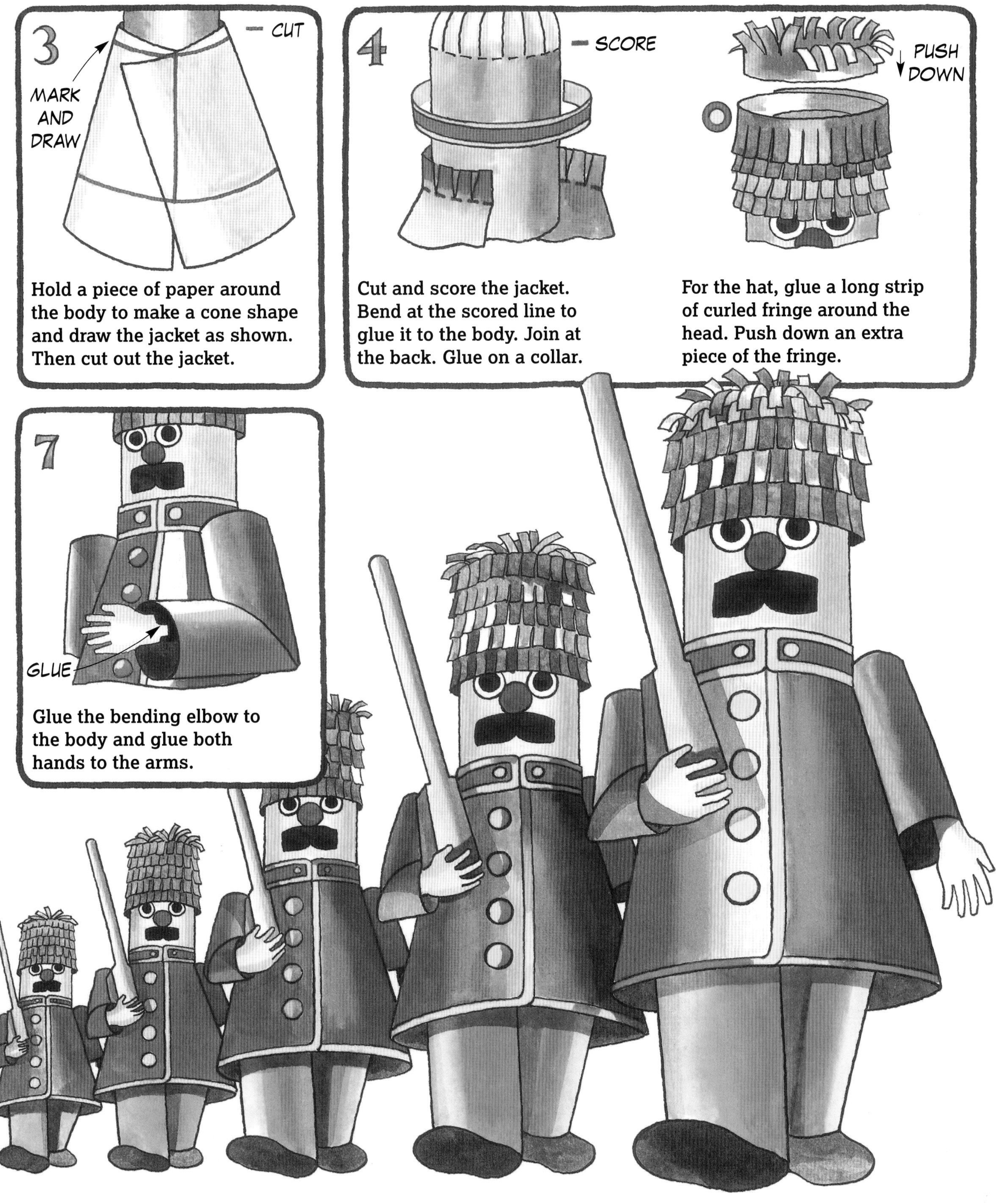
3
CUT
MARK
AND
DRAW
Hold a piece of paper around the body to make a cone shape and draw the jacket as shown. Then cut out the jacket.
4
SCORE
PUSH
DOWN
Cut and score the jacket. Bend at the scored line to glue it to the body. Join at the back. Glue on a collar.
For the hat, glue a long strip of curled fringe around the head. Push down an extra piece of the fringe.
7
GLUE
Glue the bending elbow to the body and glue both hands to the arms.

Paperville

Make one small house first, to see how the pattern works.

It's easier if you start at the edge of the paper and measure all the lines going across, then all the lines going down.

YOU WILL NEED

- large sheets of stiff paper
- scissors, ruler
- pencil, glue and paints

1 CHIMNEY

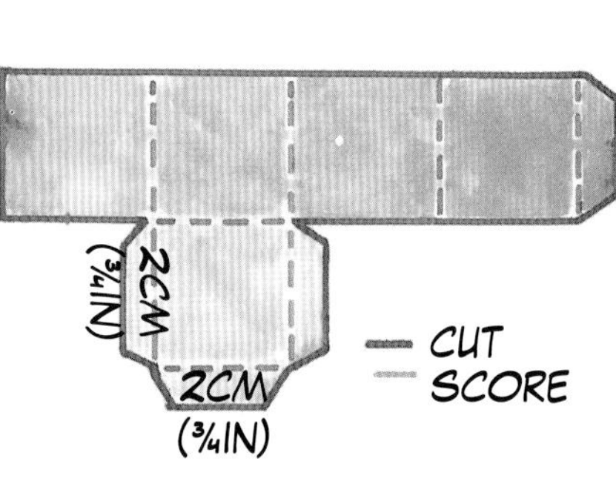

Draw a strip of four squares plus an extra square. Draw tabs. Cut out as shown.

2

MARK

CUT

SCORE

Hold the strip next to the roof and mark the shape on every other square. Cut and score both and fold in the triangles.

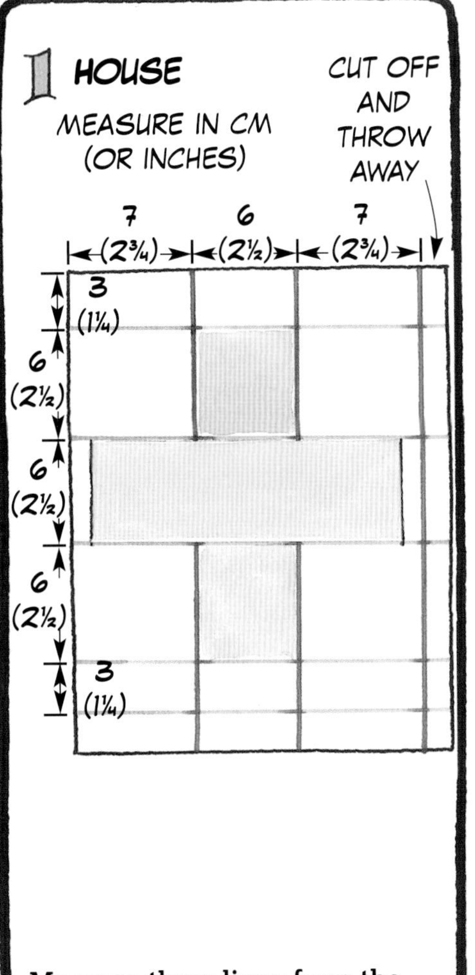

Measure three lines from the side of the paper, like the red lines. Then start from the top and measure down to make five lines, like the blue lines.

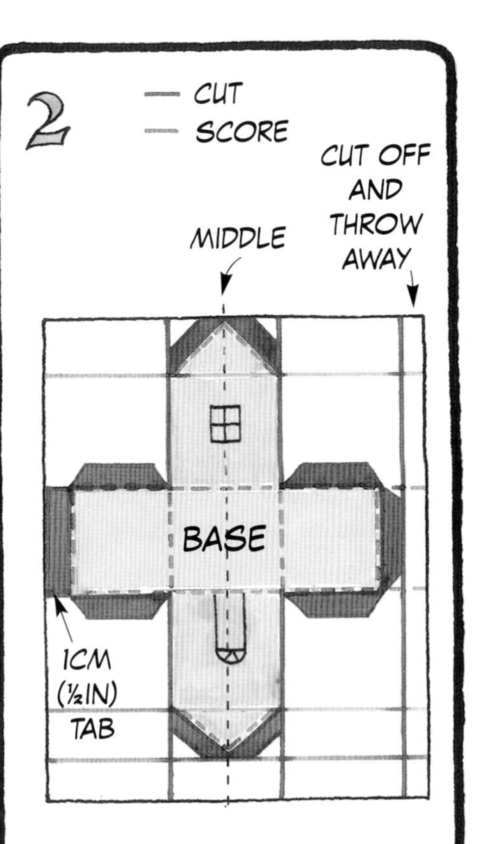

Draw lines from a central point to the sides as shown. Draw tabs. Make windows and doors. Score all around the base and along tabs. Cut out.

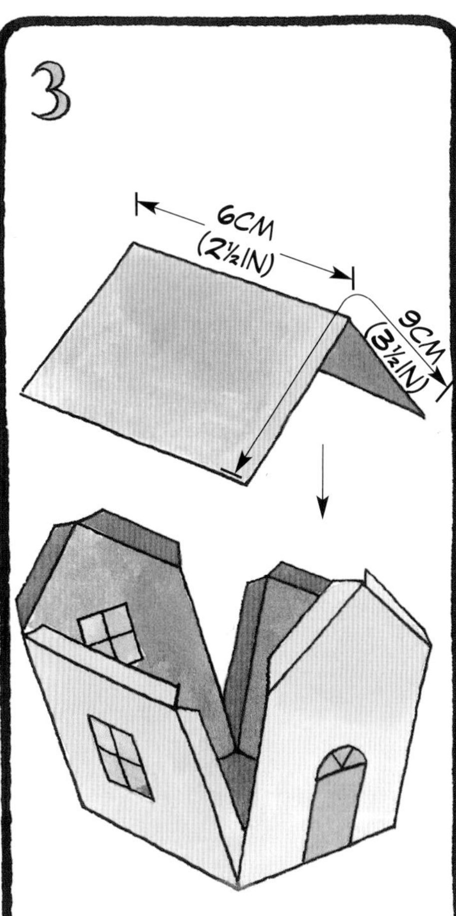

Fold the tabs all around, then fold up the house and glue it together. For a roof that just fits, fold a piece of paper measured as shown. Make it bigger if you want the roof to stick out over the walls.

Dab glue on the roof and fold the chimney around, using the folded triangles as tabs. Glue into a box shape.

For a chimney pot, make a small paper tube. Cut and score one end to bend in and then glue it to the chimney.

MAKING BOXES

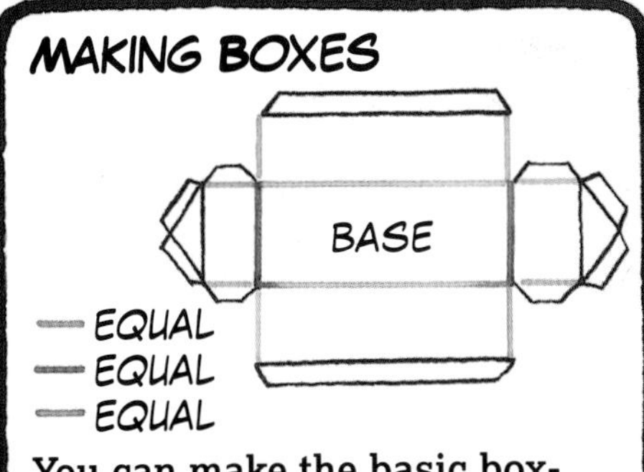

You can make the basic box-shape as long or as tall as you like. But remember...

1. Make all the sides equal.
2. Make opposite sides of the base equal.

Jack-in-the-box

YOU WILL NEED

- thin cardboard box with a lid
- bright paper
- ruler and pencil
- scissors and glue

Follow these instructions on how to make a paper spring. Glue the spring to a head made from a paper circle, and paint on a face.

As you open the box, give it a shake to make the Jack jump out.

1

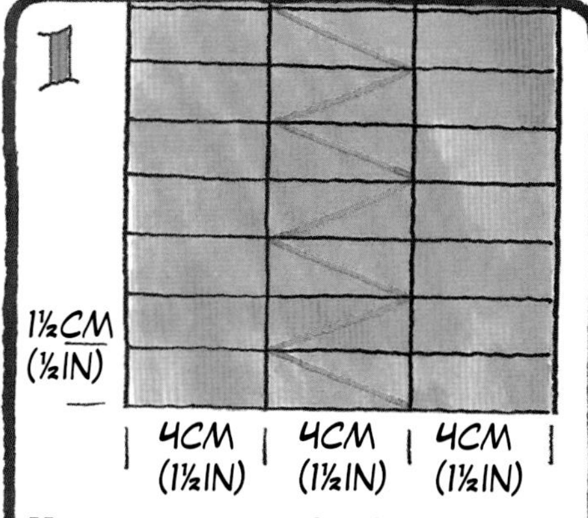

Use paper 12cm (5in) wide and as long as possible. If you glue strips together, let the glue dry before the next step. Rule lines as shown in black and make a zig-zag (shown in green).

2

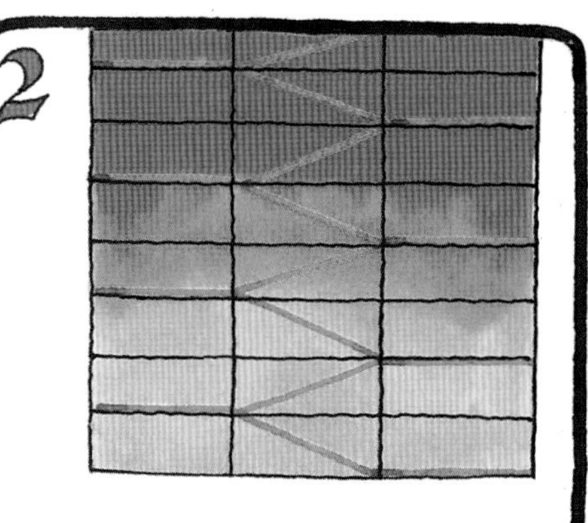

Now make more lines (shown in green) joining the points of the zig-zag to the edges. Score all the green lines and crease them firmly.

3

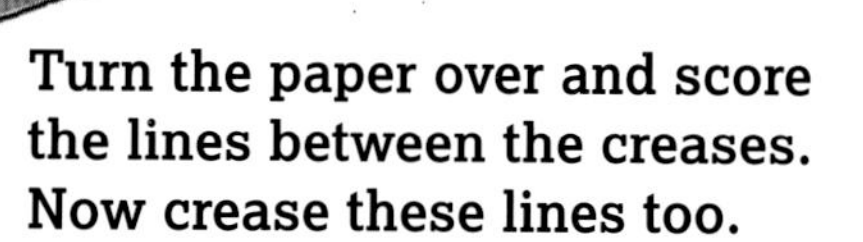

Turn the paper over and score the lines between the creases. Now crease these lines too.

4

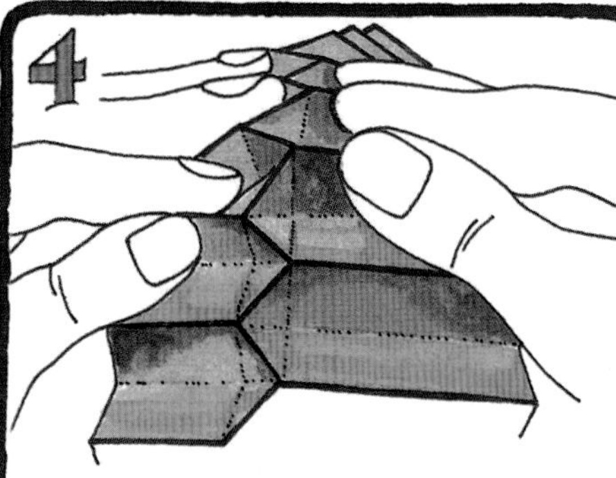

Hold the paper as shown here. Then walk your thumbs along the sides to push the creases inward and pinch the folds between your fingers.

5

Continue until all the folds can be pinched between your fingers to make this shape.

Experiments

Bubble boat

Make this boat and it will bubble its way around the bath under its own power. If you bend the tube at the back to one side, you can make the boat go around a corner.

YOU WILL NEED

- a plastic bottle with a top
- baking soda – this is used in cooking
- vinegar
- thin paper or a paper tissue
- plastic drinking straw or empty ink tube from an old ballpoint pen
- model clay and scissors

Using scissors, make a small hole in the bottom of the plastic bottle, close to the edge.

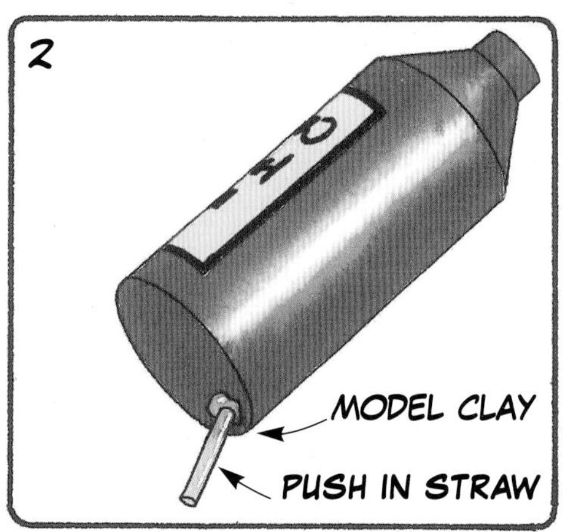

Push the plastic straw through the hole until only about 1cm (½in) sticks out. Press model clay tight around it to fix it in place.

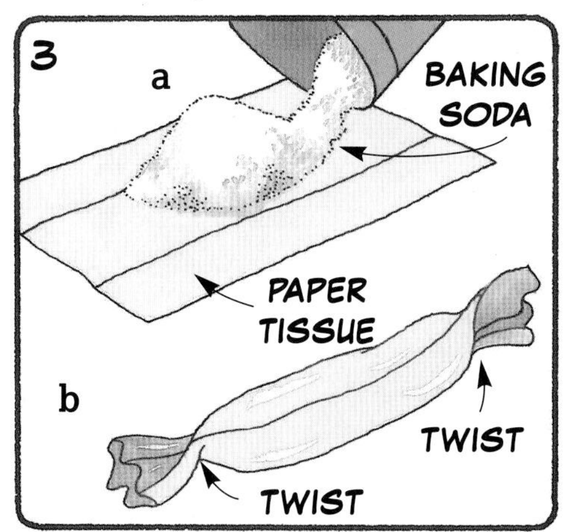

(a) Shake some baking soda on to a paper tissue or piece of paper.
(b) Wrap the paper around the soda and twist the ends, like this.

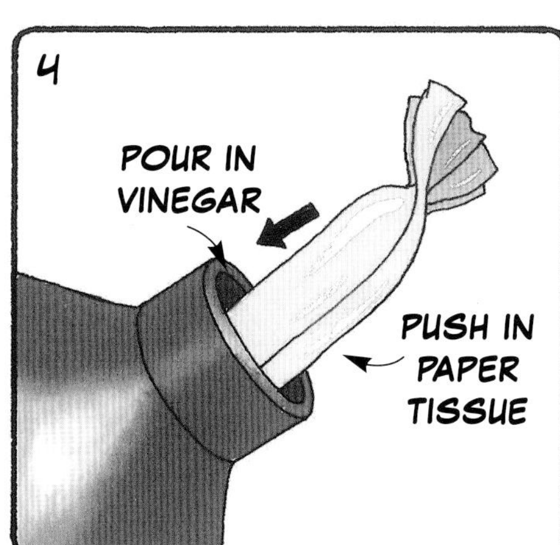

Put a few spoons of vinegar into the bottle. Push in the paper with the soda. Put the top on as quickly as you can. Place the bottle gently in a bath of water and let go.

WHY IT WORKS

When the paper gets wet in the vinegar, it untwists. The soda and vinegar mix together and make a lot of gas and foam. The gas goes out through the plastic straw and pushes the boat along.

Grow your own crystals

You can grow crystals by stirring table salt or sugar into hot water. Leave them to grow in a warm place. Every day you will see a few more, until there are lots clinging together in a lump.

YOU WILL NEED

- a clean glass jar
- a long piece of thread
- a paper clip
- sugar or table salt
- hot water
- a pencil

Put a spoon into the jar to stop the hot water from cracking it. Run the hot water a little and then fill up the jar when the water is hot.

Put several teaspoons of sugar or salt into the water and stir until it has all disappeared. Add more and stir again.

Stand the jar in a bowl of hot water to keep the water in the jar hot. Add more salt or sugar and stir again. Keep adding it until no more will dissolve.

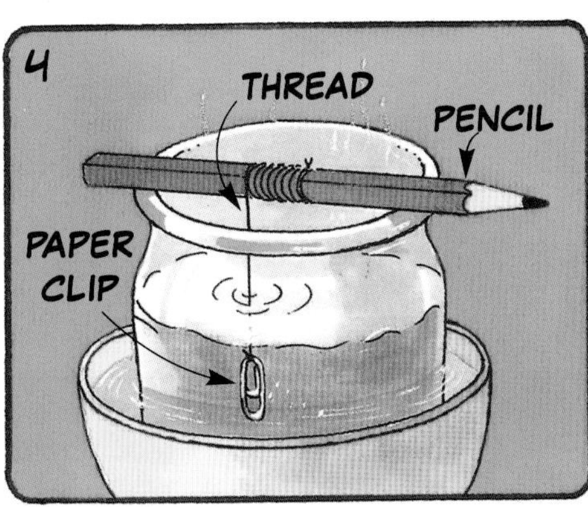

Tie a paper clip on to one end of a piece of thread. Tie the other end around a pencil. Drop the clip into the jar. Wind the thread around the pencil until the clip hangs like this.

Try mixing a few drops of poster paint or ink in the water to make bright crystals.

DID YOU KNOW?

Lots of things, such as sugar, salt, sand and precious stones are crystals. Each crystal has its own shape. You can see them with a magnifying glass.

Magic balloon bottle

Set up this experiment and amaze your friends. You can make the balloon go in and out of the bottle for as long as you like by just putting the bottle into hot water and then into cold water, and then back again into the hot.

YOU WILL NEED

- a bottle – any sort will do
- a balloon
- scissors
- a bowl of hot water
- a bowl of very cold water

Fill up the bottle with hot water. Leave it for a few minutes to warm the bottle. Pour out the water.

Cut the neck off the balloon. Then stretch the balloon over the top of the bottle and pull it down. Stand the bottle in the bowl of cold water. Now watch what happens.

WHY IT WORKS

When you warm the bottle with hot water, the air in the bottle is warmed. When air is warmed it gets bigger. This is called expansion. When you cool the bottle with cold water, the air in it is cooled and gets smaller. This is called contraction. As the air gets smaller, the air outside pushes the balloon into the bottle. If you warm the bottle the air inside expands and pushes the balloon out.

DID YOU KNOW?

If you have a ping pong ball with a dent in it, you can get the dent out of it. Put the ball in warm water. The air inside will expand and push out the dent.

A hot-air balloon floats up when the burner in the basket heats air in the balloon. This is because the air expands, some escapes and the rest weighs less.

Bottle fountain

Here is another surprise to puzzle your friends. You will have to tell them why it works because they will never guess.

YOU WILL NEED

- a small bottle with a screw-on top
- a plastic drinking straw
- model clay
- a pin or needle
- poster paint or ink
- a bowl of hot water

Take the top off the bottle. Make a hole in the top with scissors, pressing down, like this. Half-fill the bottle with cold water.

Pour a few drops of poster paint or ink into the water in the bottle. Now screw the top back on so that it is very tight.

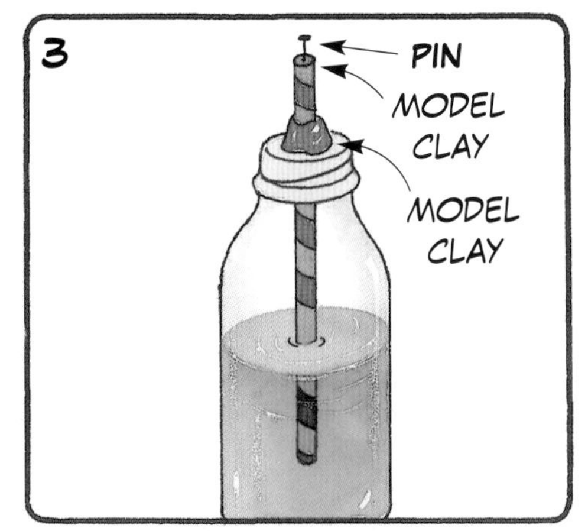

Push the straw through the hole and seal it with model clay. Put more in the end of the straw. Poke a hole through it with a pin.

Place the bottle in a bowl and fill the bowl up with hot water. Wait for a while for the fountain to work.

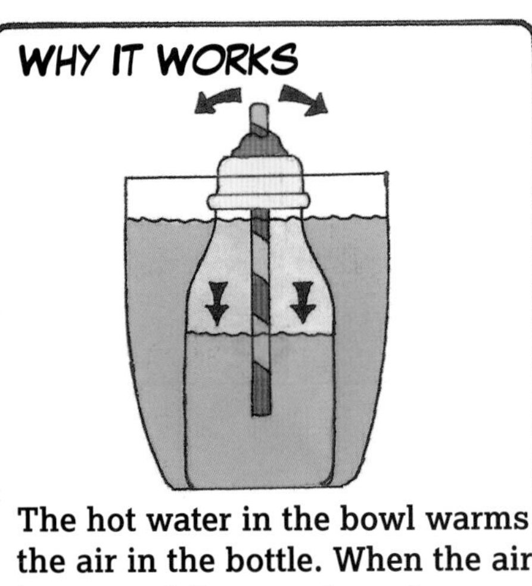

The hot water in the bowl warms the air in the bottle. When the air is warmed it expands and pushes the water up the straw and out in a spray.

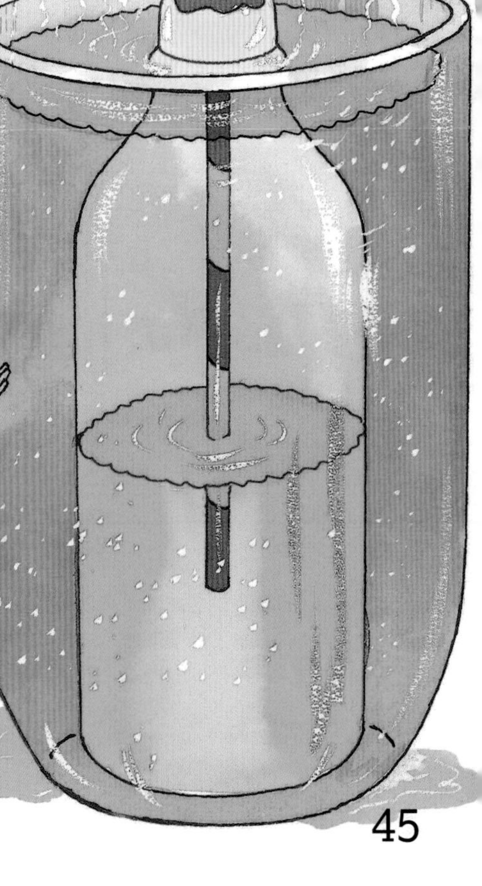

Air is everywhere

You cannot see air but it fills nearly every space in the world. Even when things look empty, they're really full of air. Air is a gas which you cannot feel except when the wind blows or when you breathe in and out. There is a thick layer of air all around the Earth, which pushes down on everything around us.

YOU WILL NEED

- 2 glasses and a bowl of water
- a piece of wood, about 45cm (18in) long and 4cm (1½in) wide
- 2 sheets of a large newspaper
- a hammer or wooden mallet

An empty glass looks as if it has nothing in it. To show it is full of air, hold it down in a bowl of water, like this. The air keeps nearly all the water out.

Tilt the glass a little. The air bubbles out through the water and water fills the glass. Now try catching the escaping air in a filled glass under the water.

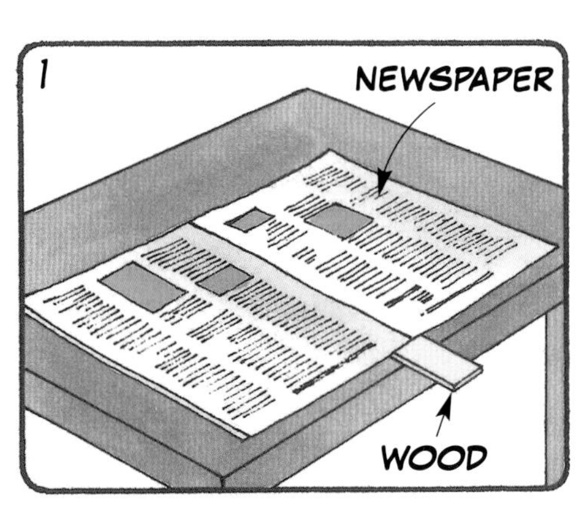

Put the thin piece of wood on the table, with a bit sticking over the edge. Spread out two sheets of newspaper over it. Smooth them down so they are very flat.

Hit the thin piece of wood very hard with a hammer or mallet. Do it quickly and the wood snaps. If you just press down on the bit of wood, the newspaper will lift up as the air gets in under the paper. So give the wood a good bang.

When you hit the wood, the air pressing on the newspaper is too heavy to be lifted up, so the wood breaks. The push of air around us is called atmospheric pressure.

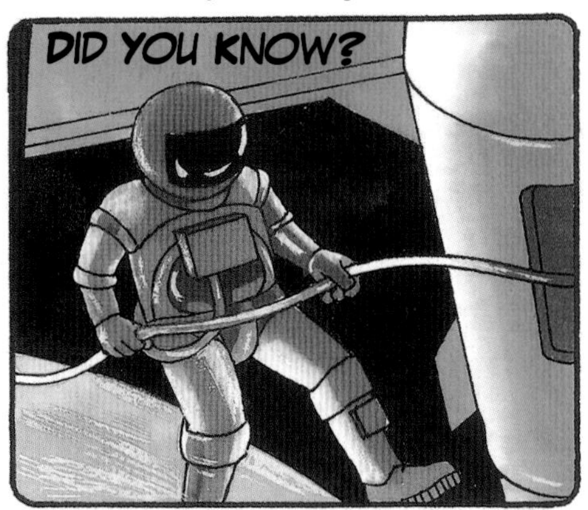

The pressure in your body equals the air pressure pushing all over you. People on the moon or in space, where there is no air, must wear suits with pressure in them.

Is air heavy?

Here is a good way to find out if air weighs anything. It's very difficult to take all the air out of a tin can or bottle without special equipment, but you can do it with balloons.

YOU WILL NEED

- a thin stick, 60cm (2ft) long
- 2 balloons, which are the same size and shape
- 3 pieces of string, each about 30cm (1ft) long
- a pin

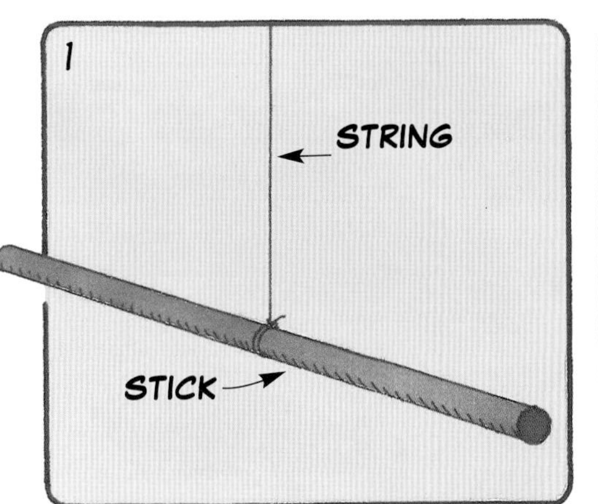

Tie the end of one string tightly to the middle of the stick. Hang the stick up by the other end. Slide the string along the stick until it hangs exactly level.

Blow up one balloon and tie the neck with a second string. Blow up the second balloon until it is about the same size as the first. Tie the neck with a third string.

Tie a balloon on to each end of the stick. Slide the strings along the stick until the stick hangs exactly level again. Now prick one balloon with a pin and watch.

DID YOU KNOW?

If a scientist weighs a bottle of air, then removes the air and weighs it again, a similar bottle with air will weigh a fraction more than the bottle without.

WHY IT WORKS

When you burst one balloon, all the air comes out. The other balloon with air in weighs more than the empty one, so the stick goes down.

Now burst the other balloon and the stick will become level again.

Bottle volcano

Here is a surprising trick to try with two bottles of water, one warm and the other cold. When you turn the bottles over, watch as the cold water sinks down and pushes the warm water up.

YOU WILL NEED

- 2 clean glass bottles – ones with wide necks are best
- cold water and warm water
- a small square of cardboard
- a few drops of ink or water paint

Fill one bottle with cold water and the other with warm water. Pour a few drops of ink or paint into the bottle with the warm water.

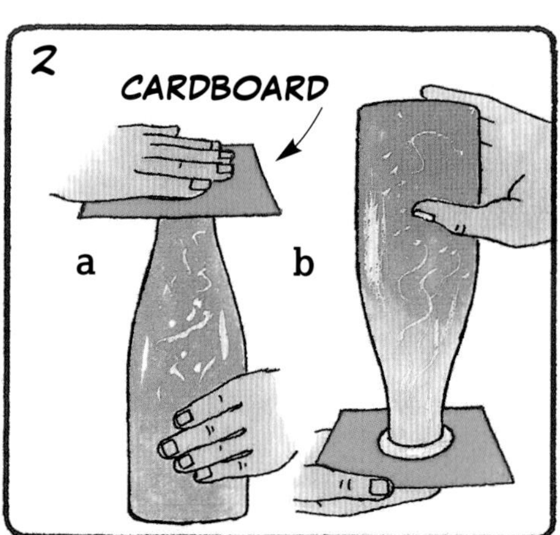

Place the cardboard over the top of the bottle holding the inky water.
(a) Hold it in place with one hand.
(b) Slowly turn the bottle over.

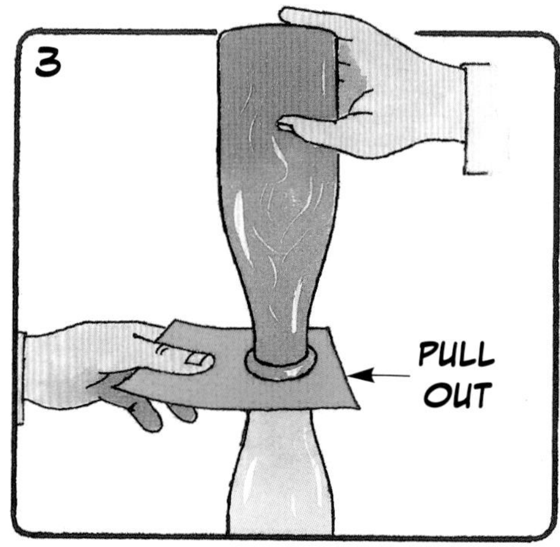

Put the bottle with inky water exactly on top of the other bottle. Hold the top bottle and slowly pull out the cardboard.

Hold both bottles like this. Very carefully turn them up the other way, without letting the tops slide apart and any of the water run out.

Warm water is lighter than cold water so it floats on the top. When you turn the bottles over, the cold is on the top and it sinks down and pushes the warm, inky water up.

At the North and South Poles, the cold water sinks down, pushing up water from the bottom. Scientists think this may cause ocean currents.

Strong ice

When water cools down and freezes into ice, something strange happens to it. For these experiments, you have to use the freezing compartment of a refrigerator. Use a plastic pot or a tin. Don't use a glass bowl as it will crack.

YOU WILL NEED

- a small plastic pot with a lid
- a small, clean tin can with a lid
- 3 pencils, sticky tape
- a bottle top
- a refrigerator

Fill the plastic pot right to the top with cold water. Press on the lid. Put the pot in the freezing compartment of a refrigerator. Leave it for about eight hours.

Take out the pot. When the water has turned to ice, it lifts up the lid and pushes it off the pot. You may find the sides have been pushed out a little too.

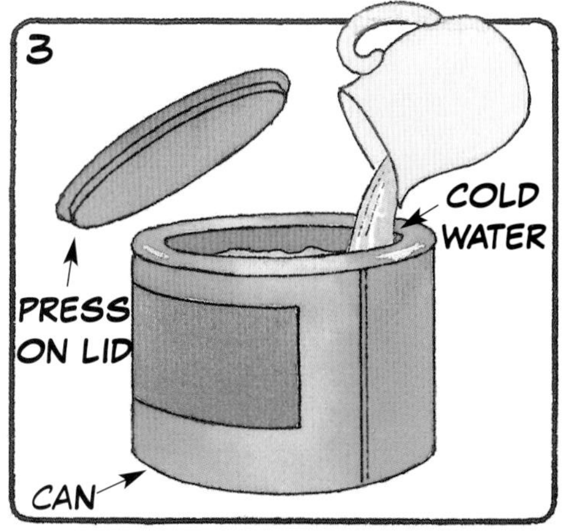

Fill a can up to the top with cold water. Press on the lid as hard as you can, without spilling the water.

Put a bottle top on the lid. Put two pencils under the can and one on the bottle top. Wind sticky tape around the pencils. Freeze it.

When the can has been in the freezing compartment for about eight hours, have a look at it. You will find the lid has been pushed up by the ice and broken the top pencil. The sides may have been pushed out as well.

When water cools and turns into ice it gets bigger and pushes outward. It presses so hard that it can sometimes break water pipes on the outside of houses.

When rain runs into cracks on mountain tops and freezes into ice, the ice pushes so hard it splits the rock. That's why some mountains have shattered rocks at the top.

Water turbine

Make this turbine and hold it under a running tap. It will spin around and around as the water spurts out. If you hold the string between your fingers, so that it can turn too, the turbine will spin as long as there is water in it.

YOU WILL NEED

- an empty plastic bottle
- a pencil
- a short piece of string, about 15cm (6in) long, and another piece about 30cm (1ft) long
- scissors

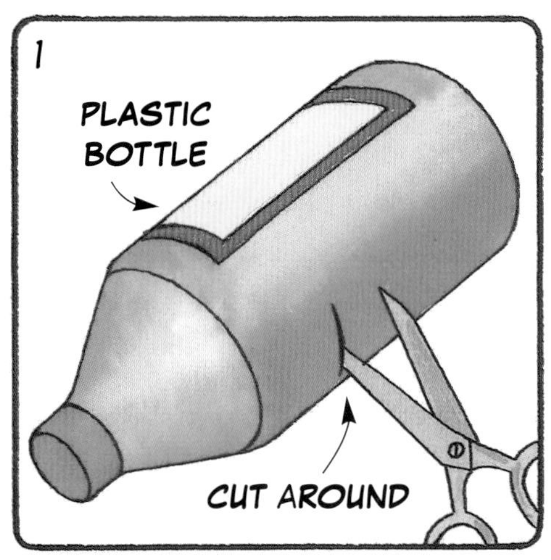

Push one blade of the scissors into the bottle, near the top, like this. Snip all the way around until you have cut the top off.

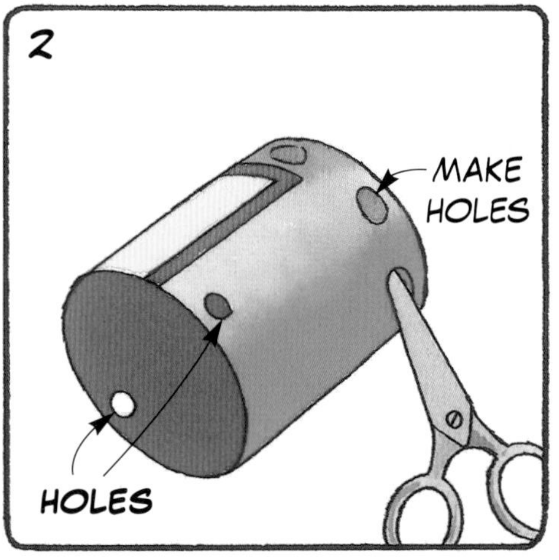

Make eight holes around the bottom of the bottle. Space them out evenly. Make two holes in the top, one on each side.

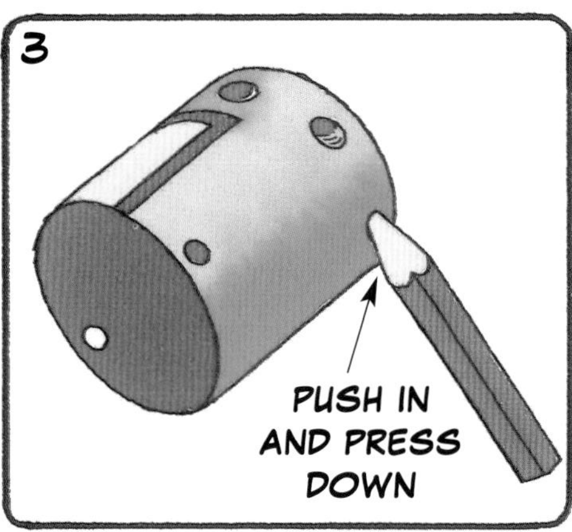

Push the point of a pencil into the bottom holes in the bottle, to slant them. Press the pencil down until it is against the side of the bottle.

Tie the short string to the holes at the top. Tie the long string to the middle of the short piece. Tie a pencil to the other end, like this.

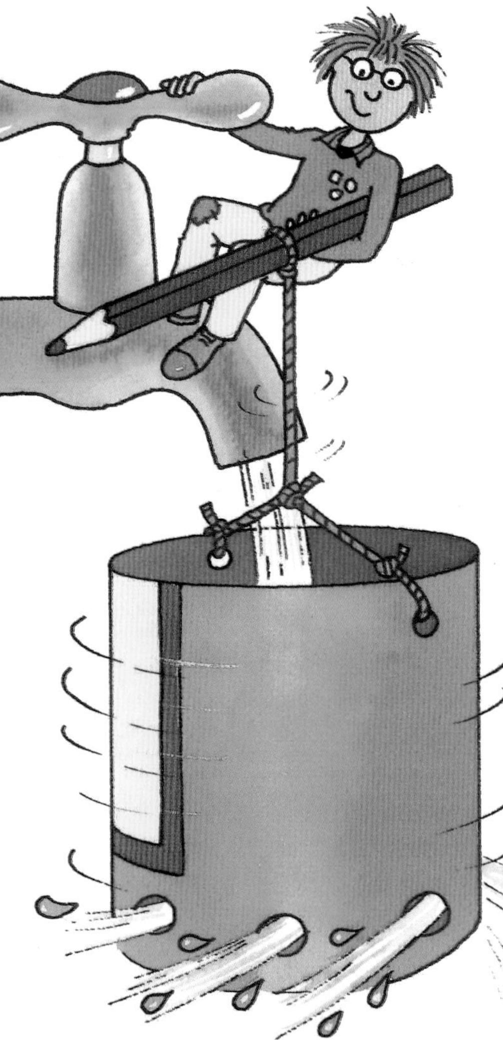

Turn on running water and hold the bottle by the string under it. As it fills up, the water squirts out and the bottle spins around.

WHY IT WORKS

When water squirts out of the holes, it comes out sideways. The jets of water push the bottle away and make it spin around in the opposite direction.

Spin drier

Spin this little drier and it will whizz the water out of wet cloth or wet paper towels. It won't make them completely dry but it will get rid of a lot of the water. It's best to do this experiment outside where it doesn't matter if other things get wet from the flying water.

YOU WILL NEED

- a plastic bottle
- a pencil, scissors
- a cotton reel
- string

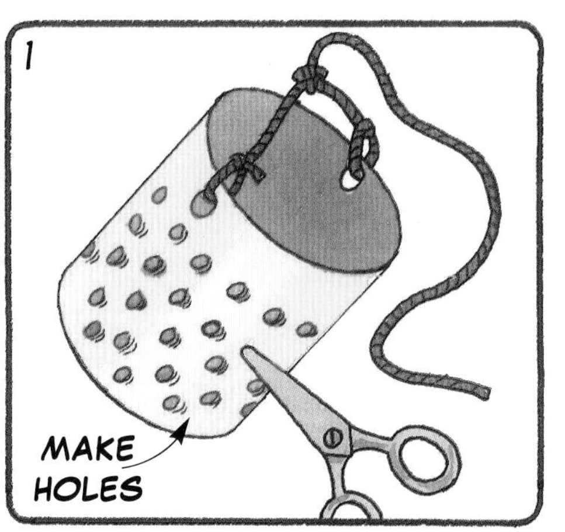

Cut off the top of the plastic bottle and tie on strings in the same way as for the water turbine. Poke lots of holes in the bottle.

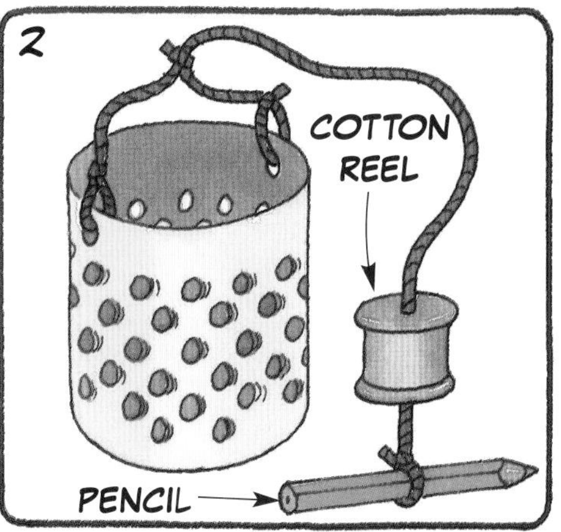

Slide a cotton reel onto the long string on the bottle. Then tie a pencil to the end of the string.

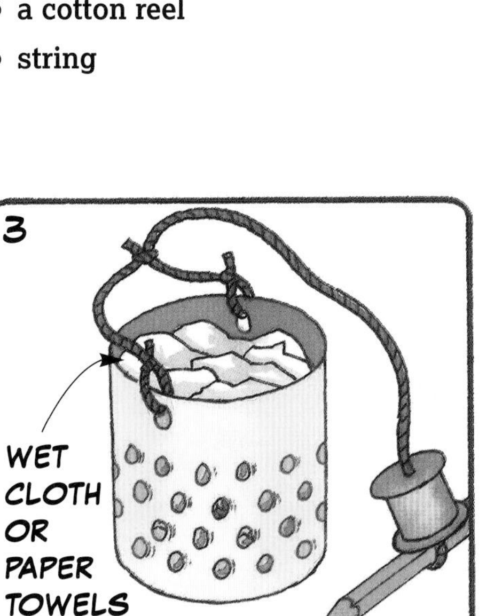

Push bits of wet cloth or wet paper towels into the bottle. Press them down. Don't pack them in too tightly or it won't work.

Hold the cotton reel in one hand. Wind the pencil around as fast as you can with the other hand.

WHY IT WORKS

When anything, like this big top, spins, things on it fly off. This is called centrifugal force. When the drier spins, the water is flung out through the holes.

If you have one, tie the string to the end of an egg whisk. Wind the handle as fast as you can to spin the drier. As it spins, water will come out of the holes.

DID YOU KNOW?

Electric spin driers and washing machines work in the same way as your drier. They whizz around very fast and the water in the wet clothes flies out through the holes in the drum.

Amazing ping pong ball

Try these two experiments on your friends and surprise them. You need a very small funnel, and a drinking straw with a bend in it. Or you can make your own. And you also need lots of puff.

YOU WILL NEED

- a ping pong ball
- paper about 20cm (8in) long and 10cm (4in) wide
- a circle of thin cardboard about 10cm (4in) across
- a piece of drinking straw, about 4cm (1½in) long
- glue, sticky tape and scissors

Hold the ping pong ball above the end of the straw. Take a deep breath and blow hard. Let go of the ball and it will stay there.

Put the ping pong ball into the funnel. Blow, pointing the funnel up. Keep blowing and point it down. The ball will stay in it.

1 MAKING A TUBE

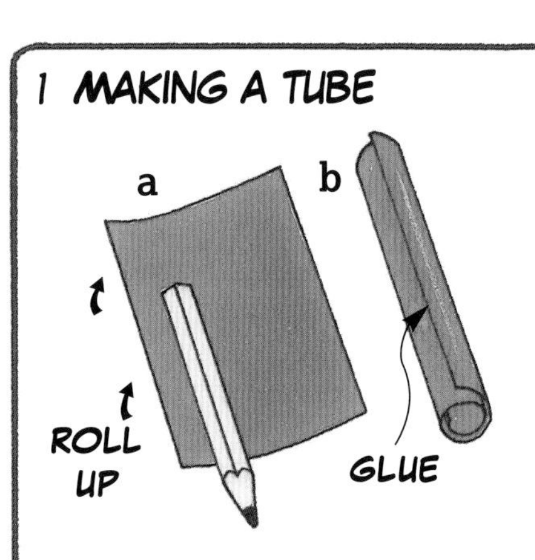

(a) Put a pencil down on the edge of the piece of paper. (b) Roll up the paper around it then stick the edge with glue to make a tube. Shake out the pencil.

2

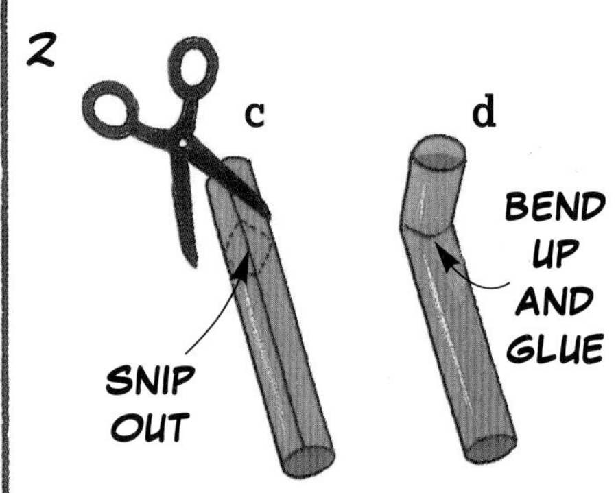

(c) Make a small snip in the tube, near one end. Then make another snip to cut out a V-shaped piece. (d) Bend up the end and glue around the join.

MAKING A FUNNEL

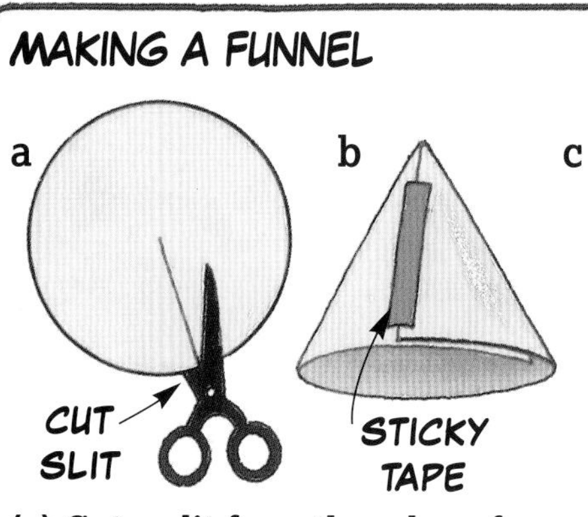

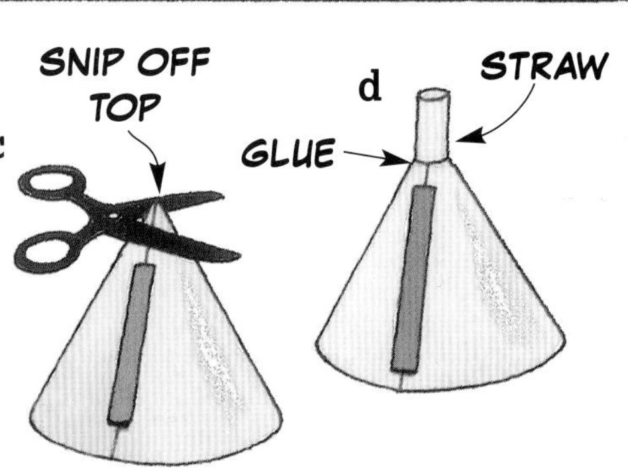

(a) Cut a slit from the edge of the cardboard circle to the middle. (b) Curl the circle up into a cone and stick the edges.

(c) Snip the top off the cone. (d) Then push the straw through the hole so it just goes down inside. Glue it to the cone. Leave to dry.

WHY IT WORKS

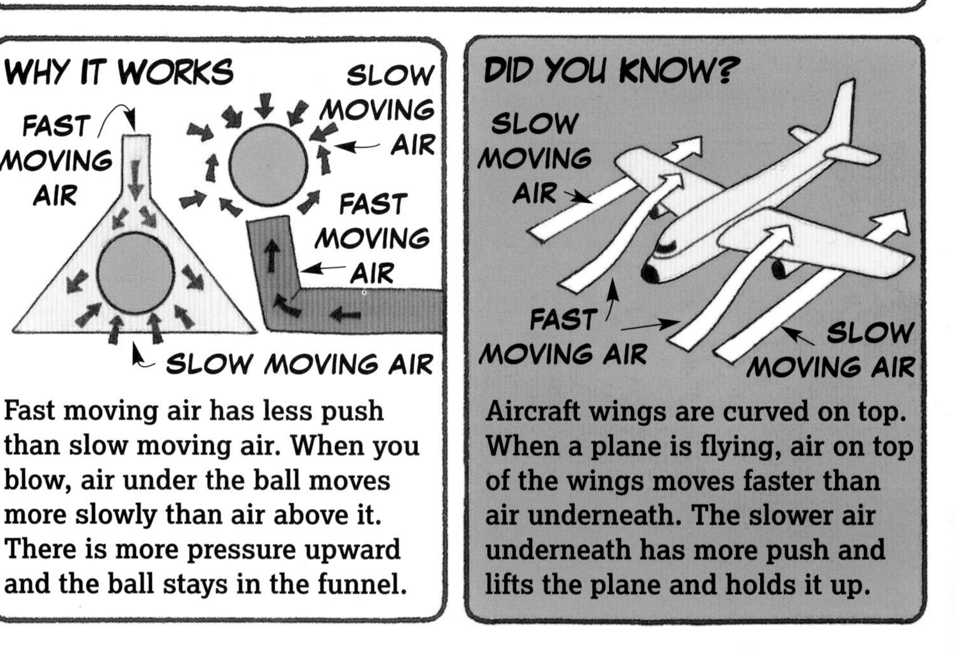

Fast moving air has less push than slow moving air. When you blow, air under the ball moves more slowly than air above it. There is more pressure upward and the ball stays in the funnel.

DID YOU KNOW?

Aircraft wings are curved on top. When a plane is flying, air on top of the wings moves faster than air underneath. The slower air underneath has more push and lifts the plane and holds it up.

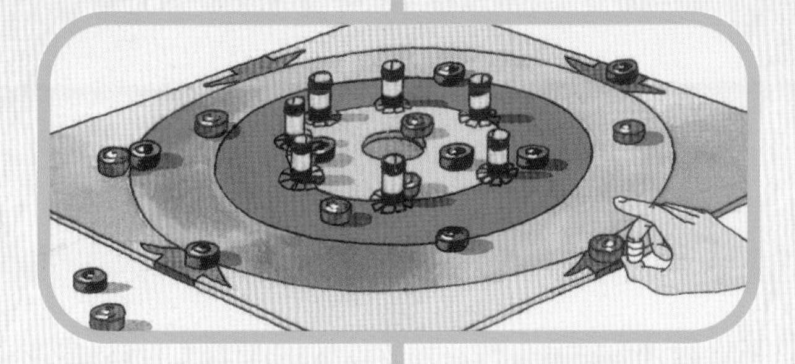

Action games

Getting ready

These are the things you need to make the games in this section:

- Thick cardboard – cut from strong cardboard boxes which you can get in stores.
- Thin cardboard – cut from empty cereal packets, backs of writing pads, or folders which you can buy in stationery stores.
- Glue – use a waterproof glue.
- Sheet sponge – artificial sponge sold in sheets in many stores.
- Model clay – sold in toy stores.
- Tiddly wink counters – flat, round plastic counters sold in packets in toy stores.
- Draught counters – wooden or plastic counters used to play draughts and sold in toy stores.
- Garden canes – buy in garden or flower stores.
- Eye screws – buy in hardware stores.
- Paint – use poster paint or water paints.
- Tracing paper – use greaseproof paper or very thin, see-through paper.

Ask your friends to help you collect things like:

Plastic and cardboard cartons, such as empty yoghurt, cream and cheese pots.

Cardboard tubes – from kitchen and toilet rolls.

Cardboard or plastic egg boxes.

Bag ties – used to tie up freezer and garbage bags.

Cardboard boxes in lots of sizes.

Empty squeezy bottles.

Corks, empty matchboxes, hairpins, pipe cleaners, marbles and cardboard cheese boxes.

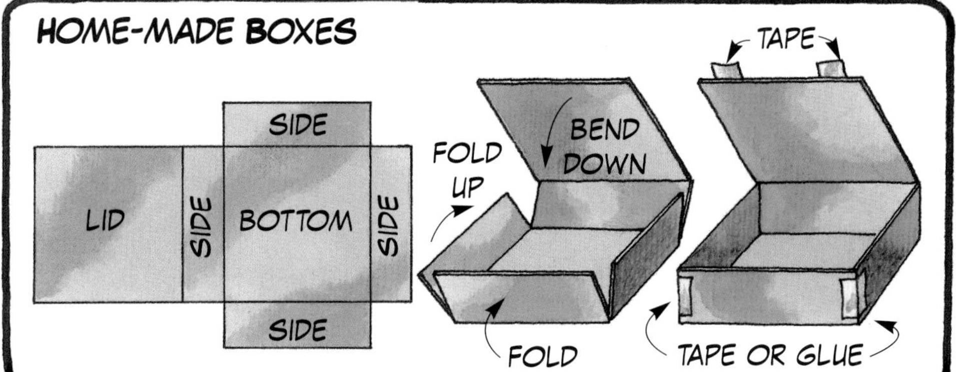

You can make a cardboard box. Use a ruler to draw the lines. The lid and bottom are the same size and the sides are all the same size.

Fold the cardboard, as shown, to make the lid, bottom and sides. Stick the side and the bottom together with glue or tape.

One way to choose the starter of a game is for all the players to throw a dice. The one with the highest number starts.

Or hold different length straws. Each player picks one. The one with the longest straw starts.

Measure and punch holes every 10cm (4in) on a cardboard strip. Stick pencils through two holes. Holding both pencils, swing one around in a circle.

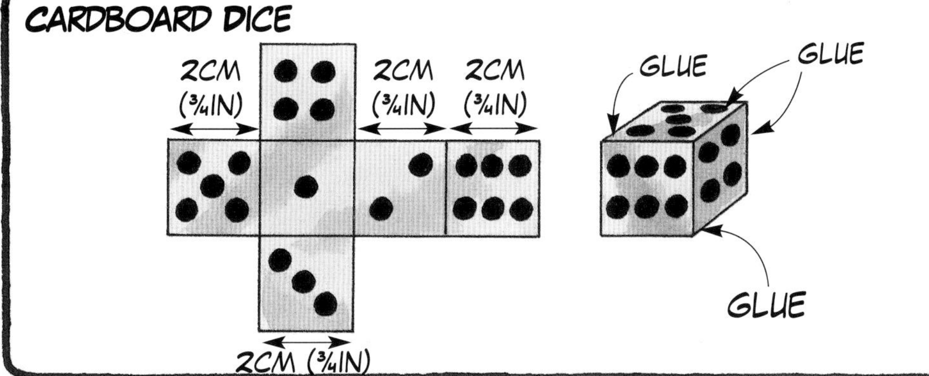

To make cardboard dice, draw this shape, with all the sides 2cm (¾in) long, on thin cardboard. Paint the dots in each square.

Fold inwards along the lines and glue the sides and top together. The two sides opposite each other should add up to seven.

To make a dice, shape some model clay into a cube and mark in the dots with a pencil point. You can also use a sugar lump.

Cut strips of paper and draw an X on one. Fold them and jumble them up. The player with the X starts. With only two players, toss a coin.

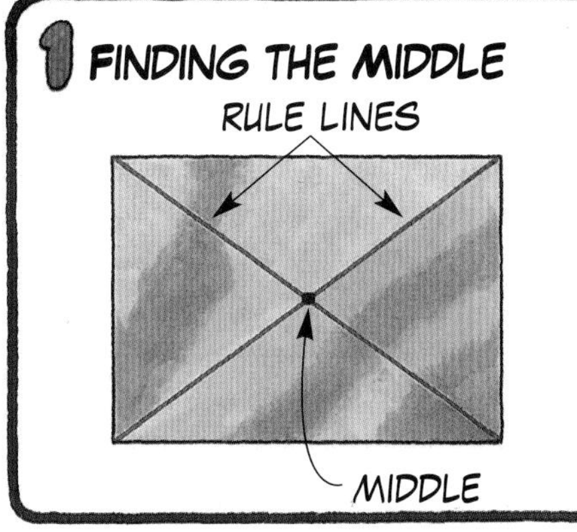

To find the middle of a box or a sheet of paper, rule lines across it from the four corners, like this. The middle is where the lines cross.

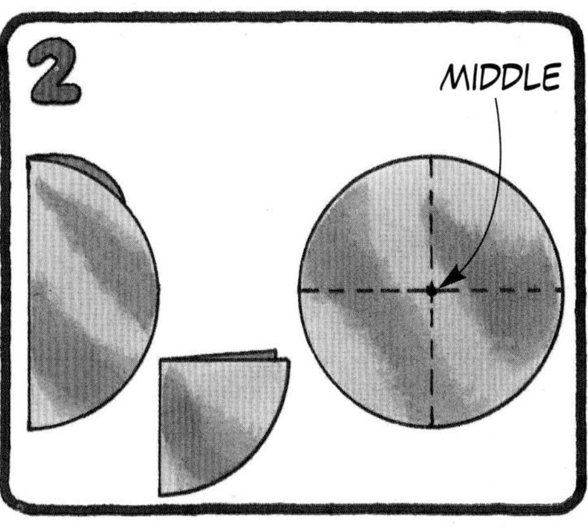

To find the middle of a circle, fold it in half twice, like this. Open the circle out again. The middle is where the two folds cross.

Five minute games

(For lots of players)

The games on these two pages are very easy to make and only take a few minutes to play.

YOU WILL NEED

For Egg Flip
- 2 card egg boxes and a fork

For Catchball
- 2 tall plastic cartons
- a ping pong ball
- 8 rubber bands
- thin and thick cardboard

For Blow Football
- 2 small cardboard boxes
- model clay and 2 straws
- a ping pong ball

For Ribbon Roll
- 1 tall, plastic carton
- 5 small yoghurt pots
- ribbon, about 90cm (3ft) long
- a pin
- thick cardboard and white paper
- 5 marbles

For Matchbox Bullseye
- thin cardboard and a matchbox

For all the games
- paint, glue, scissors, a pencil and sticky tape

(a) Cut the tops off both egg boxes and throw them away. Cut the six egg holders out of the bottom of one. (b) Paint each egg holder a different shade. Leave to dry.

(c) Paint the six holes in the bottom of the second egg box. Make them the same shades as the egg holders, like this.

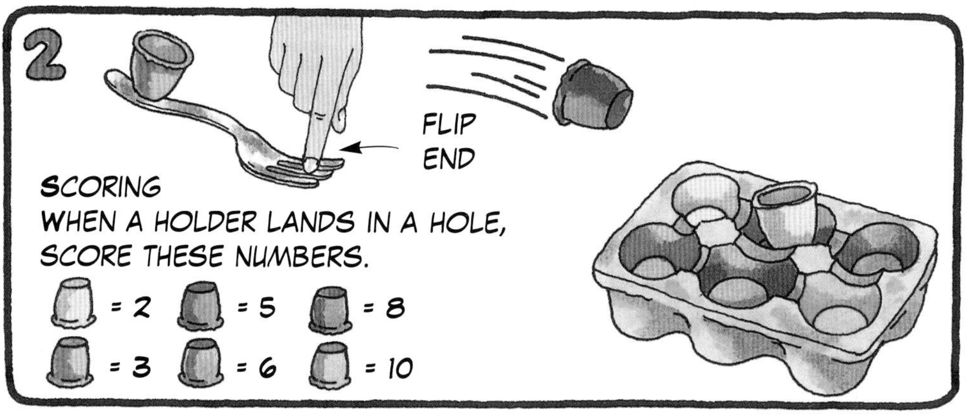

Put the painted egg box bottom on the floor. Put a fork about 45cm (1½ft) from the box. To play, balance an egg holder, open end up, on the handle end of the fork.

Push down quickly on the prongs and try to flip the holder into a hole in the egg box. Mark down the score. A holder that lands in the same-shaded hole scores double.

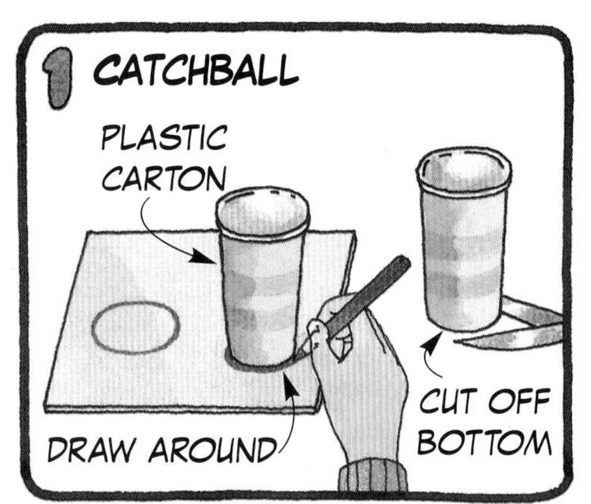

Draw two circles on cardboard. Cut them out 1-2cm (½in) smaller all the way around. Then cut off the bottom of the carton.

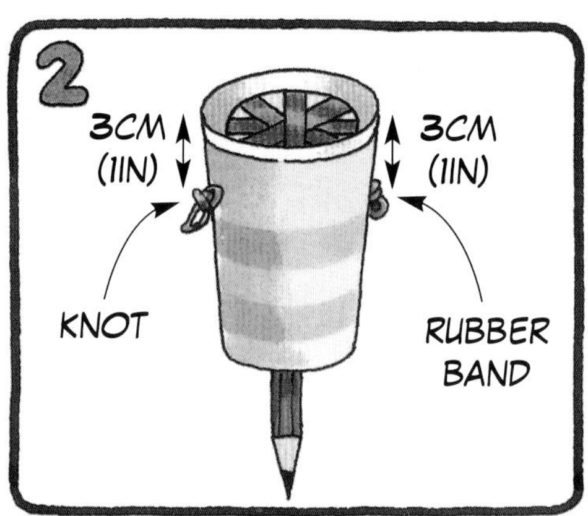

Make a catcher in the same way as a cannon (see page 61). Instead of a cardboard tube, use the carton and circles you have cut out.

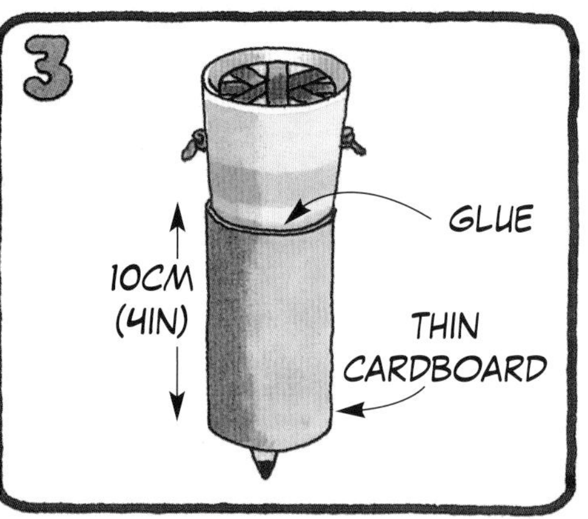

Cut some thin cardboard, 23cm (9in) wide and 10cm (4in) long. Glue it around the bottom of the catcher. Make another catcher.

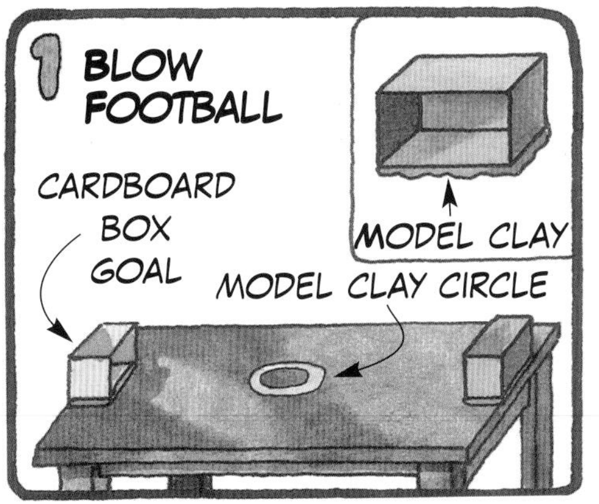

Put some model clay on the bottom of two small boxes. Push them, model clay side down, on to the ends of a table. Put a model clay circle in the middle.

Two people, or four people playing in teams of two, can play. To start, put a ping pong ball in the model clay circle in the middle of the table, like this.

The players each have a straw and stand on either side of the table. The idea is to blow the ping pong ball, using the straws, into the other team's goal.

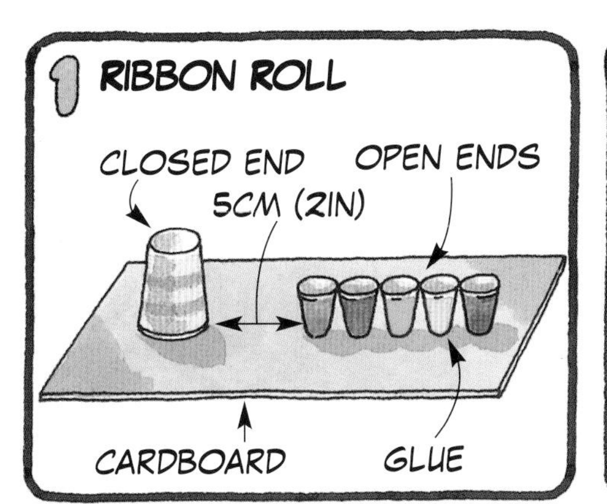

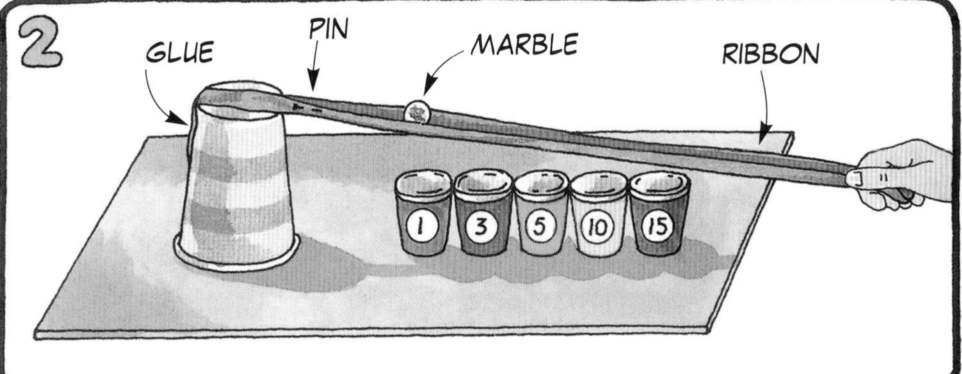

Glue five yoghurt pots, open ends up and touching each other, to cardboard. Glue a tall, plastic carton, open end down, about 5cm (2in) from the first pot.

Glue one end of some ribbon, about 3cm (1in) wide and 90cm (3ft) long, to the top of the carton. Pin the ribbon together close to the carton so that it makes a funnel.

Draw these numbers on pieces of paper. Glue them on the pots. Roll marbles, one by one, down the ribbon and try to get them into the pots. Roll five marbles in a turn.

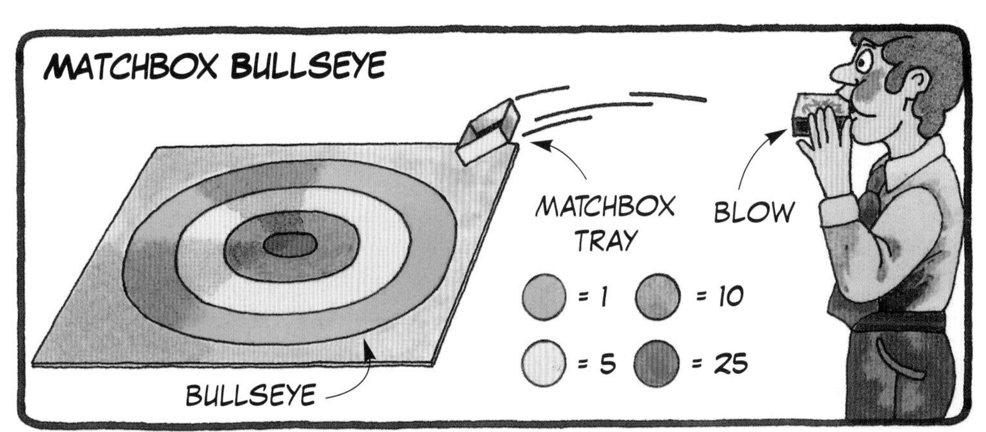

Stand 3m (10ft) apart. The game is to fire and catch a ball with the catchers. The player who catches the ball five times in a row wins.

Draw a big circle on cardboard. Draw three smaller circles inside. Paint them different shades. When they're dry, paint on the numbers.

Stand 3m (10ft) from the board. Put a matchbox to your mouth and blow so the tray shoots on to the circles. Have three blows in a turn.

Mouse trap

(For 3 or more players. Each player needs a cork mouse.)

YOU WILL NEED

- a cork for each player
- pieces of string, each about 40cm (16in) long
- a hairpin and felt cloth
- scissors and strong glue
- a big carton or little box
- thin cardboard
- a used matchstick or a toothpick
- tracing paper and a pencil
- paint and a paint brush
- a circle of cardboard for the cardboard mat

Paint the corks different shades. Leave them to dry. Then make a hole through the middle of each cork, using closed scissors or a knitting needle, like this.

Loop string around a hairpin. Then push the hairpin through the hole in a cork and double-knot the end of the string. Repeat this on all the corks.

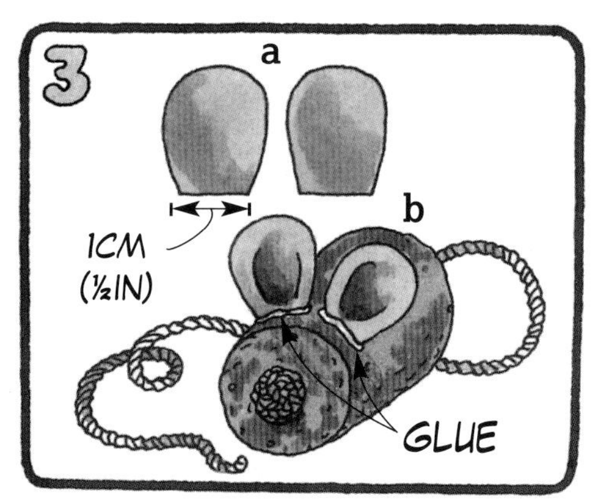

(a) To make the mouse ears, cut out two pieces of felt. (b) Glue them to the top of the cork. Put two ears on each of the cork mice.

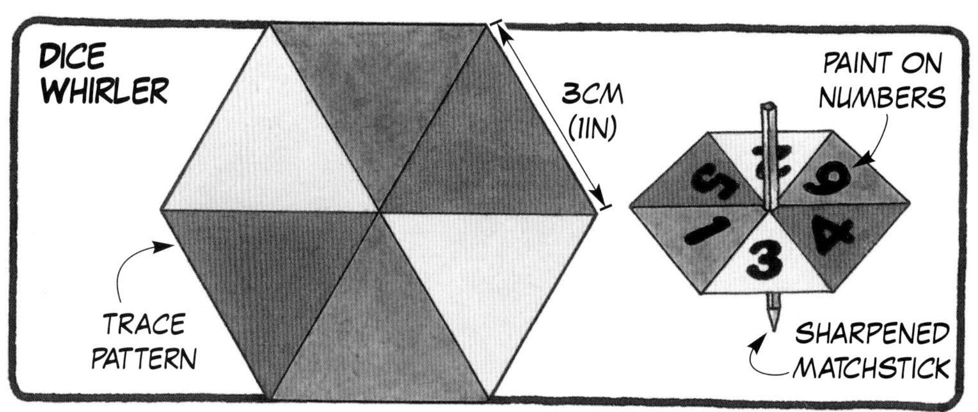

Trace this pattern onto thin cardboard. Rule lines from corner to corner, like this. Cut out the shape very carefully.

Paint the triangles and write or paint on the numbers. Sharpen one end of a used match. Push it through the middle of the whirler.

HOW TO PLAY

Players spin the whirler. The one with the highest number is the trapper. The others are the holders. Each holder puts his mouse on the mat and holds its tail. The trapper spins the whirler. When it stops on a 6 or 4 he tries to trap the mice under the carton. The holders try to pull them away. If the trapper catches a mouse he scores 5 points. Holders score 5 points if they get away in time.

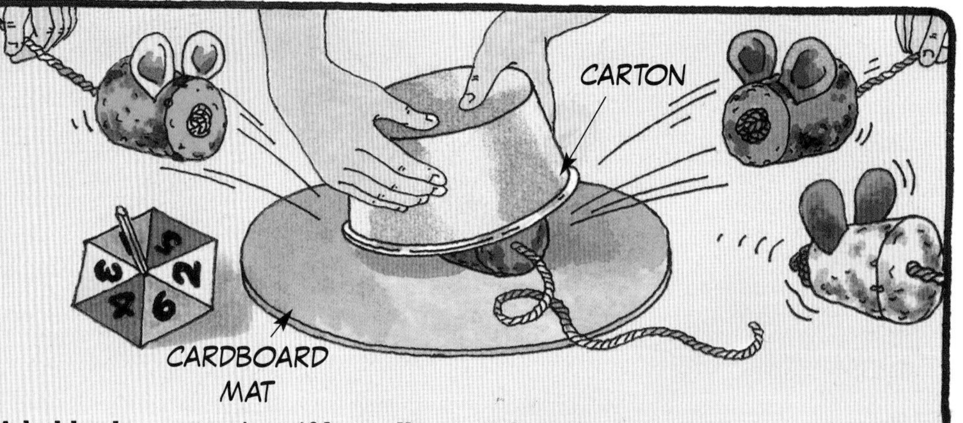

A holder loses 5 points if he pulls his mouse away when the whirler stops on a number other than 6 or 4. The first to score 50 wins.

When the trapper has spun a 6 or 4 three times, he passes the carton to the player on the left who becomes the new trapper.

Fish hook

(For 2 or more players)

Hook as many cork fish before the salt runs out of the timer.

YOU WILL NEED

- 6 corks
- 6 eye screws or hairpins
- some felt cloth
- strong glue and white paper
- a stick, about 50cm (20in) long
- salt or fine sand
- a hairpin, string
- scissors and paint
- a plastic squeezy bottle
- a glass jar

Put the fish, screw ends up, on the floor. Take it in turns to hook the fish with the rod. Add up the numbers on the fish you have hooked after each turn.

A turn lasts as long as it takes for the salt to pour out of the squeezy bottle, once the lid has been opened. The first player to score 20 points wins.

Paint six corks different shades. Screw an eye screw into the middle of each cork, or push a hairpin into the cork, like this.

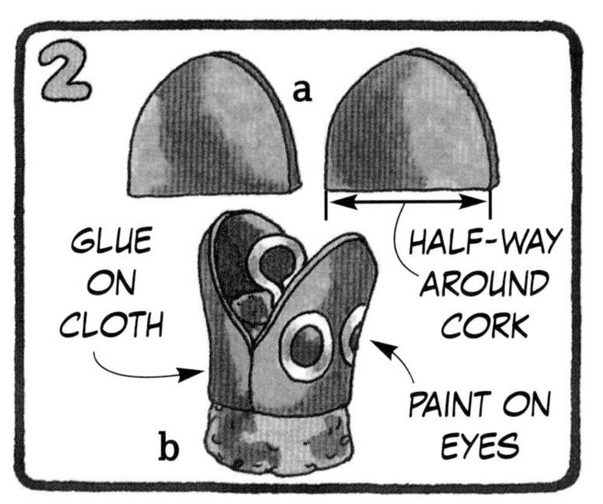

(a) Cut two pieces of felt, so each can wrap half-way around a cork. (b) Glue the felt on the cork and paint on eyes. Repeat on all corks.

Cut out six pieces of white paper and glue one to the bottom of each cork. Paint numbers from one to six on the corks, like this.

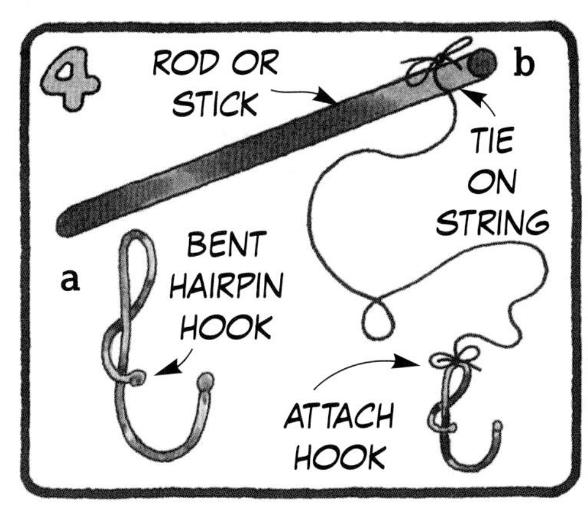

Tie string, 58cm (2ft) long, to one end of a stick. (a) Bend a hairpin or wire into a hook, and then (b) tie it to the end of the string.

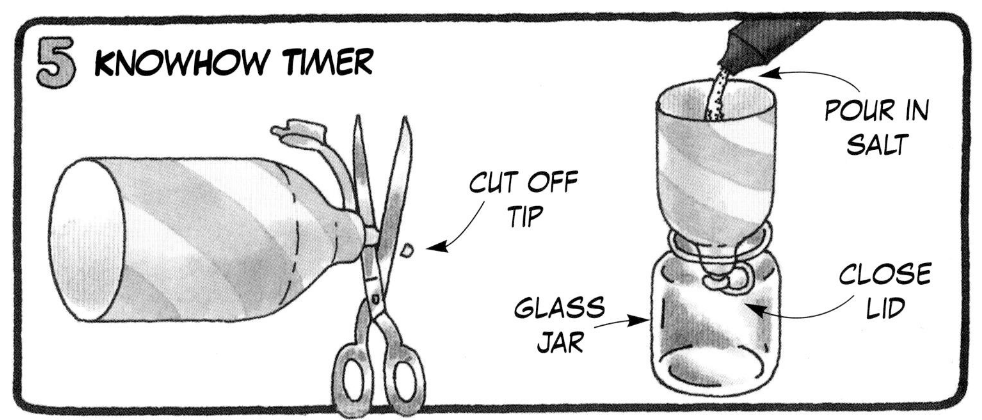

Cut a squeezy bottle in half. Cut off the very tip of the bottle. Paint the bottle with some bright paint. Leave it to dry.

Close the lid and balance the squeezy bottle, upside down, in a glass jar. Fill the bottle with salt or fine sand, like this.

Cannonboard

(For 2 or more players)

The further you pull the pencil out of the cannon, the faster the marbles will go. Pull it very gently to get marbles into the goals nearest the cannon.

YOU WILL NEED

- a cardboard box, 34cm (14in) wide, 46cm (18in) long
- a sheet of thin cardboard
- a strong cardboard tube, about 14cm (5½in) long
- 4 rubber bands
- 6 marbles
- sticky tape and strong glue
- a pencil, a ruler and scissors

HOW TO PLAY

Fire the marbles out of the cannon and try to get them into the goals with the high numbers. Each player fires six marbles in a turn. After each turn, add the plus scores and take away the minus scores. The first player with 100 wins.

To fire, put one marble at a time into the top of the cannon. Pull back the pencil and let go.

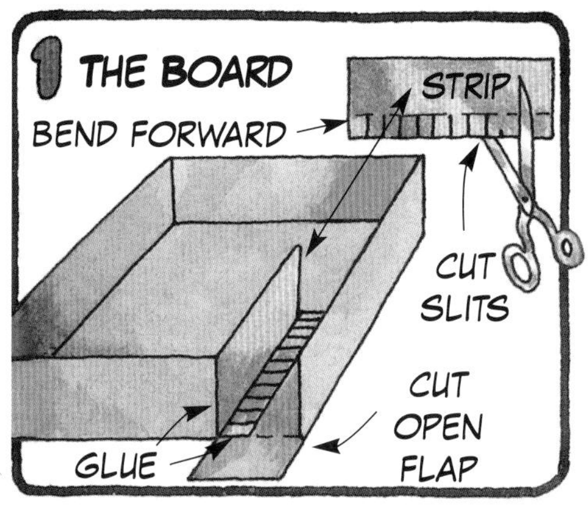

Cut a flap, 6cm (2½in) wide, at one corner of the box. Cut a strip of cardboard half the length of the box and as high. Cut slits on one side. Glue the strip to the box.

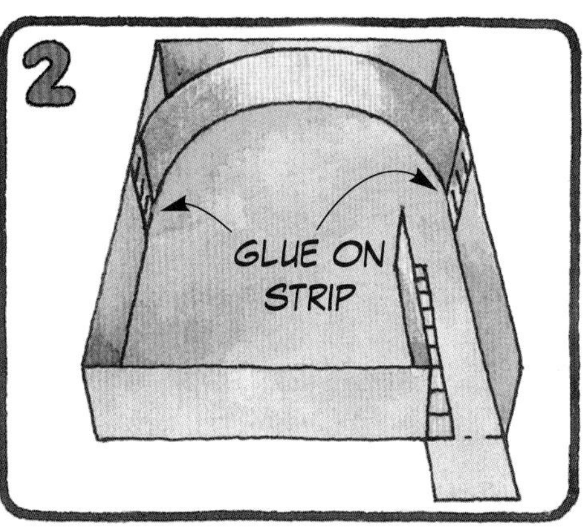

Cut a strip of cardboard 1½ times the width of the box and as high. Cut slits at both ends. Bend the strip into a half-circle and glue it to the sides of the box.

To make the goals, cut 13 pieces of cardboard, about 8cm (3in) long and 3cm (1in) wide. Cut slits at one edge of each piece. Bend them into half-circles. Glue them onto the box.

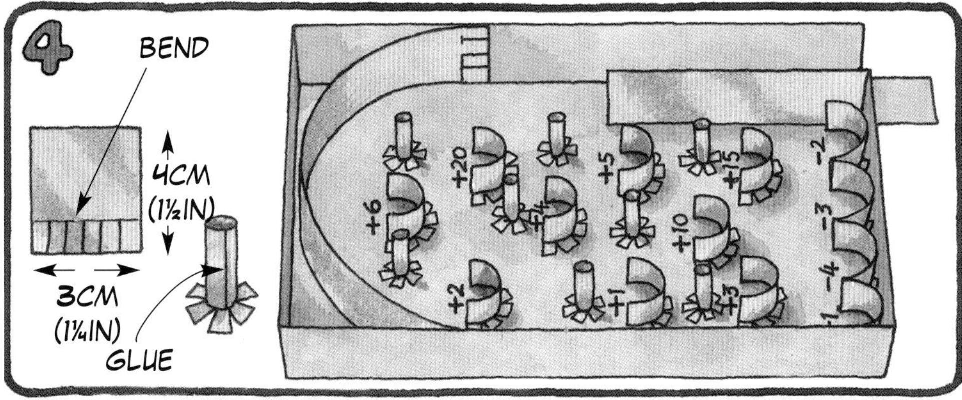

Cut out eight strips of cardboard, about 4cm (1½in) x 3cm (1¼in). Cut slits along the edge of each strip. Then roll them into small posts and glue them.

Now glue the posts onto the box, like this. They are hazards and make the game a bit harder to play. Draw or paint the plus and minus numbers inside each goal.

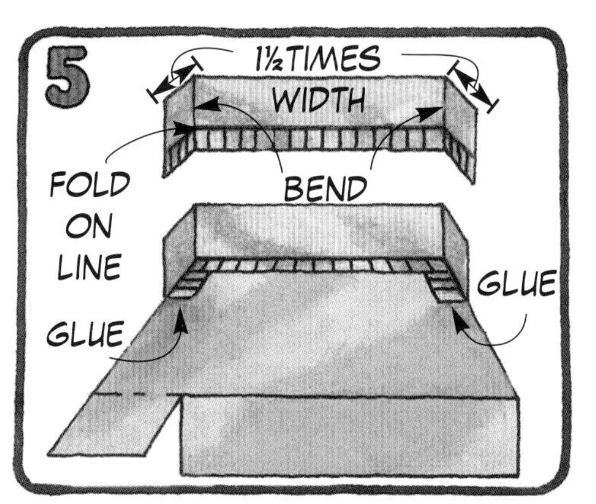

Cut some cardboard 1½ times the box width and 6cm (2½in) high. Cut slits along the edge. Bend the cardboard on the red lines. Then glue it to the back of the box.

Using the tube, draw two circles on cardboard. Cut them slightly smaller than the tube. Glue together. Make a hole in them.

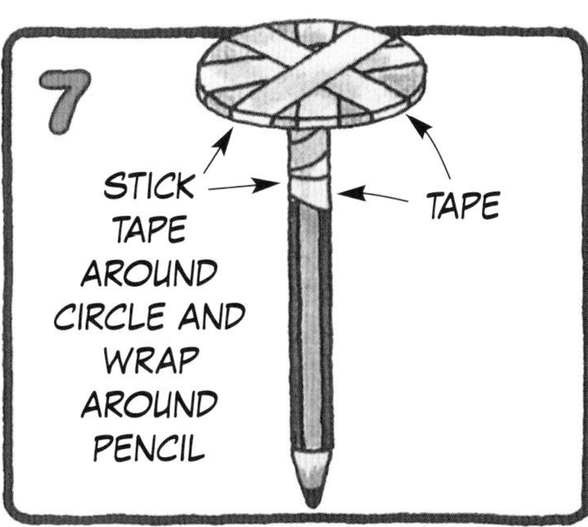

Push the end of a pencil through the hole in the cardboard circle. Tape the circle onto the pencil very firmly, like this.

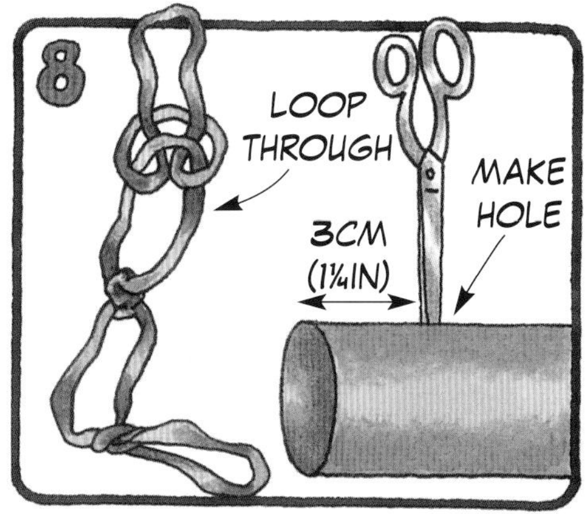

Link four strong rubber bands together, like this. Make a hole on either side of the tube, about 3cm (1¼in) from one end.

Thread the rubber bands through the holes in the cardboard tube, like this. Knot both ends very loosely.

Push the cardboard circle and pencil up the tube. Pull one rubber band over the circle then the other, like this. Untie the loose knots.

Make a hole half-way up the two pieces of cardboard, about 2cm (¾in) from the open flap. Push the rubber band ends through the holes. Double-knot each end.

Flick billiards

(For 2 players or 2 teams)

To play this game, one player or team needs ten counters of one shade. The other player or team needs ten counters of a different shade. Glue a circle of paper to the top of an extra counter. We have used black and red counters.

YOU WILL NEED

- a low cardboard box, about 72cm x 50cm (2ft 4in x 1ft 8in)
- legs cut off from nylon tights
- 21 draught counters
- a small yoghurt pot
- thin cardboard
- sticky tape and strong glue
- scissors and a pencil

Draw a circle in each corner on the inside of the box, using a small yoghurt pot as a guide. Cut out the four circles.

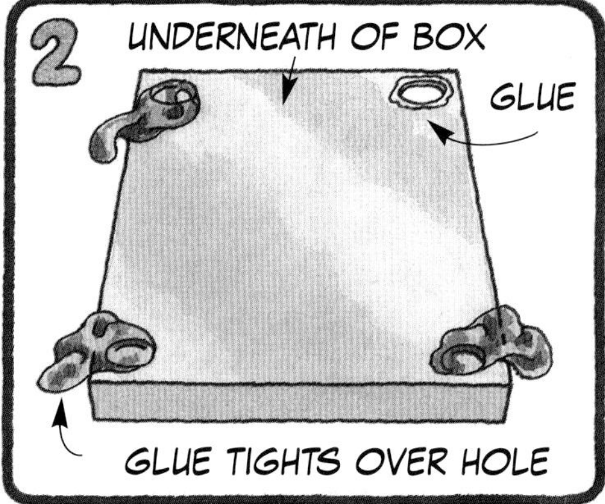

To make the corner nets, cut the feet off two pairs of old tights. Glue one foot over each hole on the underside of the box.

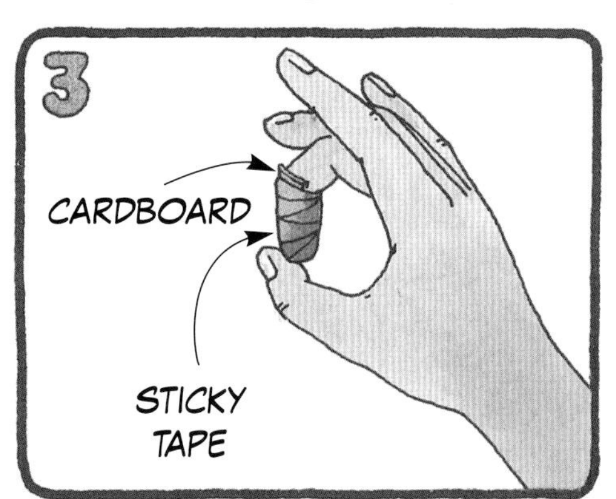

To make the finger guard, cut a strip of thin cardboard. Put it over the nail of your third finger. Wrap sticky tape around it, like this.

HOW TO PLAY

The player with black counters starts, flicking a black counter against a red one. They get another turn if they get the red one into a corner net. If not, the player with red counters tries to flick a black one into a net. If either player flicks the extra counter into a net, they pick one of their counters and the extra one out of the net and put them back on the board. The first to flick all the other side's counters into the nets wins.

This picture shows how to set out the counters at the start of the game.

Tiddly pong

(For 2 players)

This is just like ordinary ping pong except that you can play on a small table. Both players need a bat to hit the ball to each other.

YOU WILL NEED

- a sheet of thick cardboard
- thin cardboard
- a sheet of sponge
- a saucer
- an old pair of tights
- a ping pong ball
- strong glue and sticky tape
- scissors and string
- a safety pin and 4 pencils

Rule two lines, 4cm (1½in) apart and 10cm (4in) long, on thick cardboard. Draw a circle at the bottom of the lines, with a saucer. Cut out and glue together. Repeat.

Using the same saucer, draw four circles on a sheet of sponge. Cut them out. Then glue a sponge circle to both sides of a cardboard bat, like this.

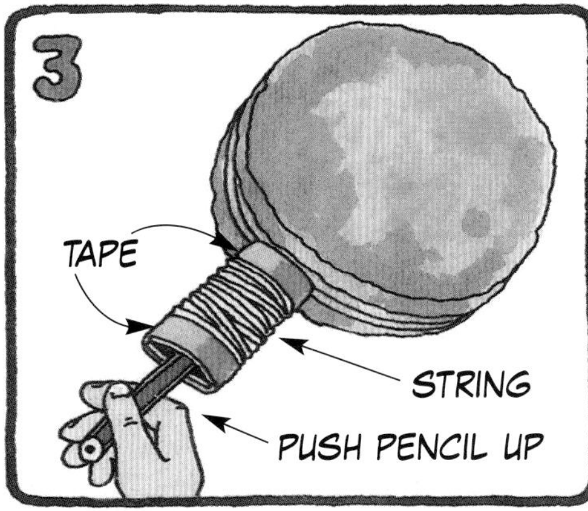

Wrap string tightly around the handle of each bat. Then glue the ends and wrap sticky tape around them. Push a pencil up the handles, between the cardboard.

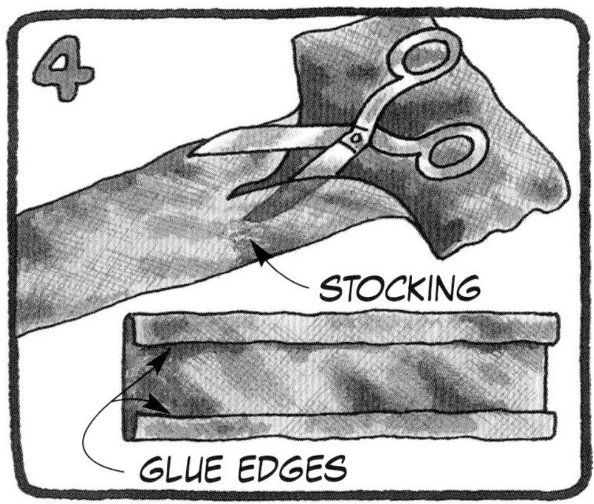

To make the net, cut the foot off an old pair of tights. Cut open the stocking. Then fold over and glue about 2cm (¾in) at both edges, as shown here.

Cut two pieces of 80cm (2ft 8in) string. Loop them, one at a time, through a closed safety pin. Thread them through the folded stocking. Tie to two pencils.

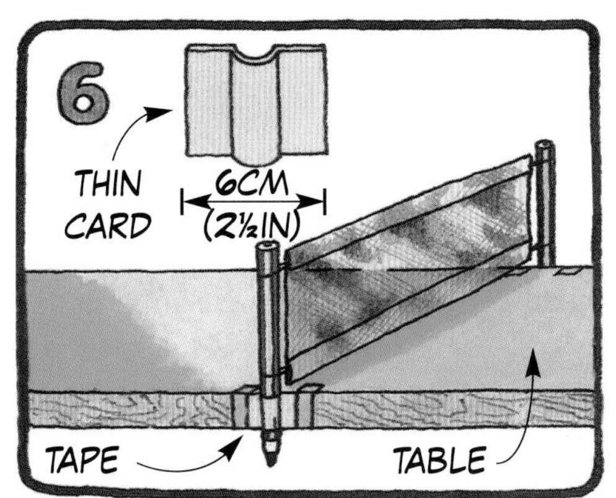

Cut two pieces of thin cardboard as deep as the lip on the table and about 6cm (2½in) wide. Tape one to the middle of each side of the table. Push the pencils into them.

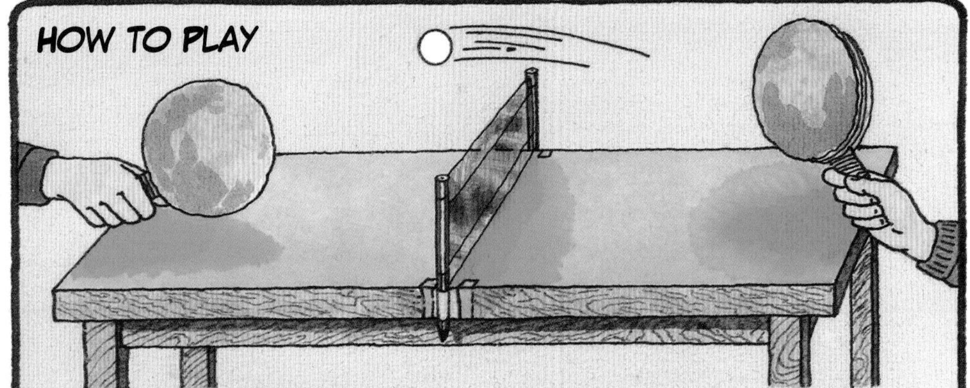

The aim is to be the first to score 21 points. You score a point when the other player can't return your shot. Take it in turns to serve the ball.

Each player has 5 serves in a turn. The ball must bounce on both sides of the table when you serve. It mustn't bounce on your side when you return a shot.

Sticks and kicks

(For 2 players)

YOU WILL NEED

- strong cardboard box, about 48cm (19in) long, 25cm (10in) wide and 8cm (3in) deep
- thick cardboard
- a cardboard egg box
- a strong cardboard tube (from a kitchen roll)
- 2 small string bags or tights
- 4 garden canes or 4 thin sticks, each about 60cm (2ft) long
- model clay and 4 corks
- 4 big rubber bands
- a pencil and paint
- a small ball or large marble

HOW TO PLAY

Put the box on a table. Put the ball inside the circle on the middle line. Players stand on either side of the table and hold a rod in each hand. Both start together.

The idea is to twist, push and pull the canes to kick the ball into the other team's goal. The first team to score three goals is the winner.

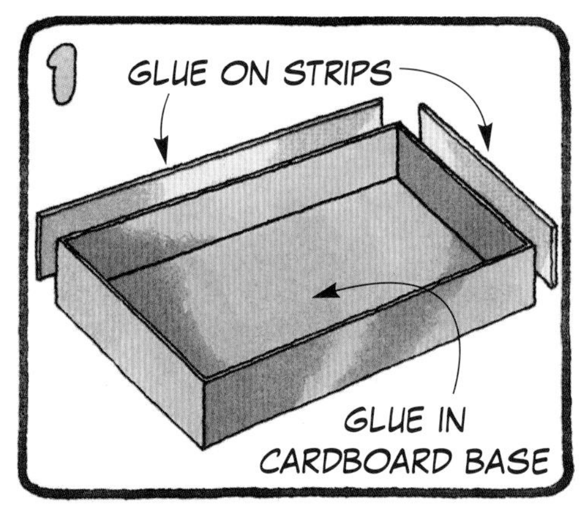

Cut some cardboard the size of the bottom of the box. Glue it inside the box, like this. Glue strips of cardboard to the sides and ends of the box too.

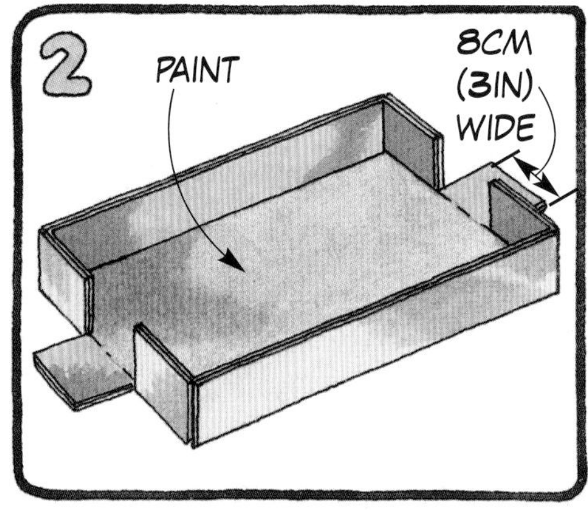

Cut a flap, about 8cm (3in) wide, at both ends of the box, like this. Then paint the cardboard base a grassy green. Leave it to dry.

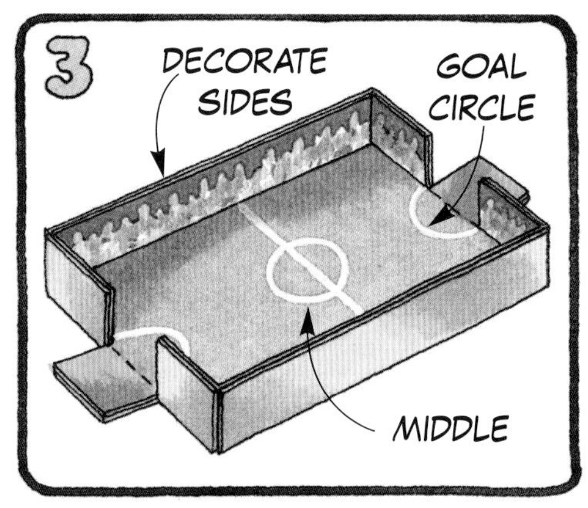

Draw a line across the middle of the inside of the box. Draw a circle on the line, like this, using a cup as a guide. Draw half-circles around the goal flaps.

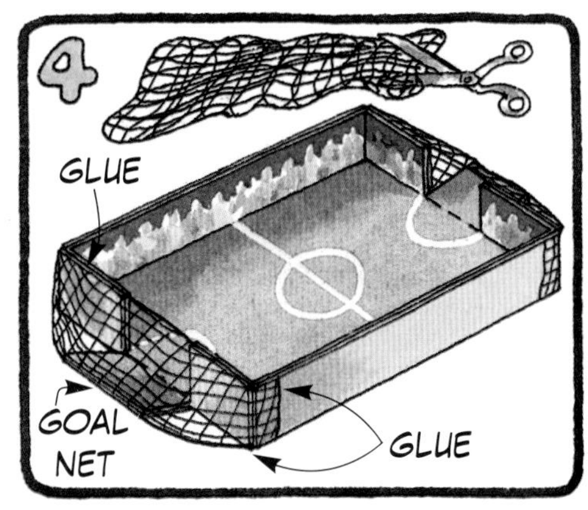

To make a goal net, cut open a string bag. Put one edge under the goal flap. Glue it underneath the box. Glue the other edge to the sides and top of the box.

To make the footballers, cut the kitchen roll into six tubes, each 6cm (2½in) long. Cut the six egg holders out of the egg box. Glue one holder to the top of each tube.

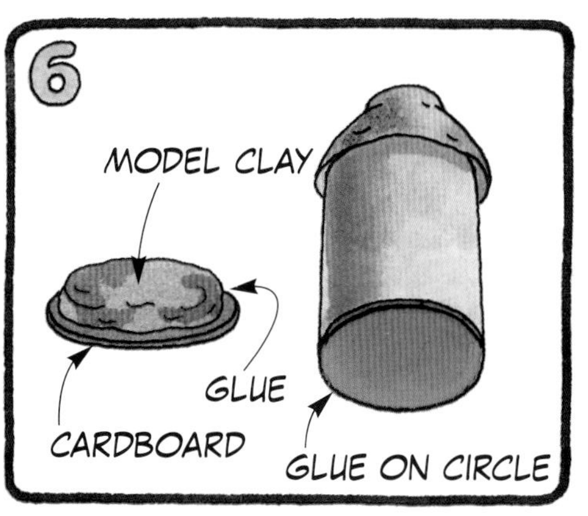

Draw around the bottom of each tube on cardboard. Cut out the circles. Glue model clay to each one. Glue a circle, model clay inside, to the bottom of each tube.

Paint faces on all the cardboard tubes. Some can look happy, some sad. Paint three footballers in one team shade and the other three in a different team shade.

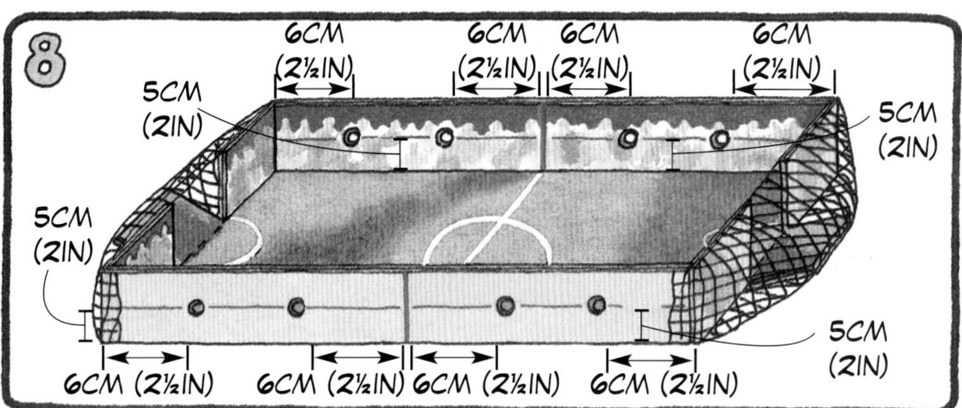

Measure the length of the sides of your box. Divide it exactly in half to find the middle. Rule lines at the middle on both sides of the box, as shown here.

Make holes 6cm (2½in) from both sides of the middle lines and 5cm (2in) from the bottom. Make holes 6cm (2½in) from both ends and 5cm (2in) from the bottom.

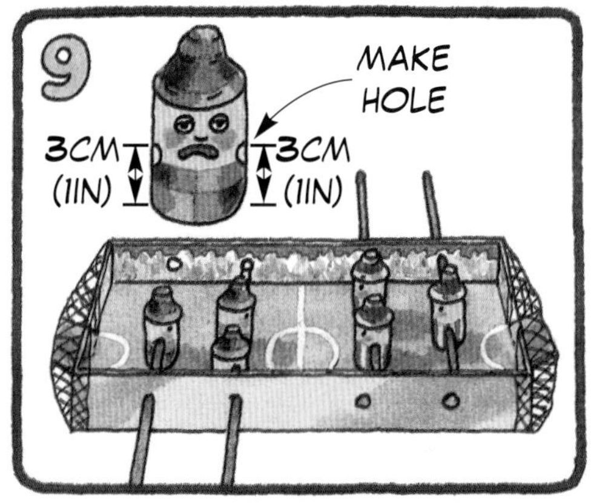

Push the canes through the holes. Make holes in each tube. Push one team on to the canes at one end and the other team on to the canes at the other end.

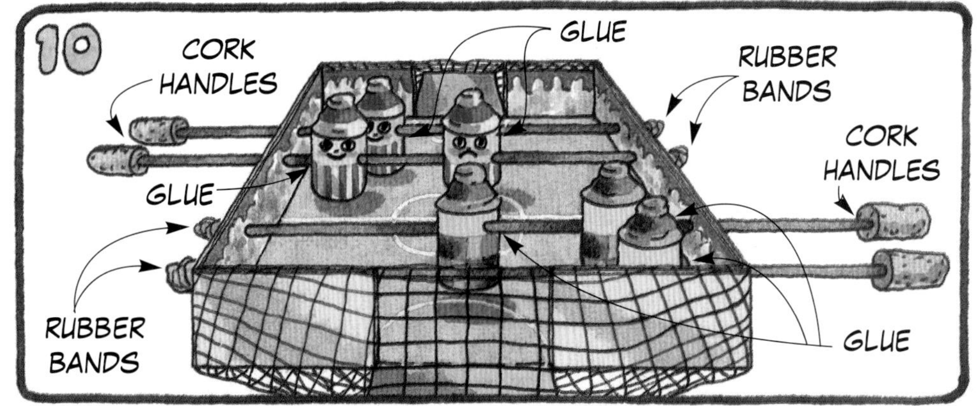

Push each cane through the hole on the other side. Wrap a rubber band around the end of each cane, to stop them from getting pulled back through the holes.

Push corks on to the other ends to make handles. Pull the rods so the rubber bands are against the box sides. Glue the footballers to the canes in position, like this.

Grand derby

(For 2 or more players)

This is a horse race which you can play on any big table. Each player needs a horse and a jockey, and a piece of string long enough to loop around the table.

YOU WILL NEED

- thin cardboard
- tracing paper
- a pencil and paint
- string and scissors
- strong glue
- model clay
- wire bag ties, pipe cleaners or thin wire

To make a horse, draw the horse, saddle and platform patterns on tracing paper. Then trace the patterns onto thin cardboard.

Cut the three shapes out of the cardboard. Cut along the red lines on the horse's feet. Paint the shapes and leave them to dry.

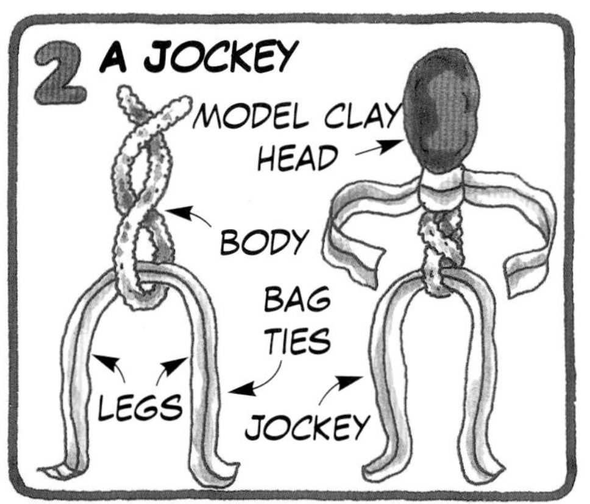

Twist two bag ties or pieces of wire together for the legs and body. Twist another around the body to make arms. Push a model clay head on the body.

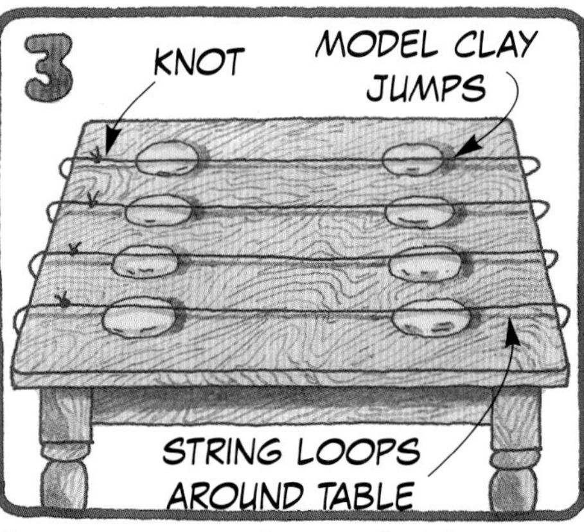

Loop as many pieces of string as there are players around a table. Knot the ends. Press pieces of model clay down on the table under the strings, to make jumps.

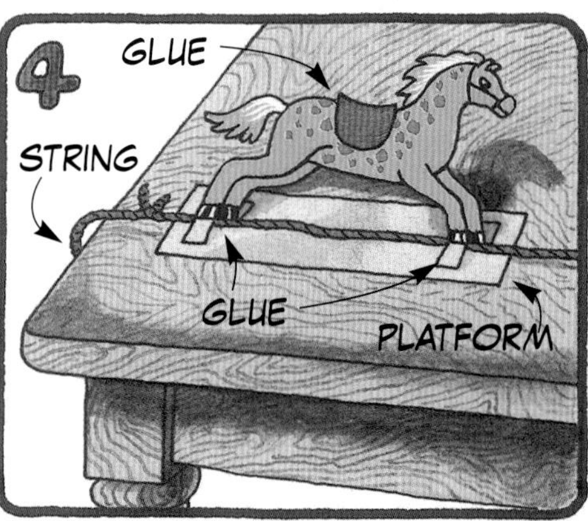

Glue a saddle on to the back of each horse. Put a horse over each string. Pull the string up the slits on the horses' feet. Bend the slits, like this. Glue them to a platform.

HOW TO PLAY

The game is to race your horse from one end of the table to the other without letting the jockey fall off. The horses must go over the jumps on the way. Anybody whose jockey falls off goes back to the beginning.

To start, put the jockeys on the saddles. Line the horses at the start. Stand at that end of the table and pull the string under the table toward you. The first player to get their horse and jockey to the other end wins.

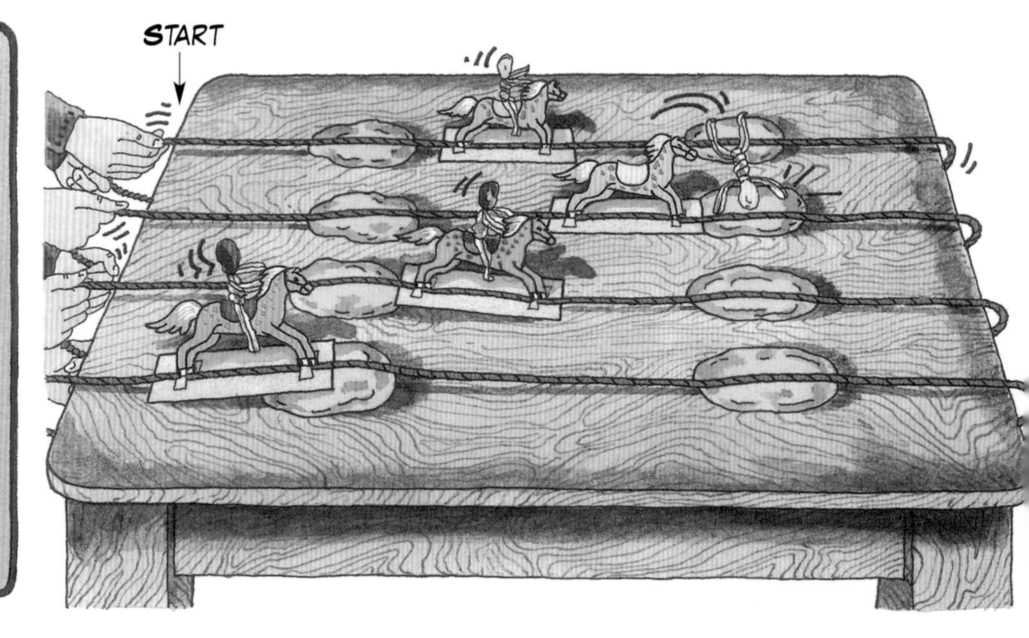

Crossing the line

(For 2 players)

Rehearse pushing the coin onto the board. Put it on the edge of the board and hit it with the palm of your hand so that it slides onto a shaded strip.

YOU WILL NEED

- thick cardboard about 30cm (1ft) wide, 32cm (12¾in) long
- thin cardboard
- a ruler and a pencil
- thin plastic wrapping and strong glue
- paint and a paint brush
- 2 coins

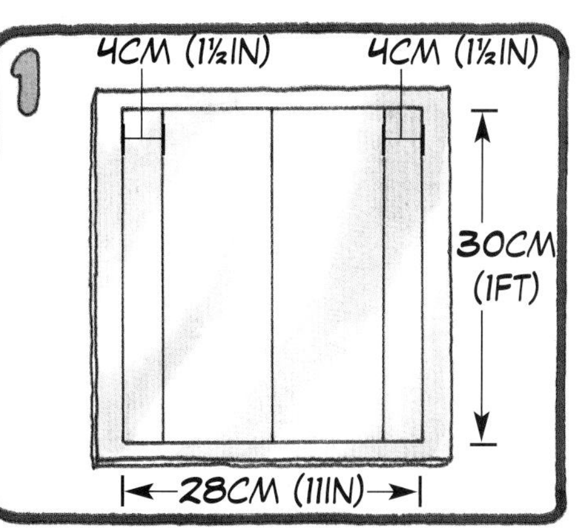

Draw a rectangle, 28cm (11in) wide and 30cm (1ft) long, on some thick cardboard. Rule lines down the middle of the rectangle and 4cm (1½in) from either side.

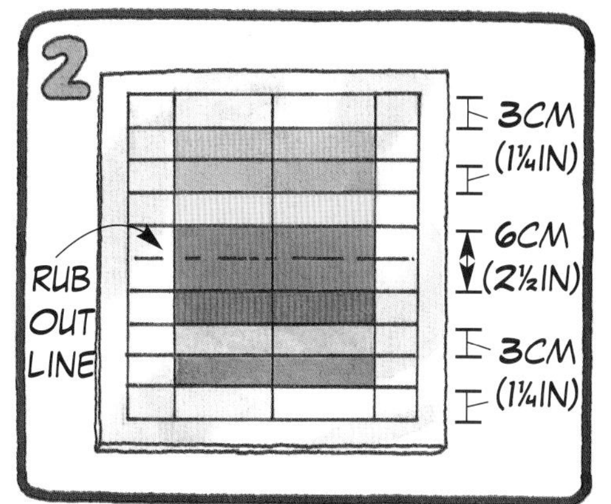

Rule 9 lines, 3cm (1¼in) apart, across the rectangle. Rub out the fifth line so that you have one 6cm (2½in) strip. Paint the seven middle strips different shades.

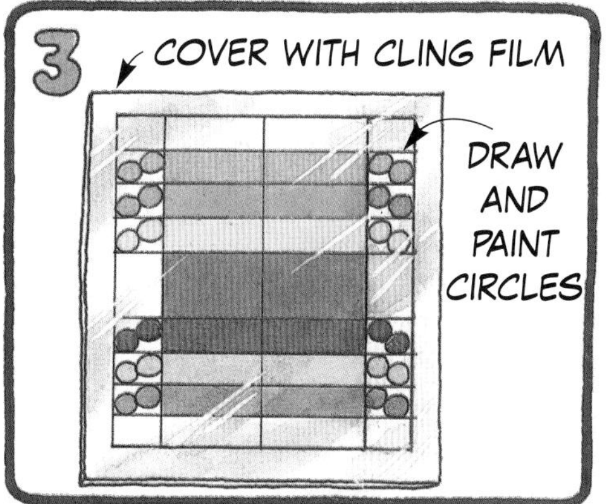

Draw two circles each side of the strips, except the middle strip, using a small coin. Paint the circles the same shades as the strips. Cover with cling film.

Using the same coin, draw 24 circles on thin cardboard. Cut them out. Then paint four circles the same shade as each of the strips, except the middle strip.

HOW TO PLAY

Put the board on the edge of a table which is not too high. Lie a heavy book behind the board, as shown above, to keep it steady while you play.

Both players have a coin of the same size and 12 cardboard circles (2 of each shade). One person plays on the left half of the board, the other player on the right half.

Start with the coins on the white strip closest to you. Take turns.

Each time the coin lands in a shaded strip, cover one of the circles beside it with the same shaded circle. If it lands on a line, wait for your next turn. If the coin lands on the middle strip, miss your next turn. The first to cover all 12 circles on their side wins.

Push and shove

(For 2 players or 2 teams)

For this board game, one player or team needs ten counters of one shade, the other needs ten of a different shade. The bigger you make the board, the more fun it is to play. Flick enemy counters off high scoring circles.

YOU WILL NEED

- a big, square sheet of thick cardboard about 64cm (25½in) long, 64cm (25½in) wide
- thin cardboard
- strong glue and scissors
- paint and a paint brush
- 20 draught counters

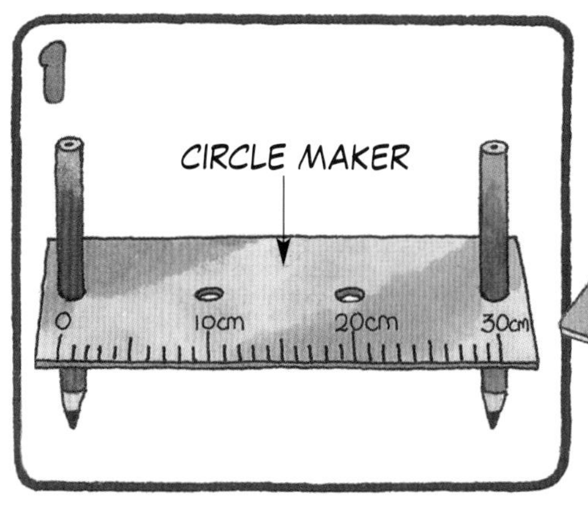

Make a KnowHow circle maker (see page 55). Punch a hole above the 0 mark, 10cm (4in) mark, 20cm (8in) mark and the 30cm (1ft) mark, as shown here.

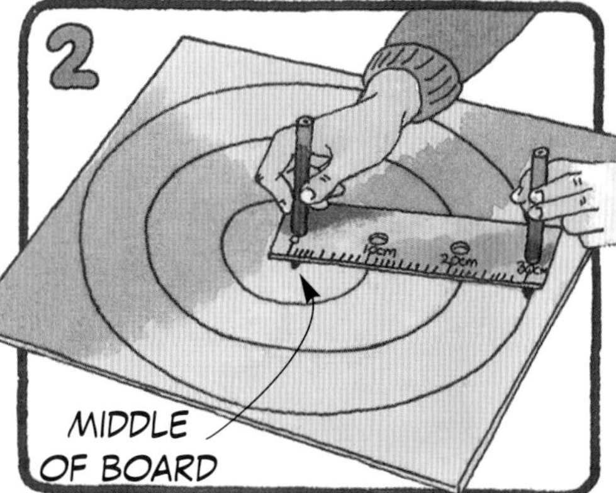

Find the middle (see page 55) of the square sheet of cardboard. Draw three circles, using the 10cm (4in), 20cm (8in) and 30cm (1ft) holes of the circle maker.

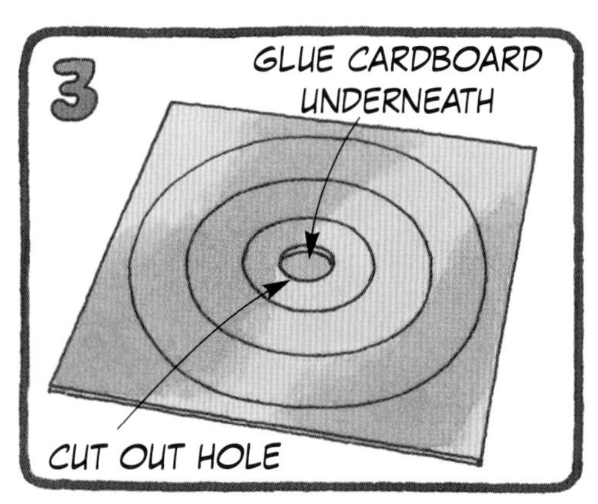

Cut a hole, a little bigger than a draught counter, out of the middle of the board. Glue a square of card underneath the hole. Then paint the circles different shades.

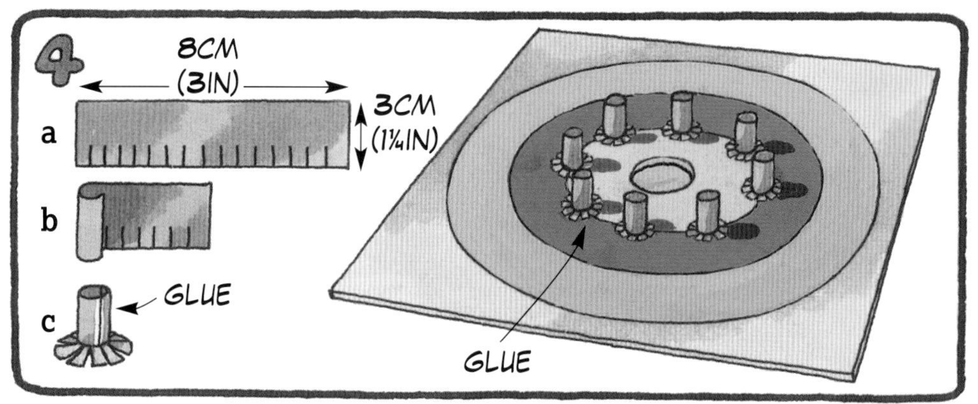

Cut eight pieces of cardboard, each 8cm (3in) x 3cm (1¼in). (a) Make cuts along one edge of each. (b) Roll them into posts. (c) Glue the ends and bend out the cuts.

Glue the posts, at equal distances, around the edge of the inside circle, like this. The space between two posts should be big enough for a draught counter to go through.

HOW TO PLAY

When two people play, each has 10 counters. If four play, in teams of two, each has 5. Partners use the same shade and sit opposite each other.

Take turns to flick the counters, one by one. Try to get them on to the high scoring circles. If a counter lands on a line, count the lower score. Try to flick them behind posts to stop being hit. The player or team with the highest score after all 20 counters have been flicked wins.

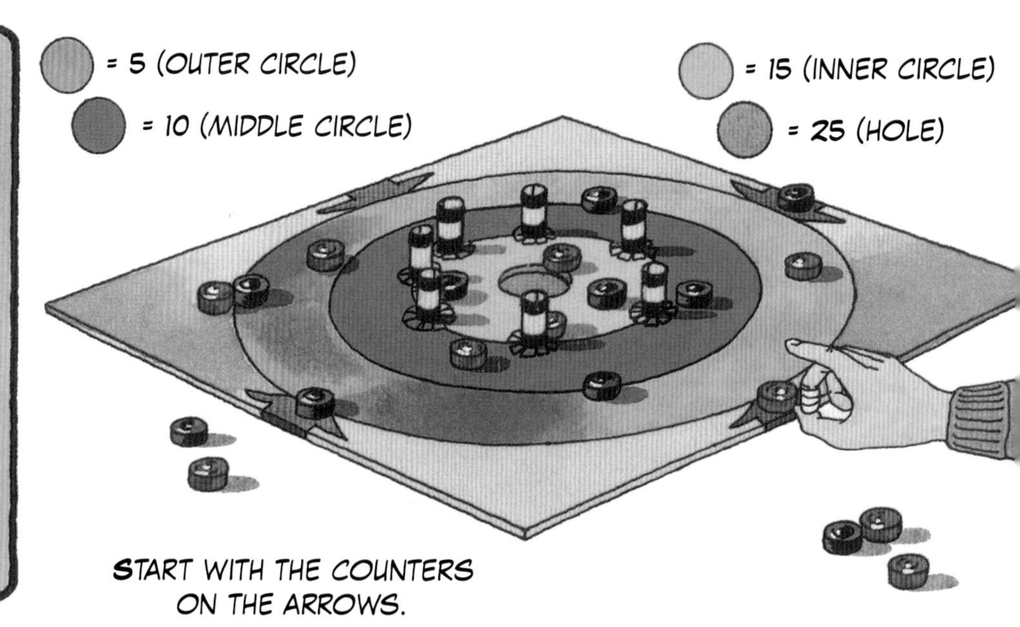

Jumpers

(For 2 or more players)

This is a different sort of tiddly winks. Try using small, very flat buttons instead of tiddly wink counters.

YOU WILL NEED

- a cardboard box, about 28cm (11in) long, 22cm (8¾in) wide and 2cm (¾in) deep
- a cardboard yoghurt pot
- a ruler, a pencil and paint
- strong glue and scissors
- one big, flat button and 5 tiddly wink counters or small, flat buttons for each player

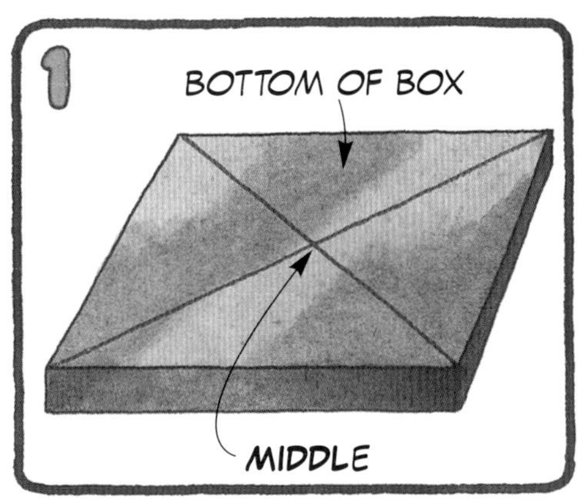

Find the middle of the box by ruling lines across it from the four corners, like this. The middle is where the lines cross.

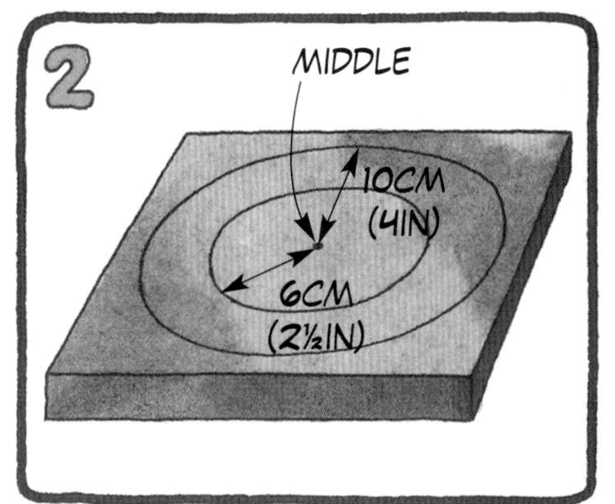

Draw a circle on the box, using the 10cm (4in) hole of the circle maker. Draw a smaller circle, using a hole punched above the 6cm (2½in) mark on the circle maker, like this.

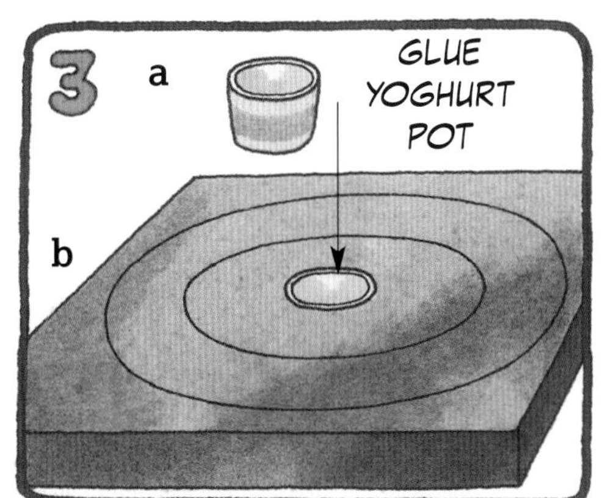

(a) Cut the top off a yoghurt pot so it is as deep as the box. Put the bottom of the pot in the middle of the box. Draw around it. Cut out the circle. (b) Glue pot in the hole.

Draw ten lines across the outside and inside circles to make ten sections in each, like this. Paint the sections different shades.

HOW TO PLAY

Draw the numbers and words in the sections. Each player has a big button and five small tiddly winks. Players sit opposite each other, about 1m (3ft) from the board.

Taking it in turns, use the button to make the tiddly winks jump onto the board. The player with the highest score after all tiddly winks have been jumped wins.

Cops and robbers

(For 2 or 4 players)

This is a hunt through a maze.

One player or team has six cops, the other has six robbers.

YOU WILL NEED

- cardboard, about 45cm (18in) long and 45cm (18in) wide
- thin cardboard and tracing paper
- model clay
- 2 yoghurt pots
- 2 big buttons
- thin rubber bands
- white paper and strong glue
- a pencil, ruler, red crayon, paint

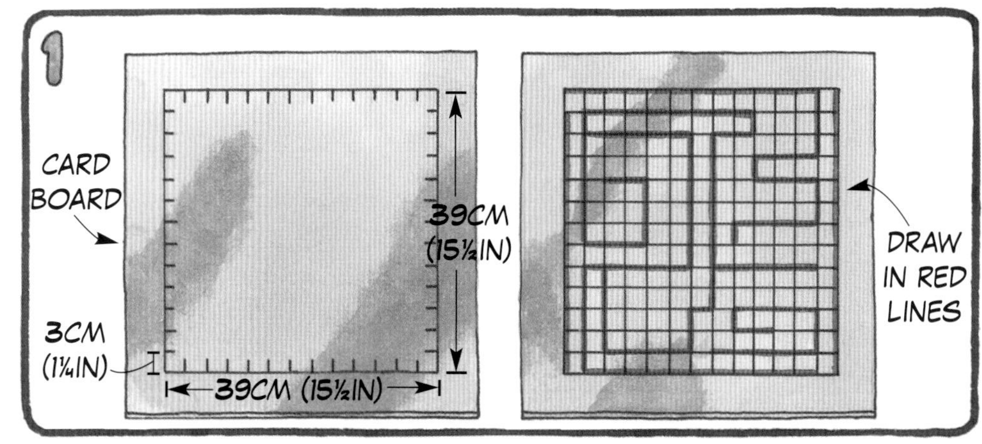

Draw a square, 39cm (15½in) long and wide, on the thick cardboard. Draw marks every 3cm (1¼in) on all sides of the square.

Rule lines from the top marks to the bottom marks and from side to side to make small squares. Draw in the red lines as shown.

To make the hedges, roll pieces of model clay into long strips, each about 1cm (½in) wide. Put the strips along the red lines drawn on the cardboard.

Push the model clay strips down gently so that they stick to the cardboard. Then pinch the model clay until the strips are about 2cm (¾in) high, like this.

Make eleven model clay tree shapes. Put them on top of the hedges, like this. Look at the big picture opposite to make sure you put the trees in the right places.

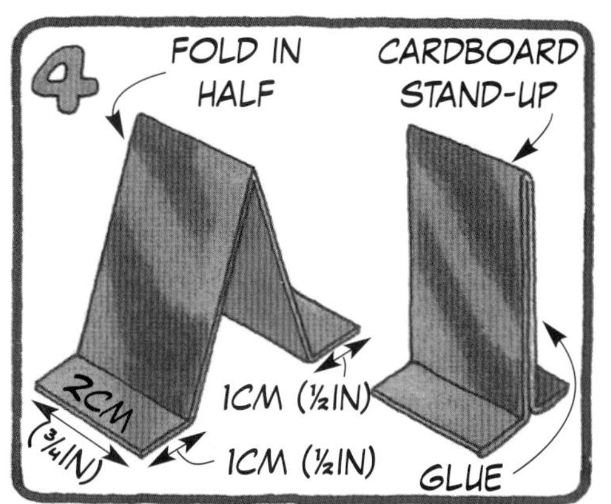

Cut out twelve strips of thin cardboard, each 2cm (¾in) wide and 7cm (2¾in) long. Fold them in half and bend out the ends. Glue the two halves together.

Draw the cop pattern and the robber pattern onto some tracing paper. Trace the cop pattern onto one side of six of the cardboard stand-ups.

Trace the robber pattern onto one side of the other six cardboard stand-ups. Then paint all the cops and robbers.

Make a hole, 1cm (½in) from the base, on either side of the pots. Thread thin elastic through the holes and thread a big button on the elastic. Knot the ends.

Cover the yoghurt pots with white paper. Paint a picture of a cop on one of the pots and a picture of a robber on the other pot. These are the handcuffs.

HOW TO PLAY

One player moves the cops and has the cop handcuffs. The other moves the robbers and has the robber handcuffs. If you play in teams of two, each player moves three men.

Put three cops at each of the cop entrances and three robbers at each of the robber entrances. Each player moves one man 5 squares in a turn, in any direction except diagonal. To catch an enemy, a player's man must land on the square next to one occupied by an enemy. He then pulls the button on his handcuffs and shouts, 'you're caught'. He takes the man off the board.

Men can only jump over a hedge where there's a tree. They can't catch through a hedge except where there is a tree. The first player or team to catch all the enemy wins.

Treasure hunts

(For lots of players)

Arrange the treasure hunts in your own house before the party begins. Try not to hide any clues in dangerous places and make sure that even the smallest player can reach them. Tell everyone which rooms are not being used in the hunt.

Players can either hunt by themselves, in pairs or teams.

In a clue-by-clue hunt, try not to let anyone else know that you have found a clue. Once you've read it, make sure you put it back where you found it.

CLUE-BY-CLUE EXAMPLE

Write the clues on pieces of paper. Hide them all around, say in a shoe or cup. Each clue tells the players where to find the next one. Read out the first clue to all the players. Here, the first clue is : 'You'll find clue number 2 if you put your foot in me.' Now follow the clues to find the treasure.

CAMOUFLAGE HUNTS

Hide 20 small, bright things, such as a red pencil, a yellow button or a green toothbrush, around the house. Hide each thing in or on something of the same shade, perhaps the yellow button on a yellow book or the green toothbrush on a green plate.

Each player gets a list of the hidden things and a pencil and starts looking. When he or she finds one, they write down its hiding place. The first player to write down the hiding places of all 20 things wins.

HIDDEN LETTERS

Hide the treasure, say in the kitchen. Write the letters that spell 'kitchen' on different pieces of paper. Hide them. Tell everyone how many letters are hidden.

As they find one, the players write down each letter. When a player thinks he or she knows which room the letters spell, they run to that room to find the treasure.

Players are shown a small object. They go out of the room. The object is hidden so only a part of it shows. Everyone comes back into the room and starts looking for it.

When a player sees it, they sit down. They don't tell anyone else they've seen it or where it is. The last person to see it is left walking around the room on their own.

Cut some magazine pictures or old cards in half. Give one half of each picture to a player and hide the other halves around the house.

The first player to find the hidden half of their picture gets a prize. You can make it more difficult by cutting the pictures into quarters and hiding three pieces.

Each player gets a list of the same ten things to find, perhaps a shoe, a nail, a potato or a paper clip. All the things are somewhere in the house. A player has to collect one of each thing on their list in a certain time, perhaps 15 minutes.

The player who has collected the most things on their list at the end of the time limit is the winner.

Frog leaps

(For 2 or more players)

This is a frog race. Each player needs a cardboard frog. The frogs start at one end of the strings and jump along to the other. The finishing line can be a mark on the floor or cardboard ponds for the frogs to jump into.

YOU WILL NEED

- thick cardboard
- a piece of string, about 2m (6½ft) long, for each player
- tracing paper
- a pencil, scissors and paint
- thin cardboard to make the cardboard ponds

Fasten one end of each string to a chair leg so the frogs stand in a line with their feet just touching the floor. Put a cardboard pond at the other end of each string.

Each player holds the end of a string and jerks it up and down to make the frog leap along it. The first frog to get into its pond or past the finishing line wins.

(a) Trace this frog on tracing paper. (b) Turn the paper over and scribble on the back. (c) Put it, right side up, on the cardboard and draw around the pattern again.

Cut out the frog shape. Paint it bright green, with eyes and a mouth. Make a hole in the middle of the body, and thread string through it.

Action toys

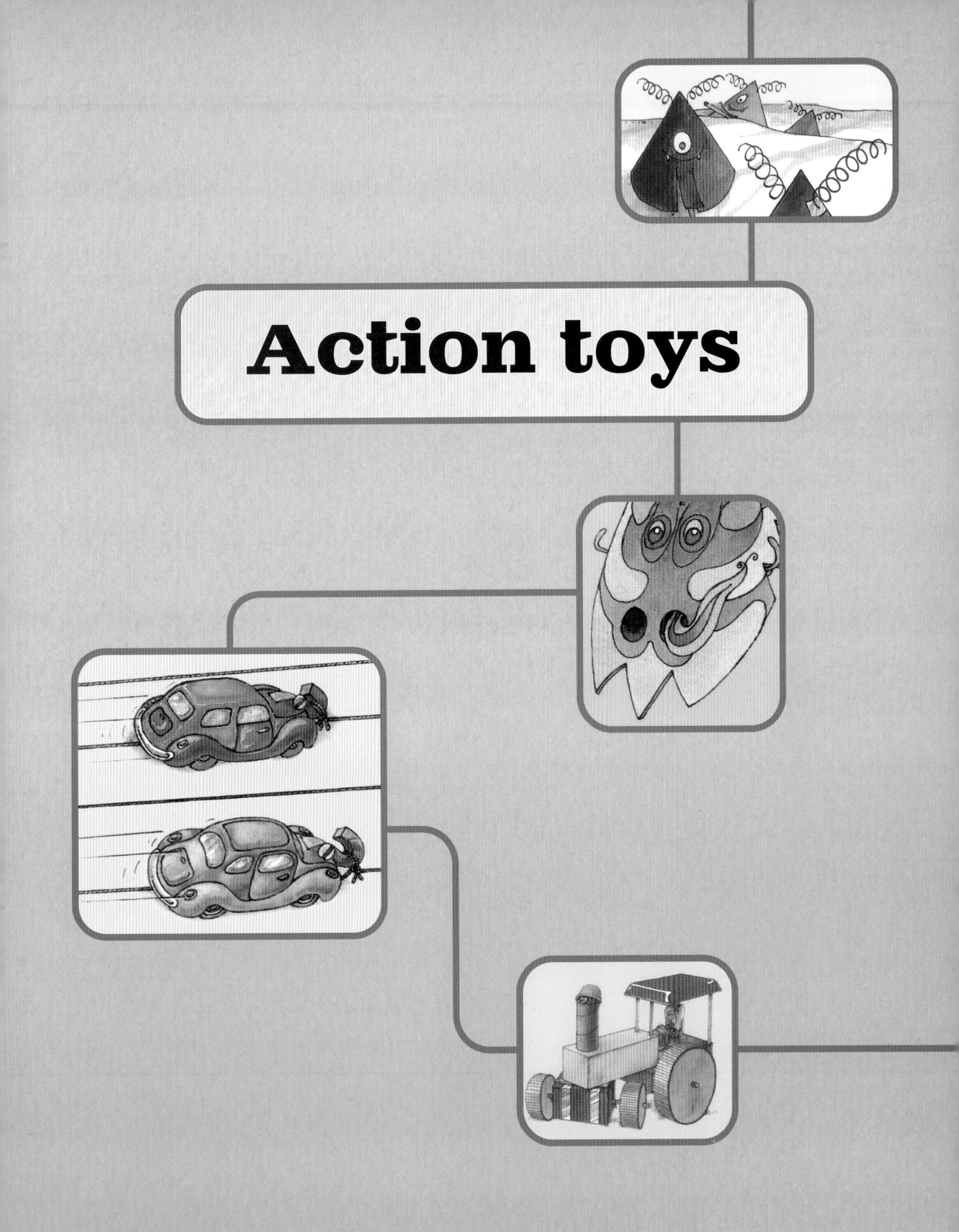

Creeping moon bug

Wind up the motor on this moon bug. Put the bug down and watch it creep along very slowly.

YOU WILL NEED

- an empty cotton reel
- a used matchstick
- a strong rubber band
- a candle
- a stick, about 10cm (4in) long
- a sheet of thick paper
- thick cardboard
- corrugated card
- thin, bendy wire
- table knife, pencil and scissors

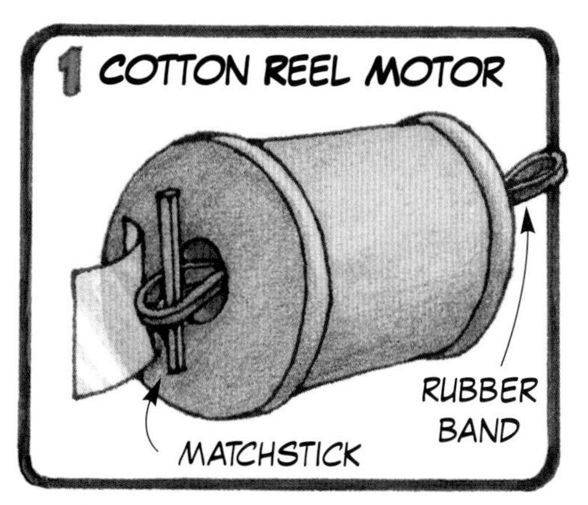

Push the rubber band through the cotton reel. Push a short piece of matchstick through the loop at one end. Stick the matchstick down with some tape.

Slice a ring, about 1cm (½in) wide, off the end of a candle with a table knife. Make a hole through it with one blade of the scissors.

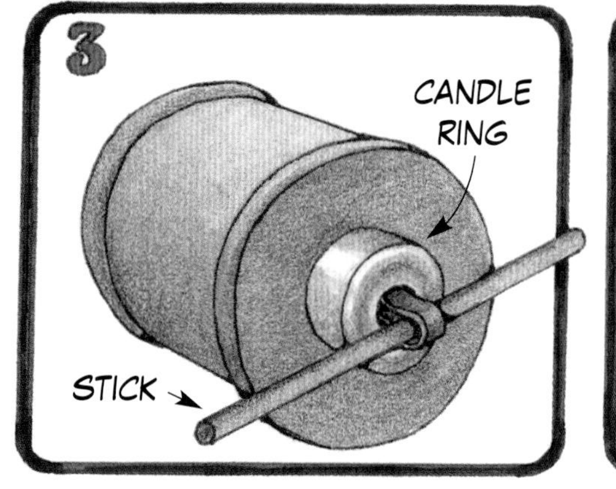

Push the free end of the rubber band through the candle ring. Put the stick through the loop.

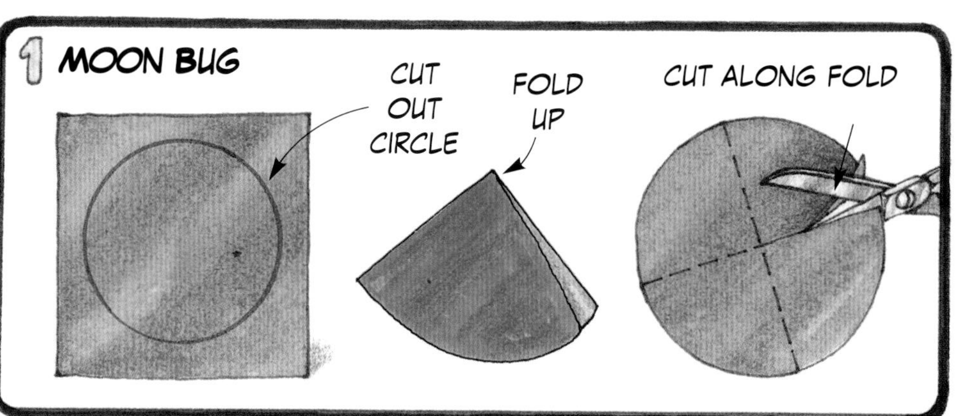

Draw a circle on thick paper. Cut it out and fold the circle in half and then in half again.

Now unfold the paper and cut along one crease to the middle.

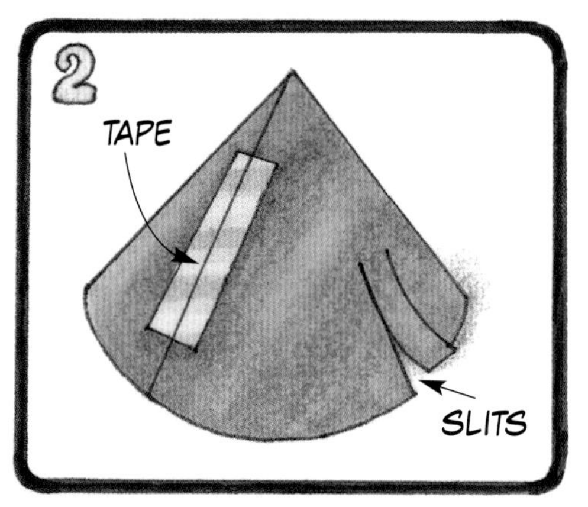

Curl the paper around to make a cone. Stick the edges together with tape. Cut two slits in the cone to make a flap.

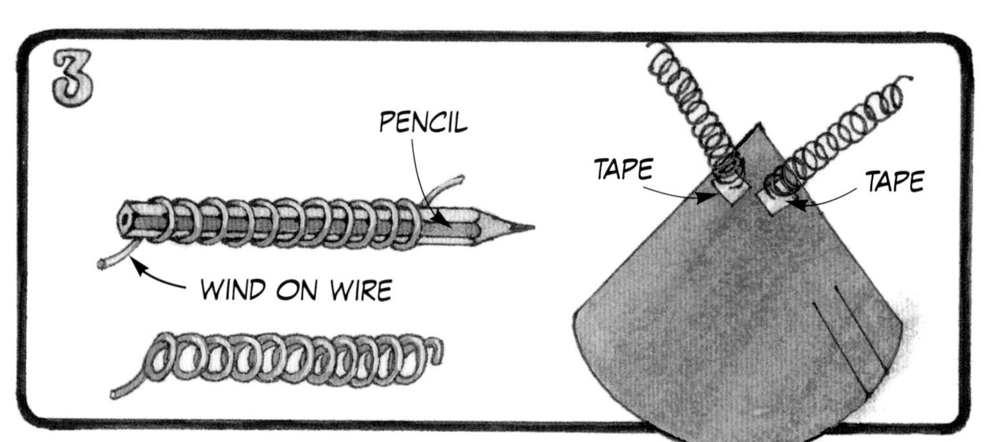

To make the antennae, wind some bendy wire around a pencil. Slide it off. Curl up a second piece and stick them on the cone.

Wind up the cotton reel motor. Put the cone of the moon bug over it, with one end of the stick poking through the flap. Watch it move.

To make a climbing motor, put a cotton reel on cardboard. Draw around it. Draw a second circle.

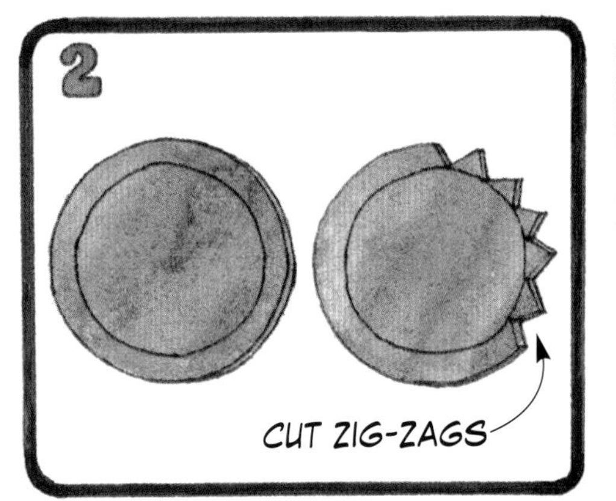

Cut out the circles a little bigger than the drawn lines. Cut out zig-zag teeth all around both circles.

Glue a circle to each end of the cotton reel. Leave it to dry. Repeat the steps for the cotton reel motor.

Wind up the climbing motor by turning the stick lots of times. Put the moon bug cone over the climbing motor, with one end of the stick poking through the flap.

Now place the moon bug on a strip of corrugated card. Put objects such as books underneath. Let go and watch as the bug slowly climbs up the card.

Titan traction engine

YOU WILL NEED

- a cardboard box, about 27cm (10½in) long, 9cm (3½in) wide, 9cm (3½in) deep
- thick cardboard, corrugated card
- 2 small boxes, each 12cm (4¾in) long and 4cm (1½in) wide
- a small, open cardboard box
- 5 cotton reels and 3 pencils
- a cardboard tube, 10cm (4in) long
- 6 thin sticks or garden canes
- a small polystyrene tray
- 1 egg holder cut from an egg box
- sandpaper, scissors, glue, tape, string, a saucer, a yoghurt pot

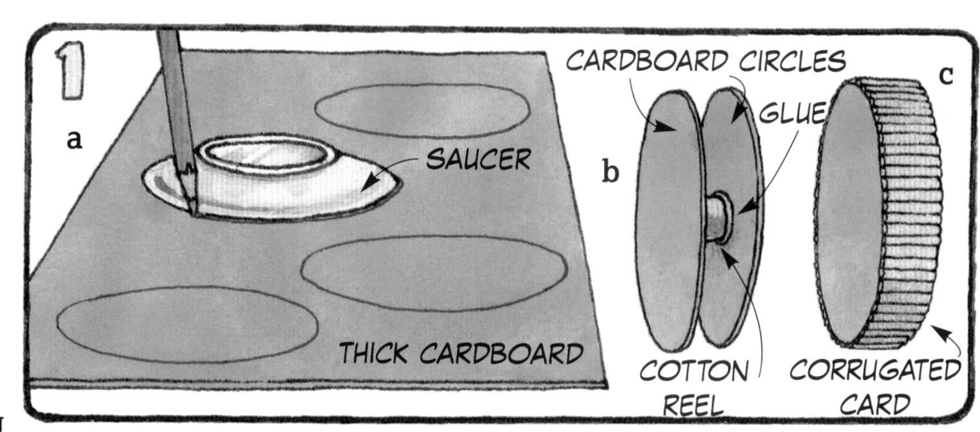

(a) Draw four circles on cardboard, using a saucer as a guide. Then cut them out. (b) Glue one circle to each end of a cotton reel. Glue the other two circles to a second reel.

(c) Glue a strip of corrugated card around the edges of two of the cardboard circles, like this.

Do the same to the other two cardboard circles.

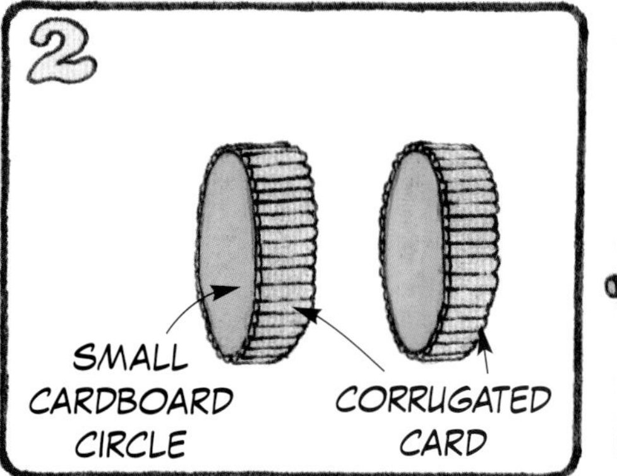

Make the front wheels in the same way as the back ones, but much smaller. The cardboard circles should be about the same size as the top of a small yoghurt pot.

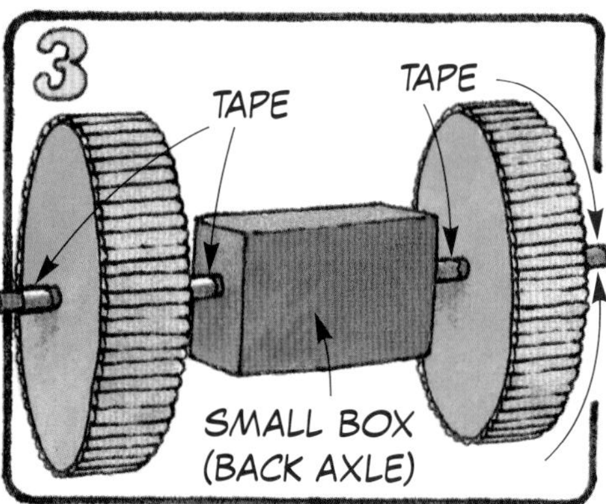

Push a thin stick, 28cm (11in) long, through the middle of a box. Push a back wheel on each end of the stick. Wrap tape around the stick on each side of the wheels.

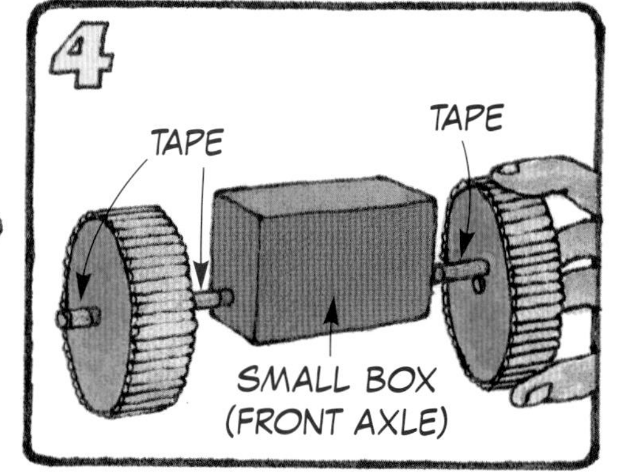

Push a stick through another box, about 1cm (½in) from the base. Push a front wheel on each end of the stick. Wrap sticky tape around the stick each side of the wheels.

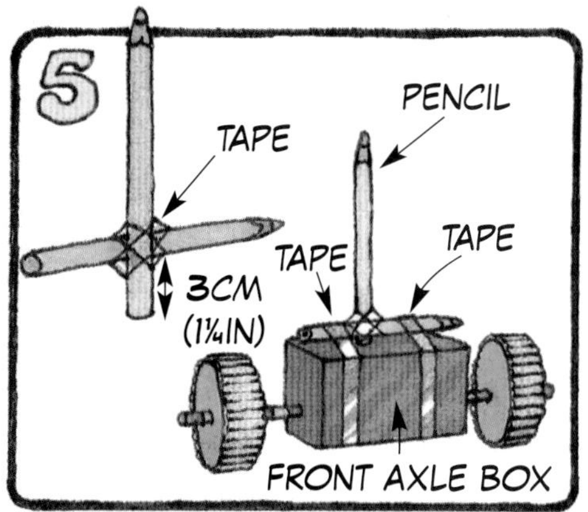

Tape two pencils together. Then push the upright pencil into the front axle box, like this. Then tape the other pencil firmly to the axle box, as shown.

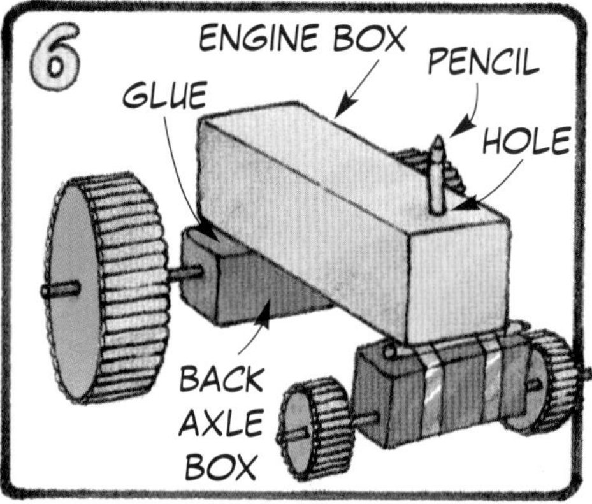

Glue the back axle box underneath one end of a strong cardboard box. Push the upright pencil on the front axle box through the hole at the other end of the box.

Glue corrugated card or sandpaper around the middle of a cotton reel, and push a pencil through the reel. Then push the pencil point into the back of the engine box.

Push this traction engine along and steer it by turning the cotton reel wheel.

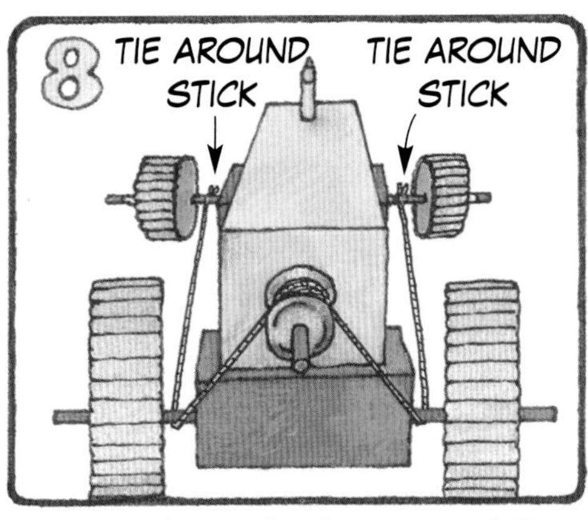

Wrap a piece of string around the cotton reel, like this. Tie one end to one side of the front axle. Pull the other end tightly and tie it to the other side of the axle.

Glue the open box to the back axle box. Tape two sticks, about 26cm (10¼in) long, to two corners. Push two sticks, about 15cm (6in) long, into the engine box, as shown.

Put a polystyrene tray on top of the four sticks, like this. Glue a cardboard tube over the pencil at the front of the engine box. Put the egg holder on top of it.

Dizzy, the dashing dragon

Pull up the ring on the dragon's head and see him rush along.

YOU WILL NEED

- a piece of cardboard, about 12cm (4¾in) long, 12cm (4¾in) wide
- a lump of model clay
- a rubber band
- a plastic drinking straw
- some nylon thread or very thin string, 70cm (2ft 4in) long
- a small curtain ring, big hairpin
- thin paper, about 12cm (4¾in) wide and 60cm (2ft) long
- sticky tape, glue and scissors

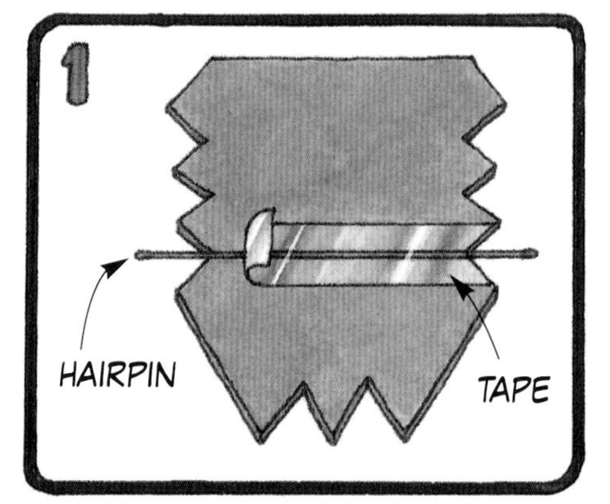

Cut a head shape out of cardboard, like this. Straighten a hairpin. Stick the pin with tape across the head, quite close to one end.

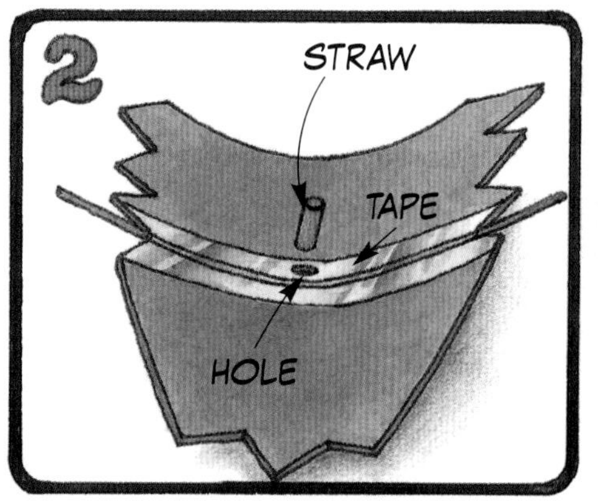

Make a hole in the middle of the head, just behind the hairpin. Push a short piece of straw into the hole. Glue it in place. Bend the head into a curved shape.

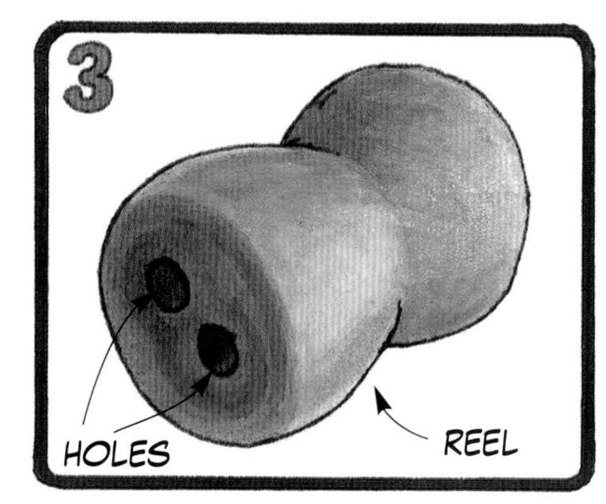

Make a reel, about 4cm (1½in) long and 3cm (1¼in) across, out of model clay in this shape. Poke two holes right through it.

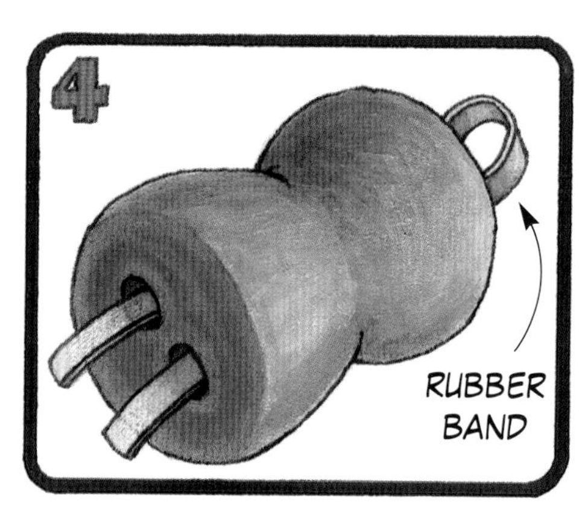

Cut a rubber band. Push the ends through the two holes in the clay reel, like this. Leave the reel until the model clay is dry.

Knot the ends of the band. Tie one end of the nylon thread on to the reel. Wind the thread onto the reel. Push the free end through the straw.

Tie one end of the thread to a curtain ring on top of the head. Then bend the ends of the hairpin down.

Turn the reel around and around to wind the thread very tight. Give one twist to each end of the rubber band.

Hook each end of the rubber band onto the ends of the hairpin. Bend the head again to make sure the reel will not rub on it.

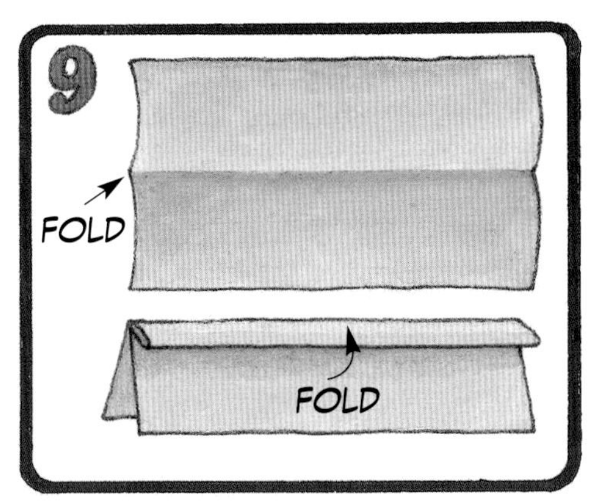

To make the dragon's body, fold the long piece of paper in half. Then fold over the folded edge to make a flap about 1cm (½in) wide.

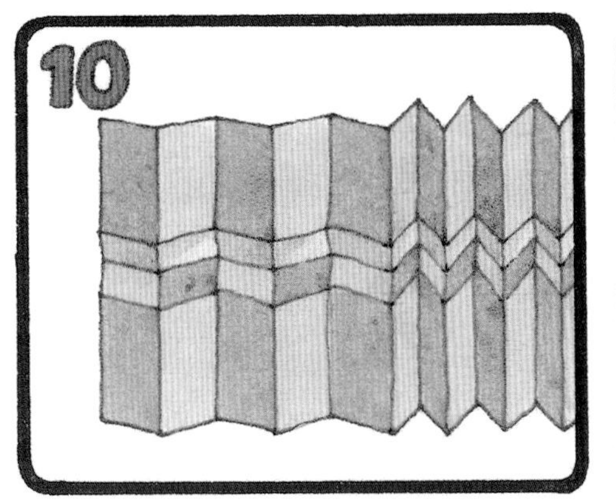

Open out the paper. Make folds, about 2cm (¾in) wide, all along it, like this. Turn over the paper and crease all the folds the other way.

Open the paper again. Draw zig-zag lines from the top fold line to the bottom fold line, like this.

Fold the paper along all the drawn lines. Pinch together all the drawn lines and pleat the paper with your fingers, like this.

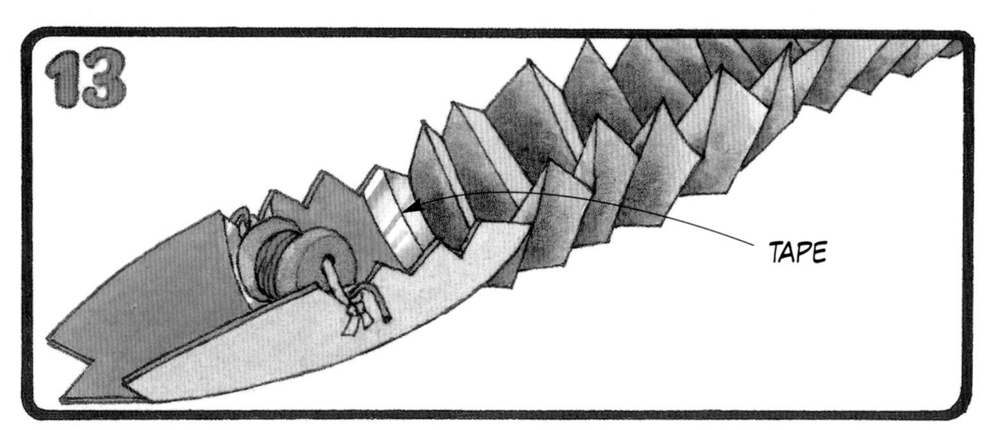

Stick one end of the paper body to the edge of the cardboard head, like this. Paint the dragon's head in lots of different shades.

To make a longer tail, fold up a second strip of thin paper in the same way as the first. Glue it to the end of the first strip.

Fire-fighting truck

YOU WILL NEED

- an oblong cardboard box
- a small cardboard box
- 4 empty cotton reels
- very thin string
- 3 rubber bands
- 3 strips of thick cardboard, each about 30cm (1ft) long and 6cm (2½in) wide
- 2 paper fasteners, glue
- 2 used matchsticks
- 3 pencils, a ballpoint pen, without the ink tube, a balloon
- a plastic carton, scissors

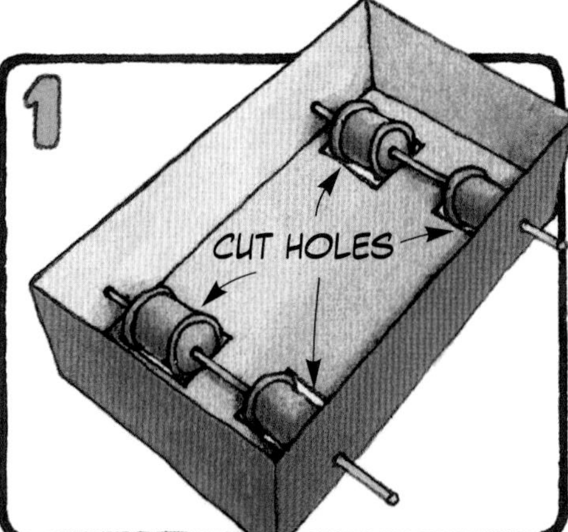

Cut four square holes in the shoe box bottom. Make two holes in each side. Push two pencils through one side. Slide two cotton reels on to each pencil and push out the side.

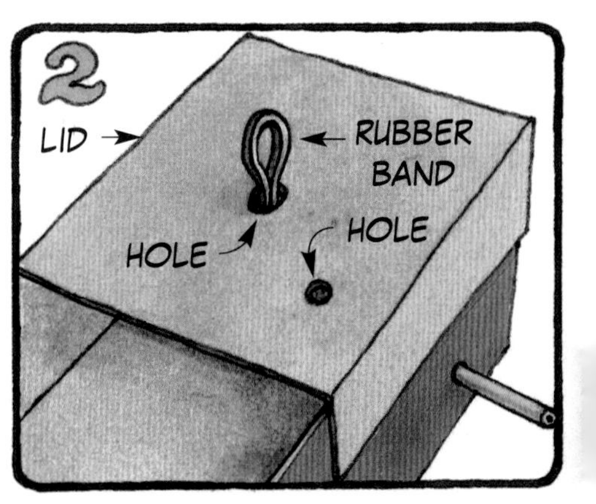

Cut the box lid in half. Make a hole in the middle of one half. Push a rubber band through and slide a matchstick underneath. Make a second hole. Put on lid.

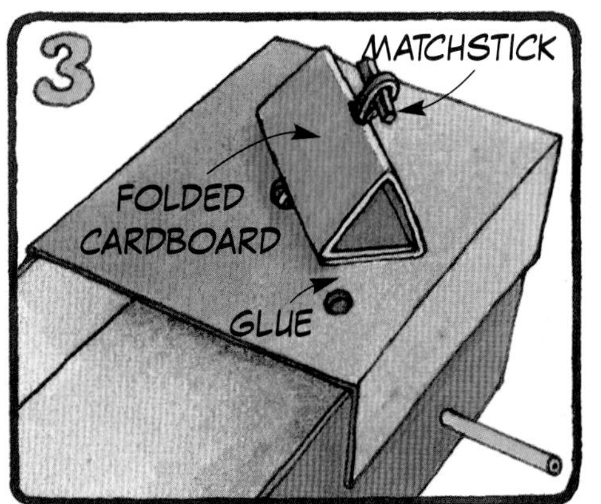

Fold up a strip of cardboard to make a triangle. Make a hole in one flat side and one fold. Push the band through. Slide a matchstick through the loop of the band.

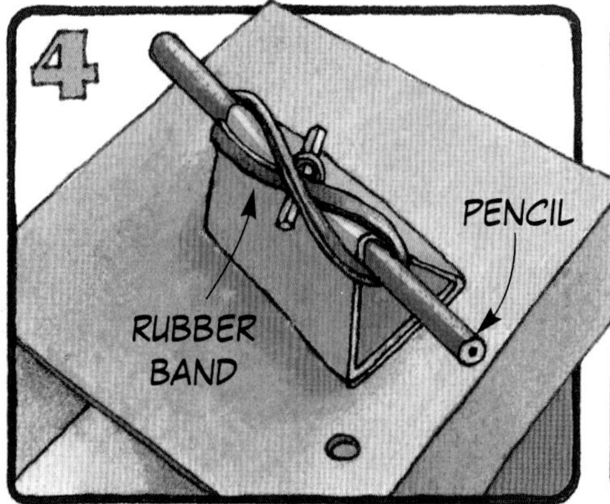

Put a pencil through the cardboard triangle. Loop a rubber band over one end of the pencil. Twist it in the middle and hook it over the other end of the pencil.

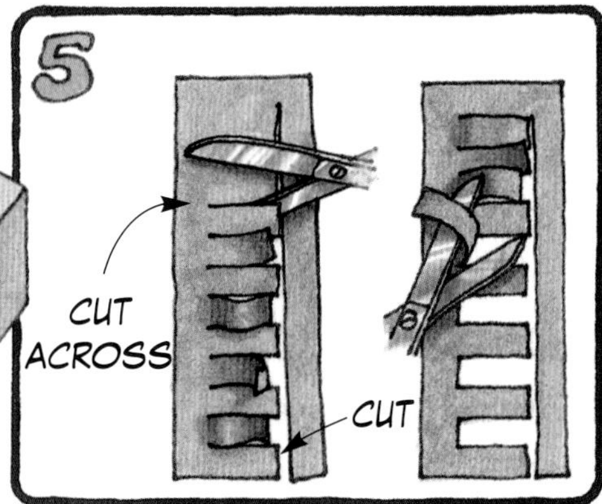

Cut up one side of the second cardboard strip and cut across. Then cut out every other flap to make a ladder. Cut a second ladder in the same way.

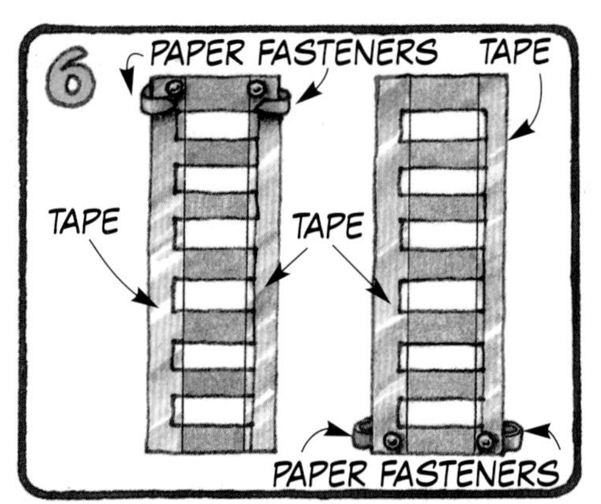

Put sticky tape down the sides of each ladder. Push two paper fasteners through the top of one ladder and the bottom of the other. Bend over the ends, like this.

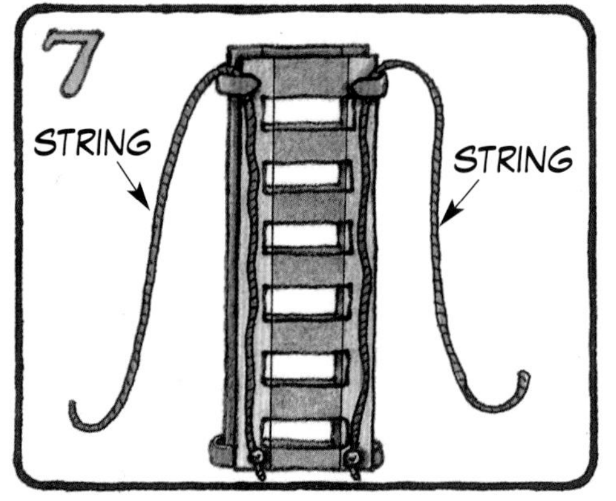

Cut two pieces of string, each twice as long as the ladders. Put the two ladders together. Tie a string to each bottom fastener and loop it over the top ones.

Glue the underneath ladder to the triangle on the box lid. Wind the end of each string around the pencil and stick it with tape.

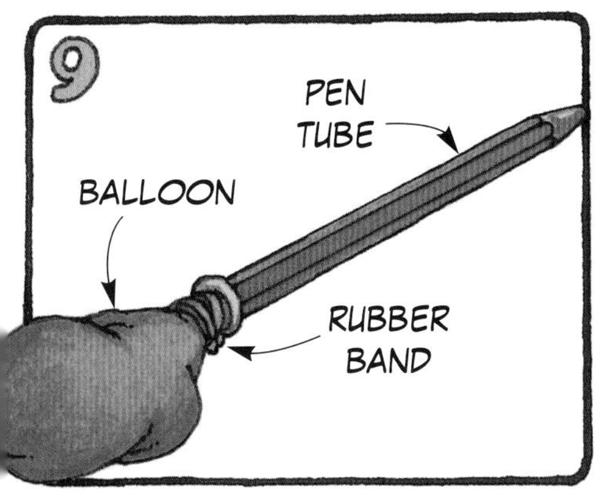

Push the pen tube into the neck of the balloon. Wind a rubber band around the balloon neck several times, to make it very tight.

Fill the balloon with water through the pen tube. When the balloon is about as big as an orange, put the pen top on very quickly.

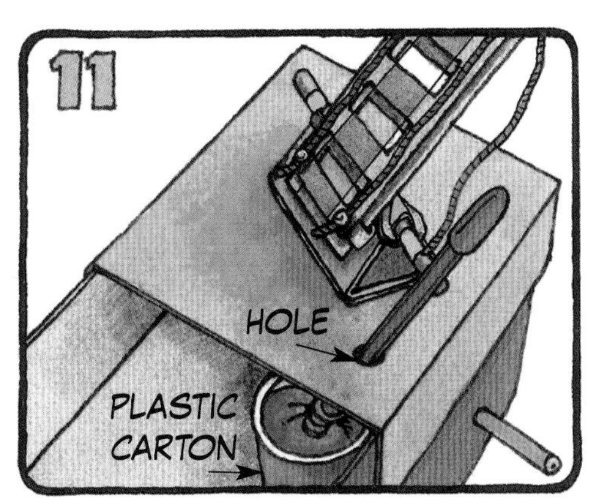

Put the balloon in a plastic carton to catch the drips of water. Push the pen tube through the hole in the box lid from the inside.

12
CUT OUT WINDOWS
GLUE ON

To make a cab, cut out the sides of a small box for the front window and side windows. Glue the box to the front of the fire truck.

Push the fire engine to a pretend fire. Twist the pencil to wind up the ladder and take off the pen top to squirt the water.

Eager weaver

Wind the two tubes around to move the woven part along the box. Use different wools on the shuttle to make patterns. Or tie different shades to the tubes.

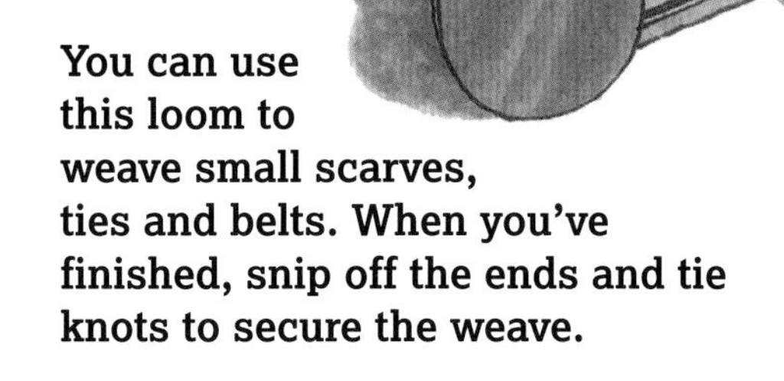

You can use this loom to weave small scarves, ties and belts. When you've finished, snip off the ends and tie knots to secure the weave.

YOU WILL NEED

- a cardboard shoe box or strong cardboard box
- thick cardboard
- 2 long cardboard tubes
- 4 large rubber bands
- brightly shaded wools
- a pencil and a ruler
- glue, sticky tape and scissors

Cut out the sides of the box, like this. Cut a piece of cardboard for the handle, about 9cm (3½in) wide and as long as the width of the box. Make sure it fits the box.

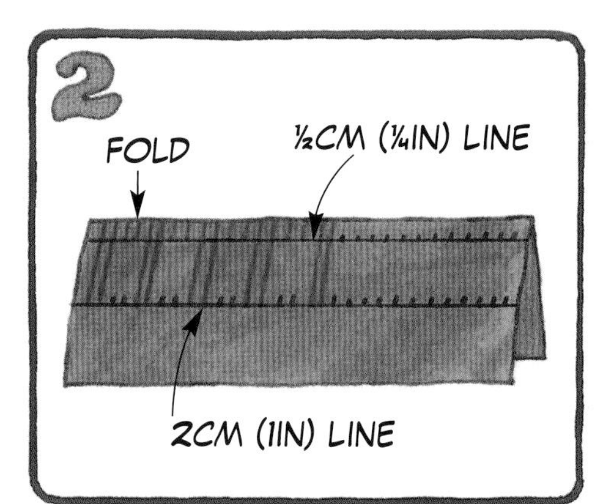

Fold the cardboard in half. Rule lines ½cm (¼in) and 2cm (1in) from the fold. Mark every ½cm (¼in) along both lines. Rule long and short boxes, as shown here.

Cut along all the lines from the fold, like this, and unfold the cardboard. Then snip every other cut bit along the fold.

When you've finished cutting, fold the short cuts back to the ½cm (¼in) line and the long cuts back to the 2cm (1in) line. Stick all the flaps down with tape.

Stick tape along the fold on both sides of the cardboard. Snip out all the pieces of tape that cover the holes. This part of the loom is called the heddle.

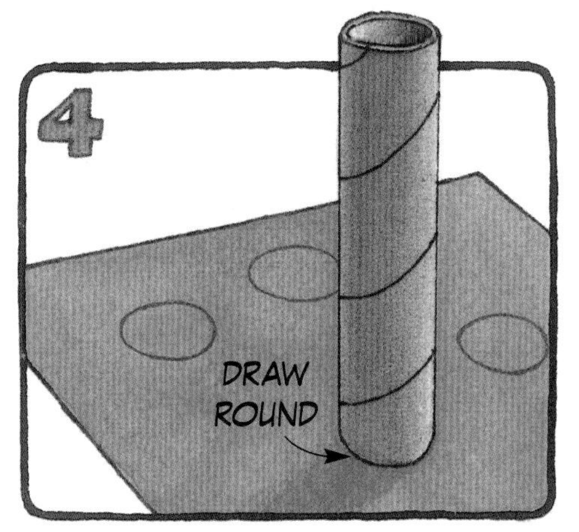

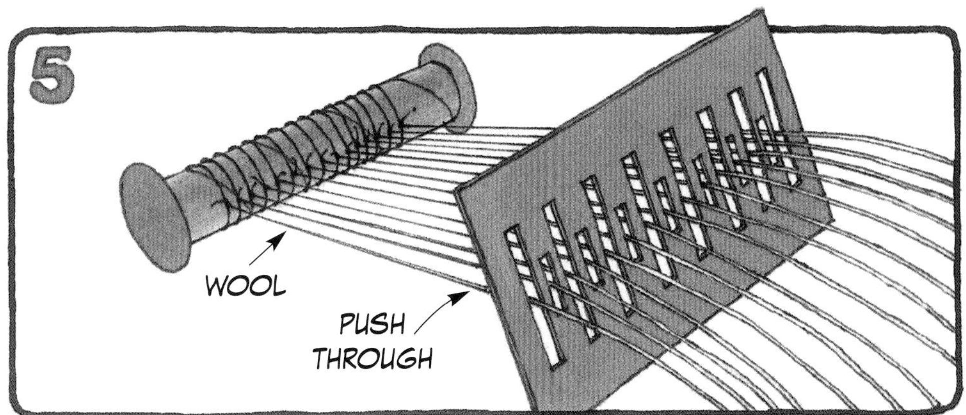

Using the end of a tube as a guide, draw four circles on cardboard. Cut out around the outside of the circles. Glue a circle to each end of the tubes.

Cut 15 pieces of wool at least 50cm (20in) long. Knot one piece around one end of a tube. Push the other end through the first hole in the end of the heddle.

Tie on another piece of wool. Push it through the second hole in the heddle. Tie on the rest of the wool, pushing it through the holes in the heddle, like this.

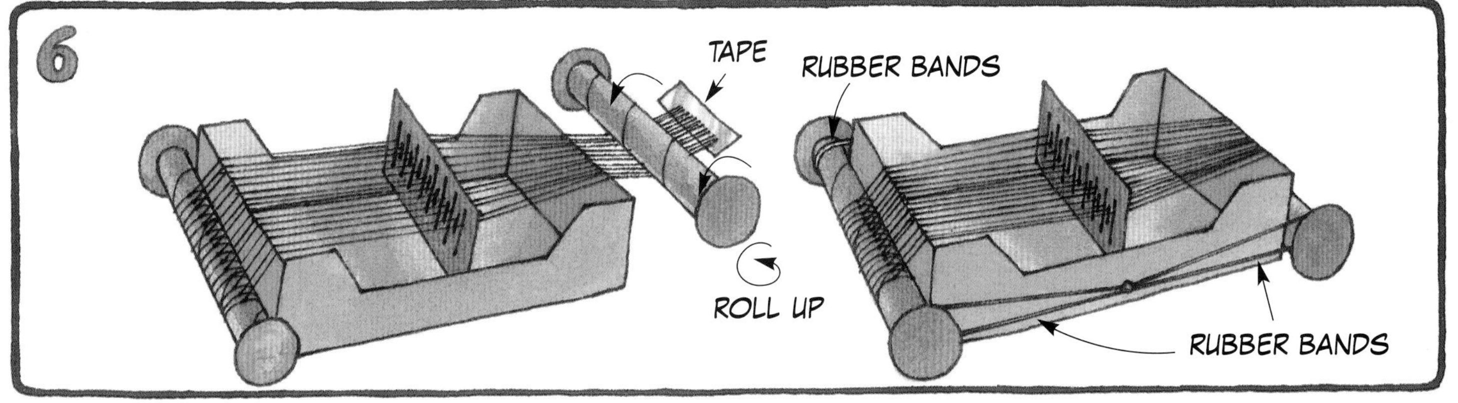

Put the heddle in the middle of the box. Put the tube with the wool on the outside at one end. Pull all the free ends of the wool over the other end of the box.

Put a second tube over the ends of the wool. Stick the ends to the tube with tape.

Knot two rubber bands together. Hook them over the tubes on one side of the box. Knot two more bands and hook them onto the other ends of the tubes.

Cut out a piece of cardboard a little longer than the width of the box. Cut it into this shape. This is the shuttle. Wind on a very long piece of wool, like this.

Tie the end of the wool on the shuttle to a strand of wool on the loom. Press the heddle down and push the shuttle through between the strands of wool.

To weave the next line, lift the heddle up. Push the shuttle through from the other side. Push the heddle against the woven part each time you weave a new line.

Mr. Twitch

Turn Mr. Twitch upside down to make his arms go around. When they stop, turn him up again.

YOU WILL NEED

- 2 plastic cartons or yoghurt pots
- a piece of thin cardboard
- 4 used matchsticks
- 2 long needles
- table salt
- a drinking straw
- glue and sticky tape
- a needle and thread
- a pencil and scissors

Draw four circles on a piece of thick cardboard, using the top of a plastic carton as your guide. Then cut out the circles.

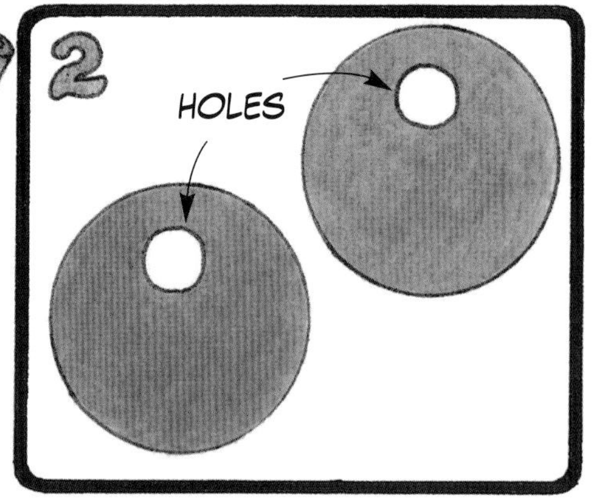

Cut a round hole in each of the cardboard circles, near one edge, like this.

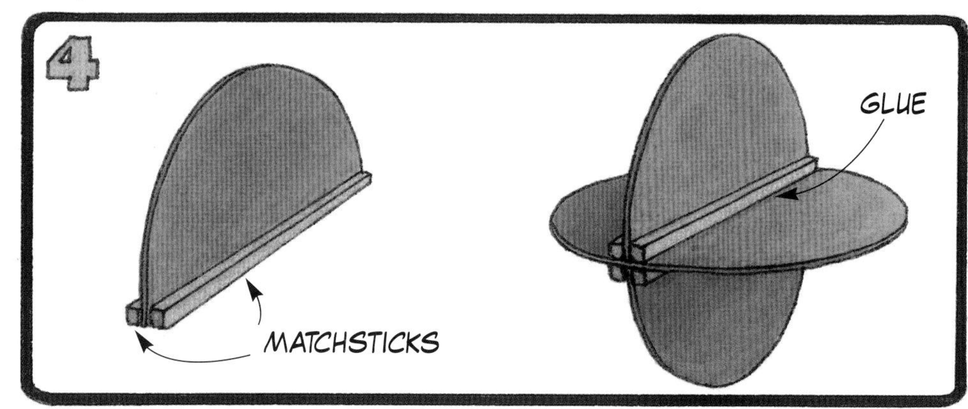

Fold a third cardboard circle in half. Cut along the fold. Glue a matchstick to each side of one half-circle.

Glue matchsticks to the other half-circle. Glue the uncut circle to the matchsticks on one half-circle. Glue the second half-circle to the circle, like this.

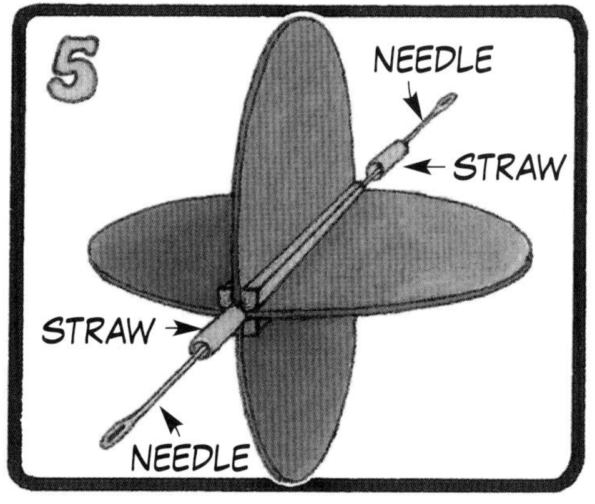

Slide a very short piece of drinking straw onto the end of each needle. Push the needles into each end of the matchsticks.

Stand the tube on end and cut two slits about half-way down it on both sides. Make a small hole at the end of each slit.

Push the cardboard circles down inside the tube with the needles in the slits. Spin the circles to make sure they turn easily. If not, trim a little off the circles.

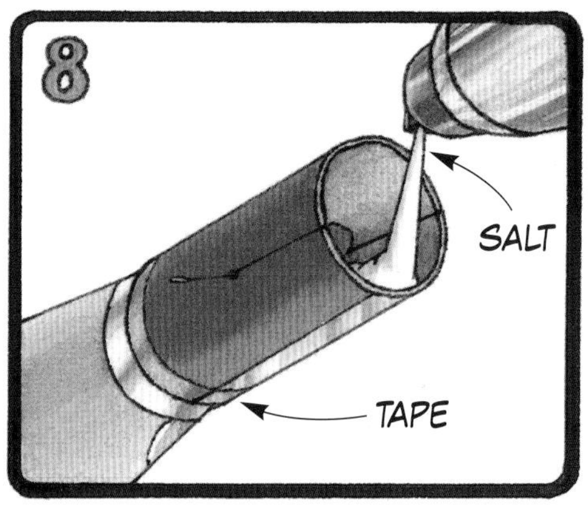

Pour some table salt into the tube. Put in enough to almost fill the plastic carton.

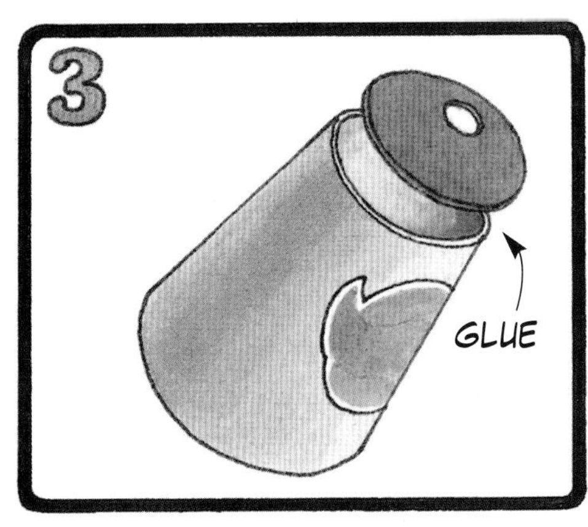

Glue one cardboard circle to the top of each of the plastic cartons. Use lots of glue to stick them very firmly onto the cartons.

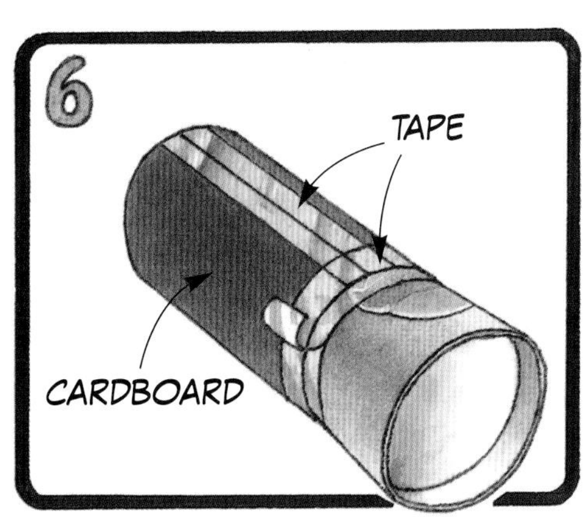

Roll some thin cardboard tightly around the top of a plastic carton. Stick it with tape to make a tube. Tape the tube firmly to the carton.

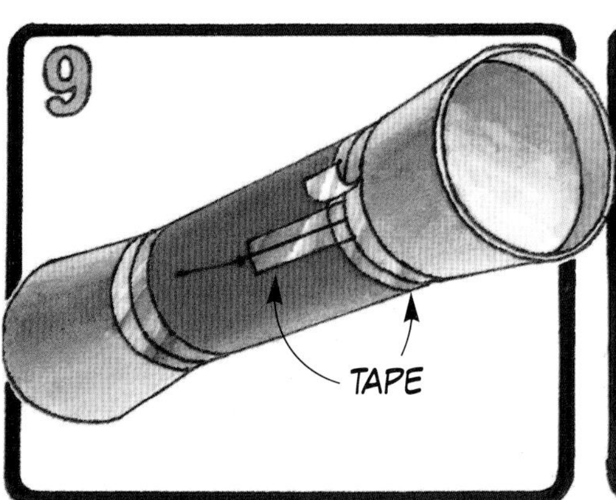

Push the top of the second plastic carton into the top of the tube. Wrap sticky tape very tightly around the end of the tube to stick it to the carton.

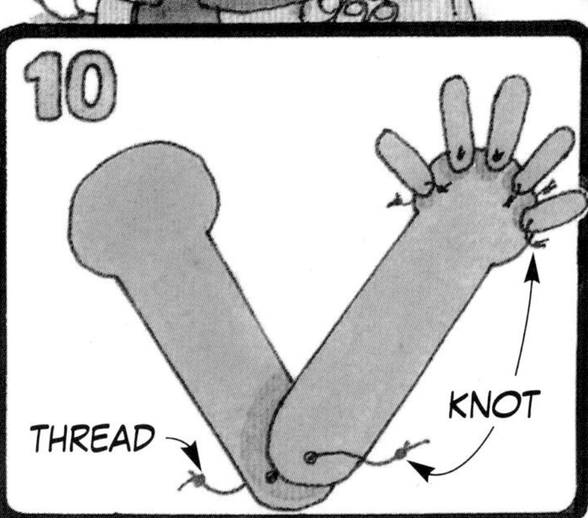

Cut the shape of two long arms out of thin paper. Cut them at the elbows. Cut out fingers and thumbs. Use a needle and thread to join the arms and fingers.

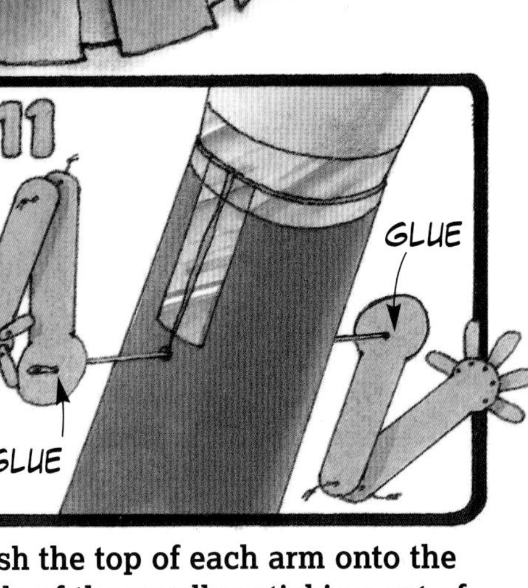
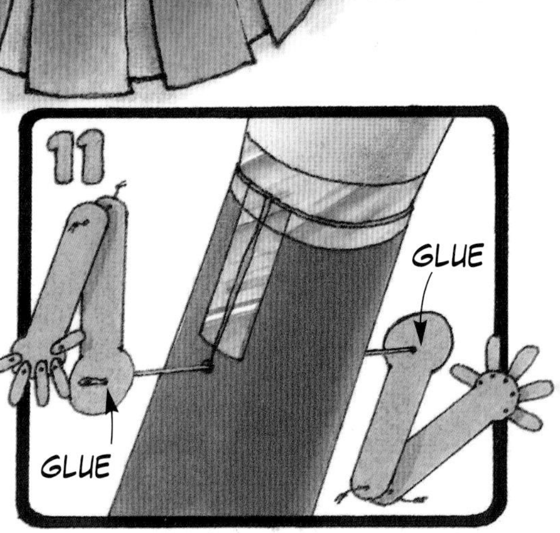

Push the top of each arm onto the ends of the needles sticking out of the cardboard tube. Put one arm up and the other down. Glue them to the needles.

Formula XF bullet

YOU WILL NEED

- a sheet of paper, 29cm (11½in) long and 21cm (8¼in) wide
- 2 ballpoint pens, without the ink tubes
- a ballpoint pen top
- 2 plastic drinking straws or very thin sticks
- a bead and strong rubber band
- bendy wire and a paper clip
- a matchbox cover
- thick cardboard, glue, sticky tape, pencil and scissors
- stiff plastic from a plastic bottle

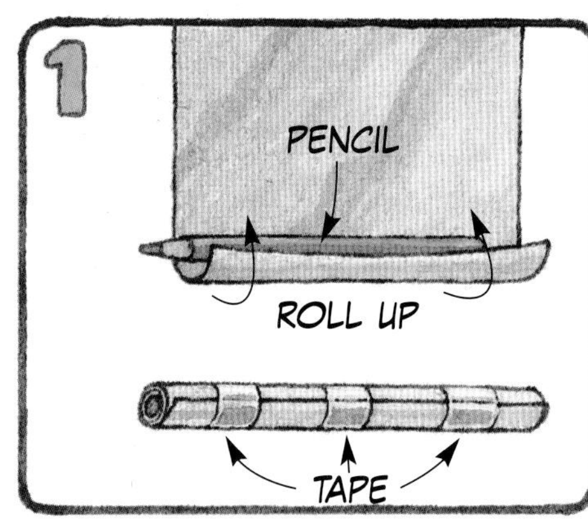

Put the pencil on one edge of the paper. Roll the paper very tightly around the pencil. Stick the end of the rolled paper with tape. Shake out the pencil.

Cut two small circles out of cardboard, for the front wheels. Use a cotton reel as a guide. Cut out two big circles for the back wheels. Use a cup as a guide.

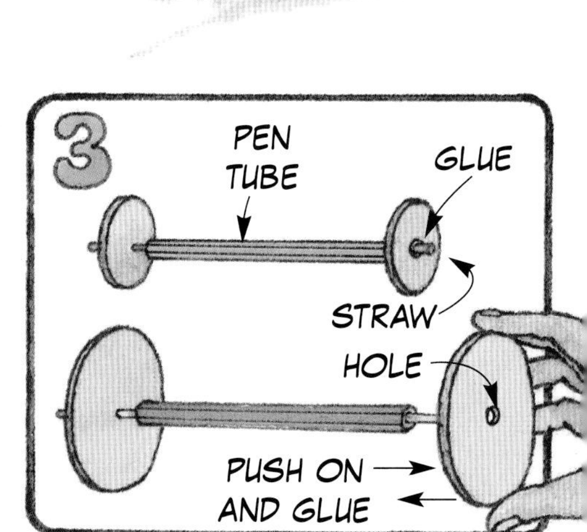

Make a hole in the middle of each wheel. Push a straw through a pen tube. Push a small wheel on each end and glue them on. Do the same with the back wheels.

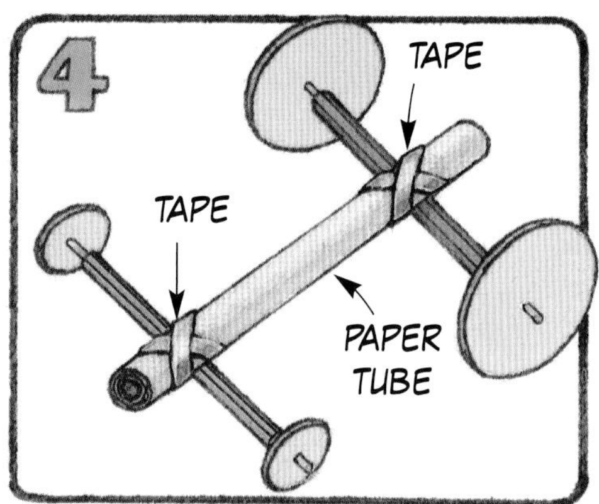

Put the paper tube across the two pen tubes, like this. Wind sticky tape around the paper tube and each pen tube to fix them in place.

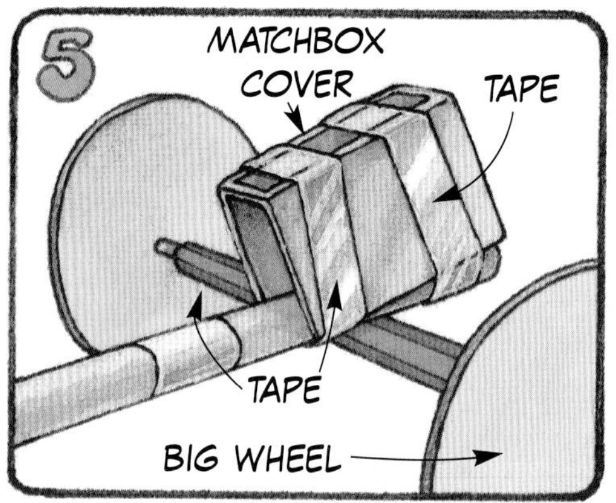

Cut one side off a matchbox cover. Put it, cut side down, on the paper tube at the end with the big wheels. Tilt it forward a little and stick it to the tube with tape.

Cut the end off a pen top with scissors. Put it on top of the matchbox cover, like this. Stick it down very firmly with tape.

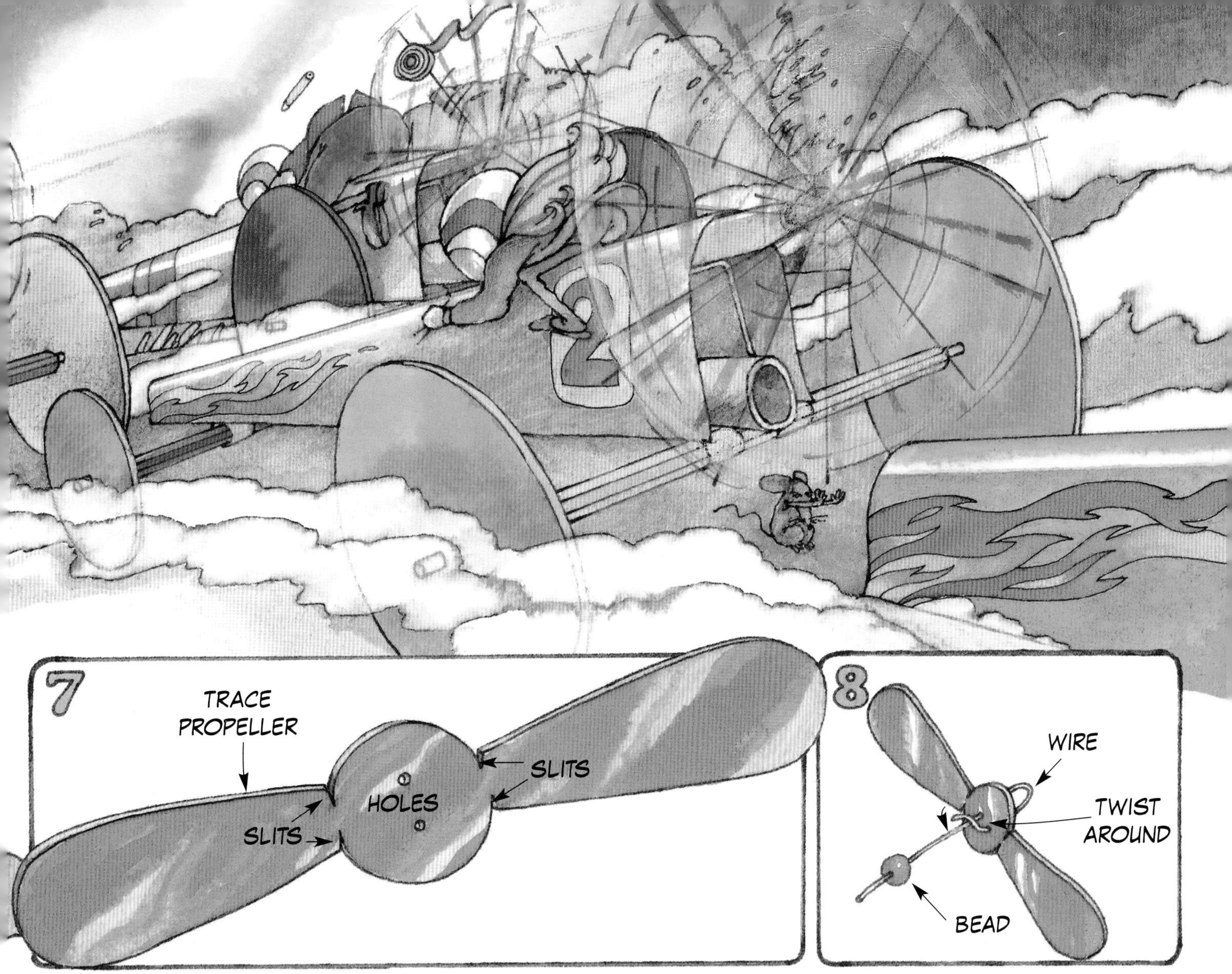

7

TRACE PROPELLER
SLITS
HOLES
SLITS

8

WIRE
TWIST AROUND
BEAD

Trace this propeller shape on thin or see-through paper. Cut out the shape. Hold it down on a piece of plastic. Draw around the shape.

Cut out the shape very carefully. Cut two little slits on each side of the round part. Make two holes in the round middle part.

Loop a piece of bendy wire through the holes in the propeller. Twist one end around the other end, like this. Push the long end through a bead and pull it tight.

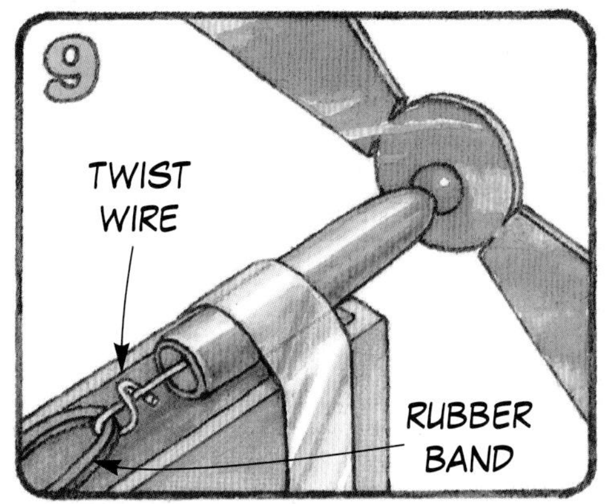

Push the long end of the wire through the pen top. Loop the other end of the wire around a rubber band and twist the wire around, as shown here.

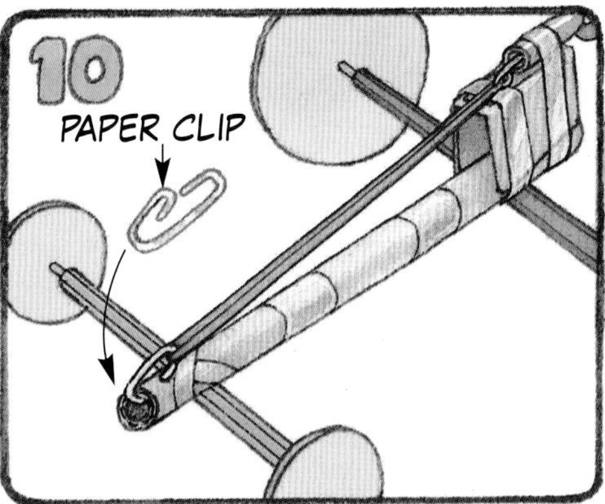

Bend open a paper clip. Push one loop into the end of the paper tube. Hook the end of the rubber band on to the other loop of the paper clip.

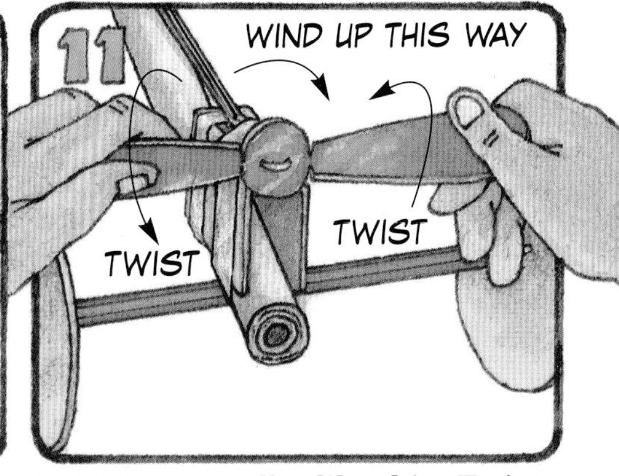

Hold the propeller like this. Twist the left side towards you, and twist the right side away from you. Then wind up the propeller about 20 times.

Water clock

Make this water clock and use it to help you tell the time. If the hand goes around too fast, drop a drawing pin into the bottom of the plastic bottle, or push a thin piece of stick into the hole.

If the cork doesn't go down with the water, put a little more model clay on the string. Empty the pot or bowl in the bottom of the box when it is full of water.

YOU WILL NEED

- a plastic squeezy bottle
- a large, strong cardboard box, about 40cm (16in) high
- 2 knitting needles
- 2 corks
- 4 pieces of string, each about as long as the width of the box
- a sheet of paper
- a piece of cardboard
- model clay
- a pot or bowl
- a pencil
- scissors and glue

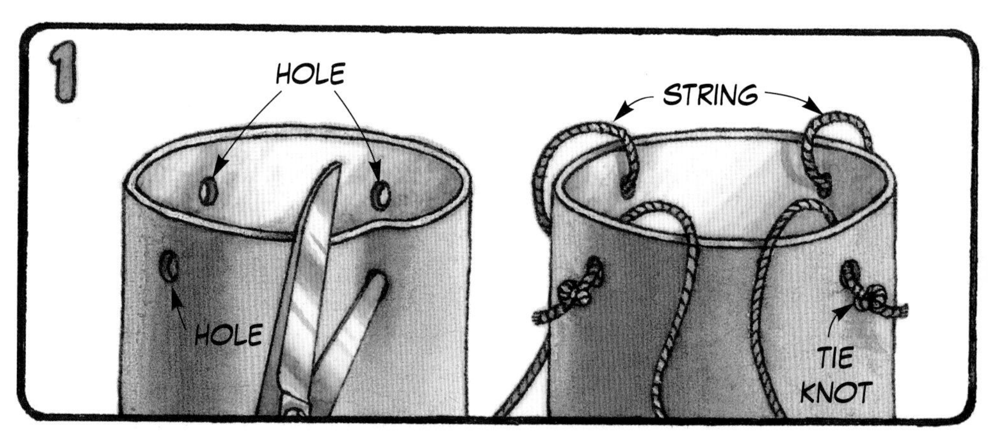

Cut the bottom off a plastic bottle. Make four holes in it, near the bottom edge.

Push some string through each hole. Tie a knot on the end of each string on the outside.

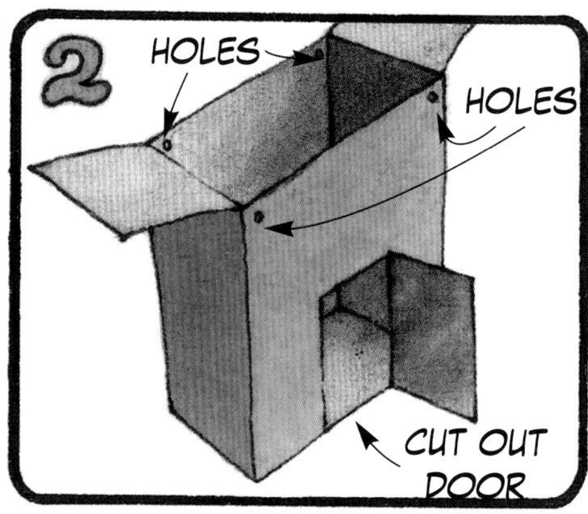

Open the top of the box. Cut a door in one side, near the bottom. Make a hole in each corner near the top of the box.

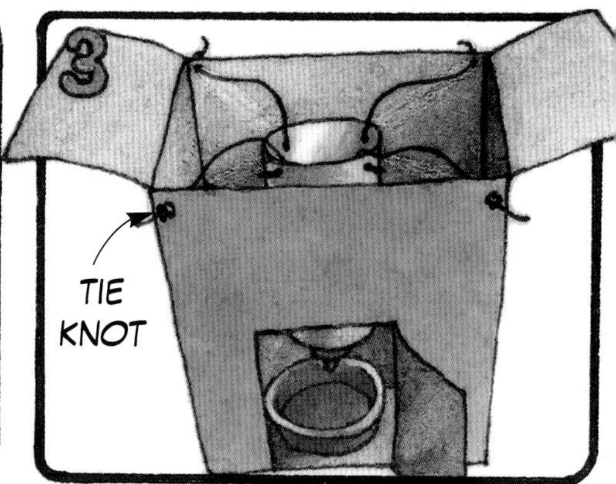

Put the bottle inside the box. Push one string through each hole in the top of the box and tie a knot on the end. Place a pot or bowl in the bottom of the box.

Cut out a paper circle. Write on it the numbers 1 to 12, like the face of a clock. Stick it to the front of the box, near the top. Make a hole in the middle of the circle.

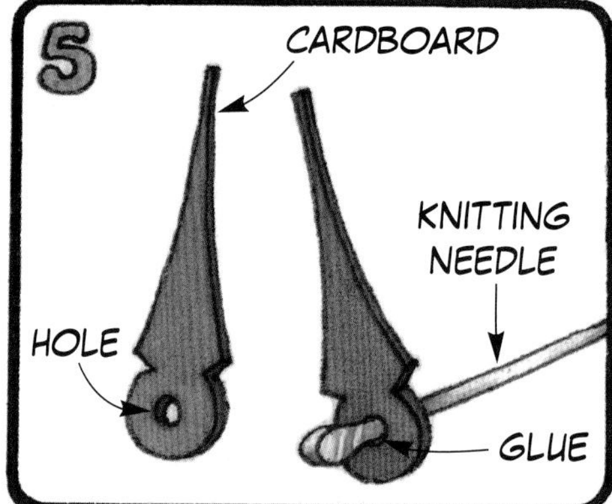

Cut a clock hand from a piece of cardboard. Make a hole in the round end. Push a knitting needle through the hole and glue the hand to the end.

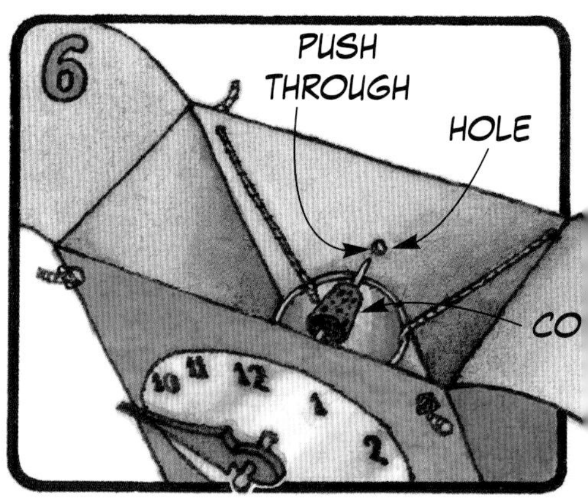

Make a hole through a cork with scissors. Push the knitting needle through the clock face. Push the cork onto the needle and push the needle out of the back of the box.

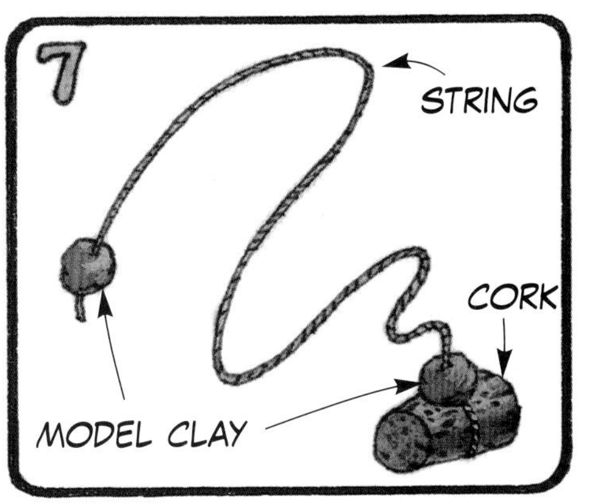

Cut a piece of string a little longer than the height of the box. Tie a cork on one end, and put some model clay next to it. Put another lump on the other end.

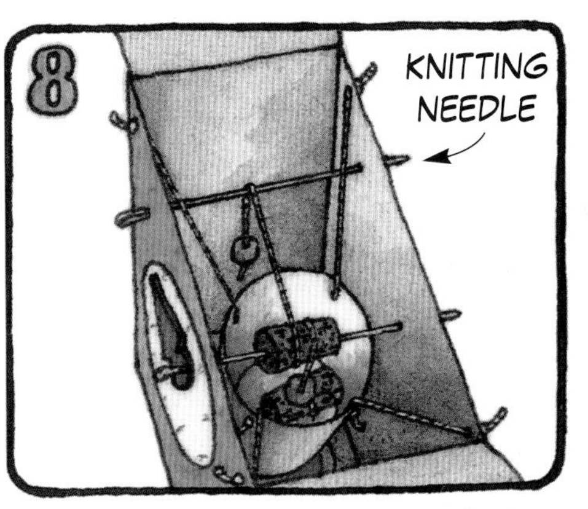

Put the string around the cork, like this. Drop the cork end into the bottle. Push a second knitting needle through the box near the first one. Loop the string over it.

Pour some water into the plastic bottle. Pull up the model clay end of the string so that the cork just rests on the surface of the water.

Grand Prix car races

Make this track and race your toy cars all around the floor. It will work best on a floor without a carpet.

You can make the circuits any shape by putting the strings around more chair legs. If the strings slip on the wheels, push the chairs away from the wheels to make them tight again.

Before a race, decide how many times the cars should go around the tracks. It could be twice for a short race or ten times for a long one. The winner is the first car to reach the finishing line.

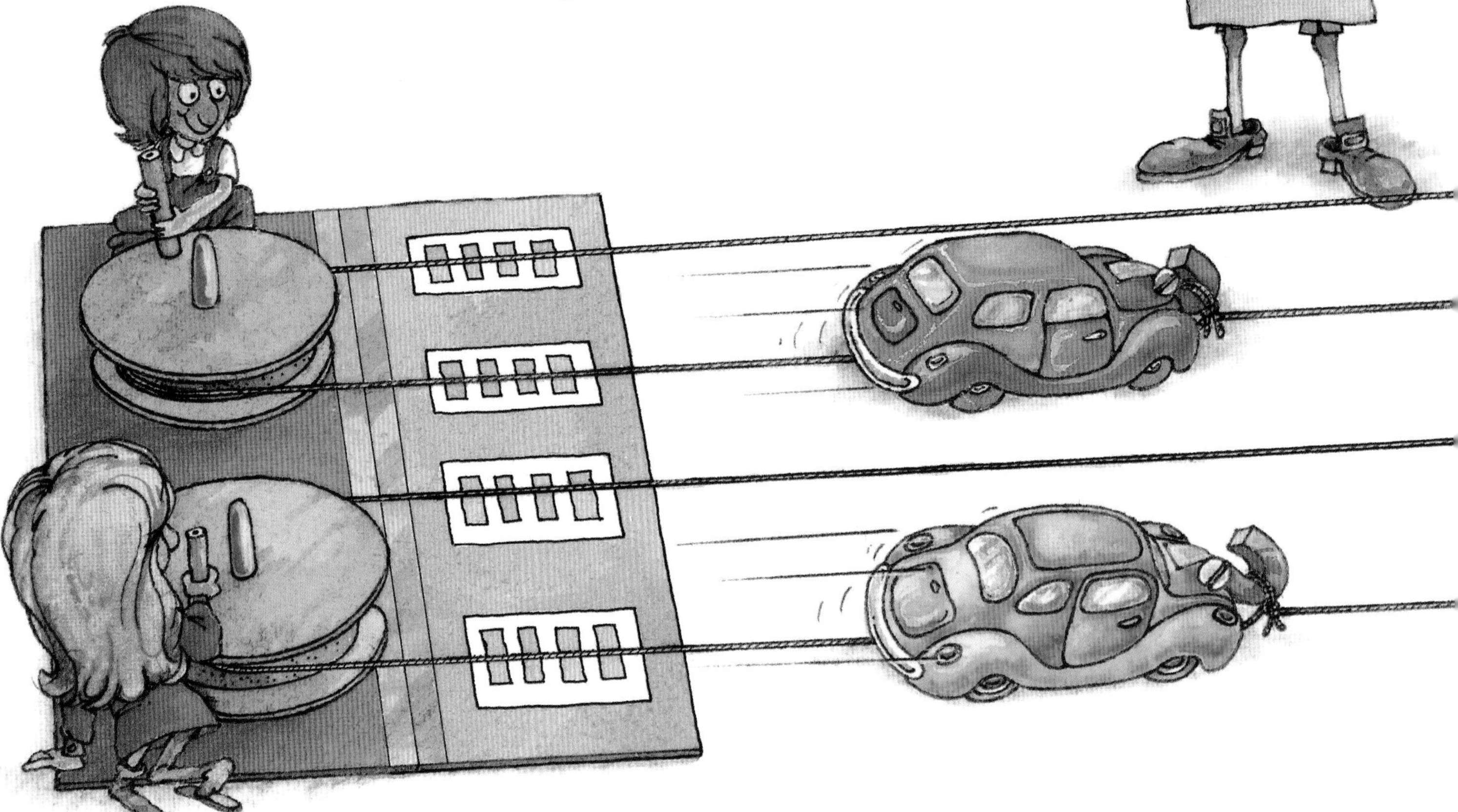

YOU WILL NEED

- 2 small toy cars
- a round cardboard cheese box
- 2 pieces of thick string, each about 5m (16ft) long
- 2 horseshoe magnets
- a sheet of sandpaper
- 2 big nails
- 2 pencils
- 2 ballpoint pen tops
- cardboard
- 4 empty tin cans
- strong glue

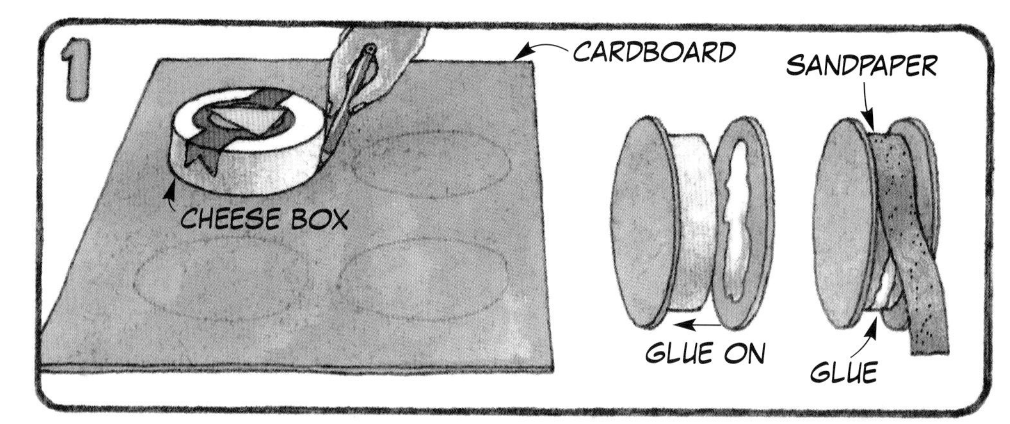

Draw four circles on cardboard, using the cheese box as a guide. Cut out the four circles, making them about 1cm (½in) bigger than the drawn lines.

Separate the box lid and bottom. Then glue one circle on each side of the lid and the bottom, to make two wheels. Glue a strip of sandpaper around the wheels.

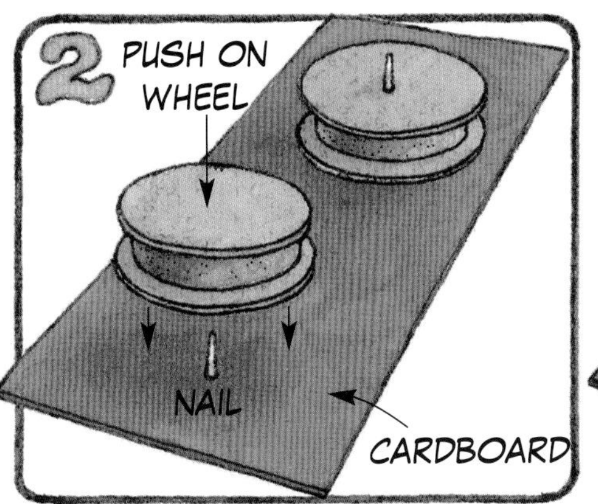

Push two nails through each end of a large sheet of cardboard. Stick a piece of tape over each nail head. Push a nail through the middle of each wheel, like this.

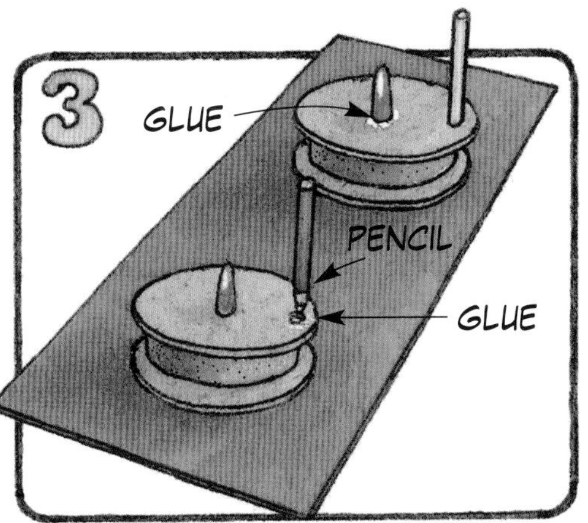

Glue a ballpoint pen top over each nail. Make sure no glue goes on the nails. Push a pencil through each wheel near the edge. Glue them in place.

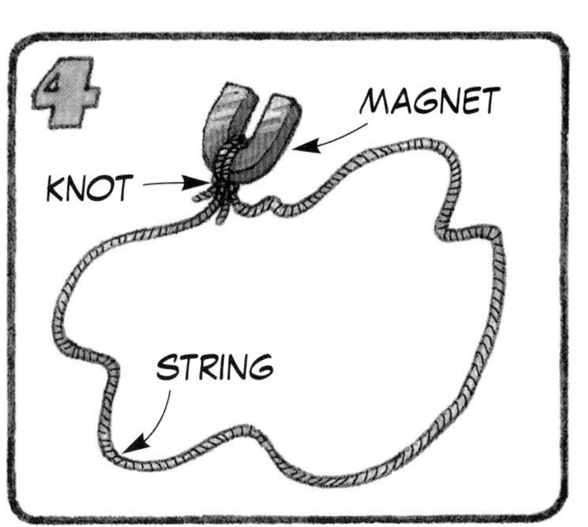

Tie the ends of each piece of string together. Tie a magnet to the knot in each piece of string.

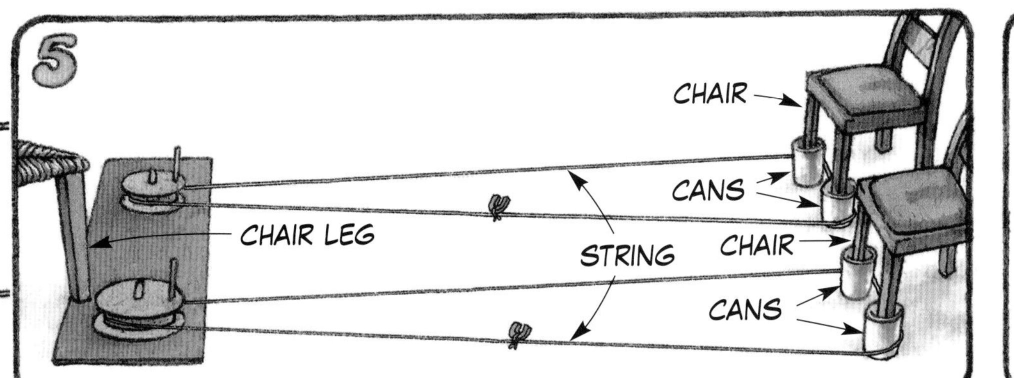

Put the cardboard with the wheels down on the floor. Put a table or chair leg on it. Loop one string around each wheel. Put tin cans under the front legs of two chairs.

Put two chair legs over each string, like this.

Push the chairs gently away from the wheels until the strings are stretched tight.

Try sticking the cars to the magnets. If they won't stick, put a small, fat iron screw on the front of each car. Stick it firmly in place with tape.

Stick a second piece of cardboard in front of the first one with tape. Draw or paint a starting and finishing line under each string.

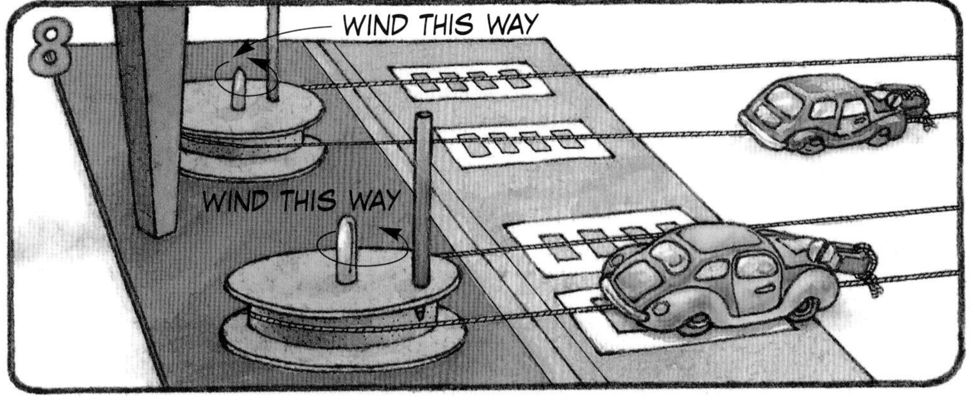

To race, wind the magnets back to the starting lines. Stick a car to each magnet. When someone says 'go', two players each wind a handle to move the cars forward.

If a car comes off a magnet, wind the handle the other way to move the magnet back again to the car. Or go to the car and stick it by hand on the magnet again.

Power pacer

Wind the propeller on this boat about 20 times. Put the boat in water and let it go.

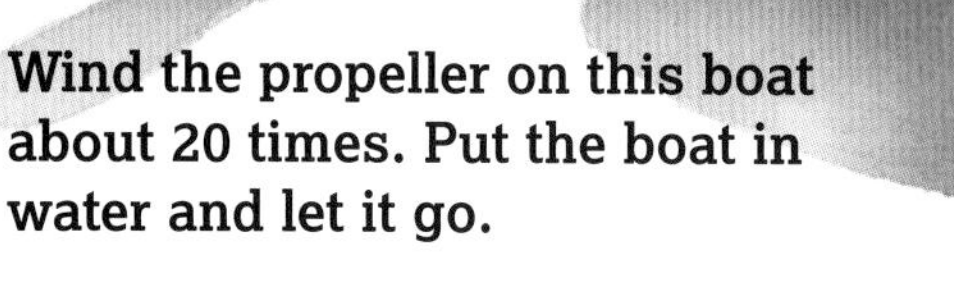

YOU WILL NEED

- a plastic squeezy bottle
- a piece of plastic cut from the side of a plastic bottle
- a ballpoint pen, with the ink tube taken out
- 3 strong rubber bands
- a piece of thin bendy wire, about 10cm (4in) long
- a used matchstick
- kitchen foil
- scissors

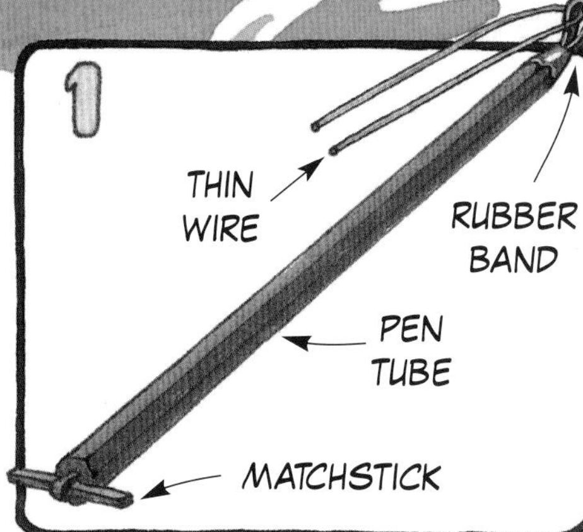

Push a rubber band through the pen tube. Push a matchstick through the loop at one end. Hook a piece of bendy wire through the loop at the other end.

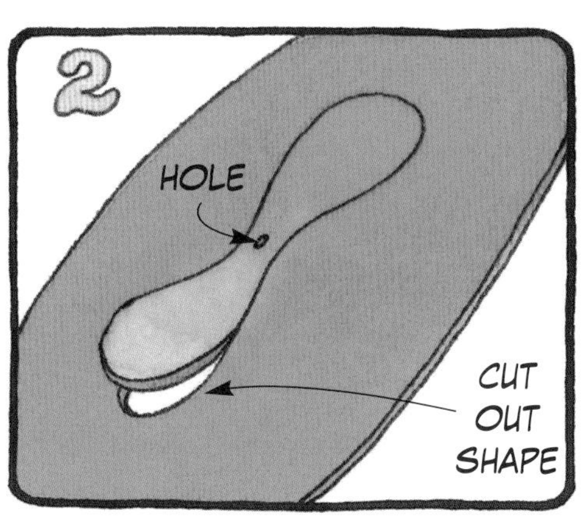

To make the propeller, draw the shape of a figure eight, about 6cm (2½in) long, on the plastic piece. Cut it out. Make a small hole in the middle of the propeller.

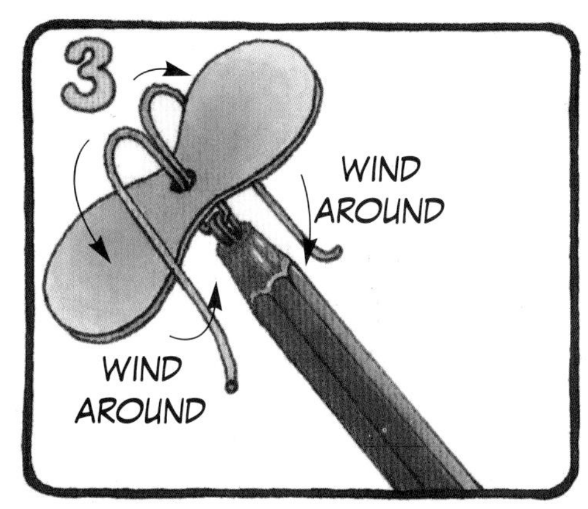

Push the ends of the wire through the hole in the propeller. Then wind them tightly around, as shown here.

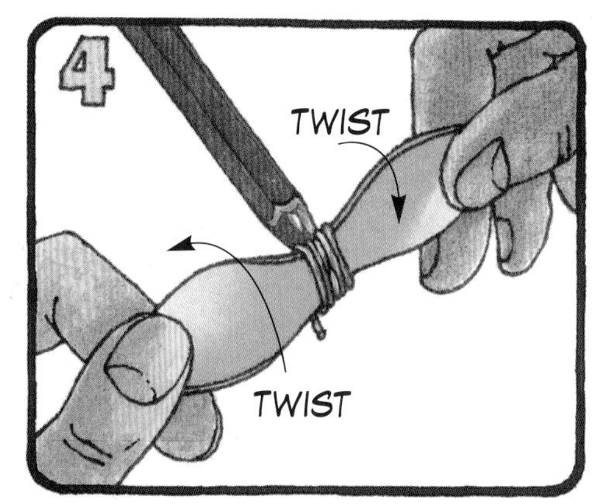

Hold the ends of the propeller. Twist the right side toward you and the left side away from you.

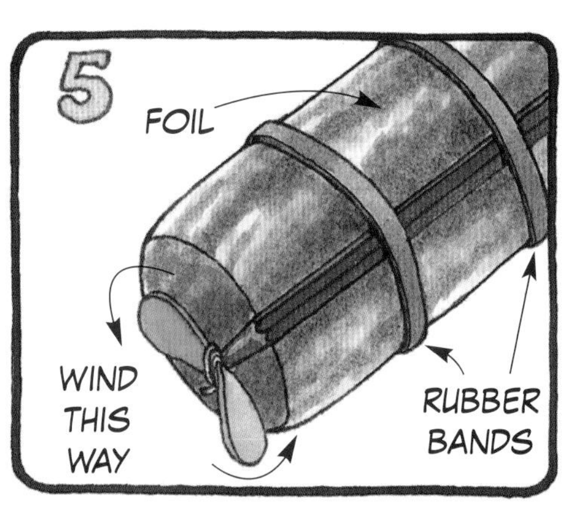

Wrap the bottle tightly in foil. Put the pen tube on one side, with the propeller sticking out of the flat end. Fix with two rubber bands.

Batteries & magnets

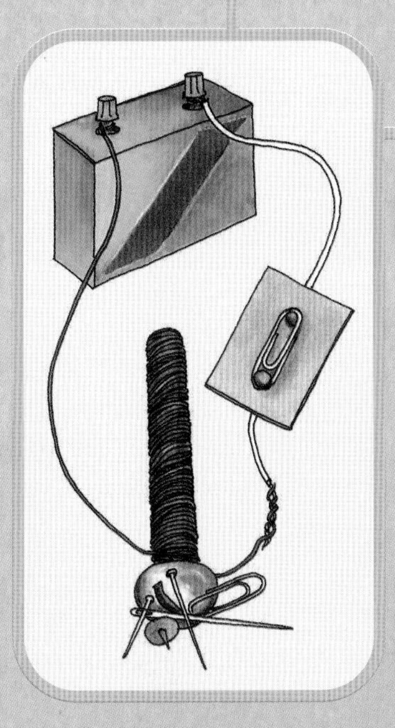

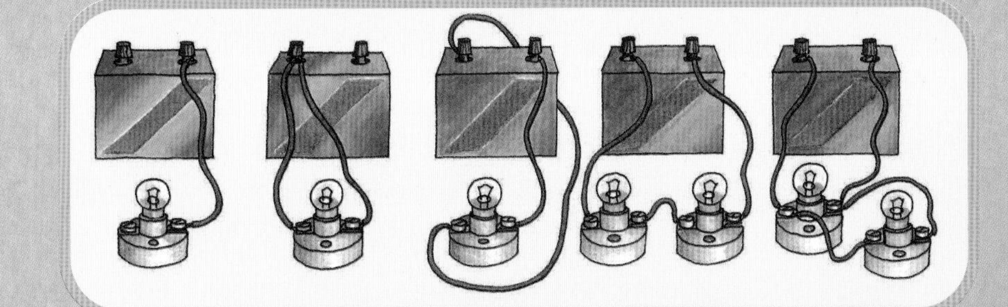

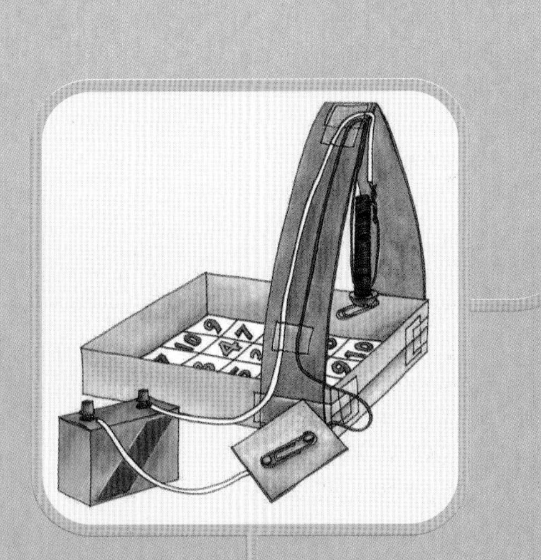

Lots of tricks with magnets

You can't actually see why a magnet works, but even so you can have lots of fun picking up and moving things with it. Buy a strong horseshoe or bar magnet and find out what it will do. The stronger the magnet the more it will pick up.

Remember to treat your magnet gently. If you drop or bang it, it will lose some of its magnetism. Try to keep magnets away from your watch, or it may be damaged and stop working.

You can make another magnet by stroking a needle eight or nine times with a magnet. Always stroke it in the same direction. Then try picking up a pin with the magnetized needle.

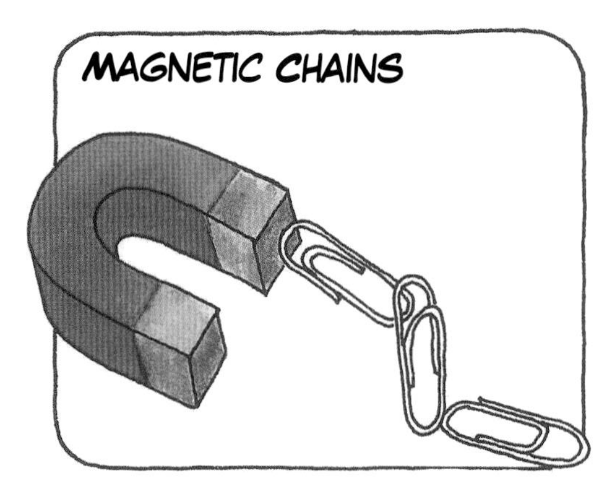

Pick up a paper clip with a magnet. Then try to make a chain by sticking more clips to the first one. The stronger the magnet, the longer will be the chain.

Try this trick and puzzle your friends. The paper clip will hang in the air for as long as you like to leave it. It looks like magic but the paper clip is held up by a magnet in a matchbox.

YOU WILL NEED

- a small horseshoe magnet
- a matchbox
- a long piece of thin thread
- a paper clip
- sticky tape
- scissors

Place the magnet in a matchbox, like this. Hold the box against the edge of a shelf and stick it in place with some sticky tape.

Try picking up lots of different things with a magnet and discover what will stick to it. Or try sticking a small magnet to larger objects.

Find out if a magnet will work through paper, cardboard and wood. Hold a magnet under the table and try moving pins and nails around on top.

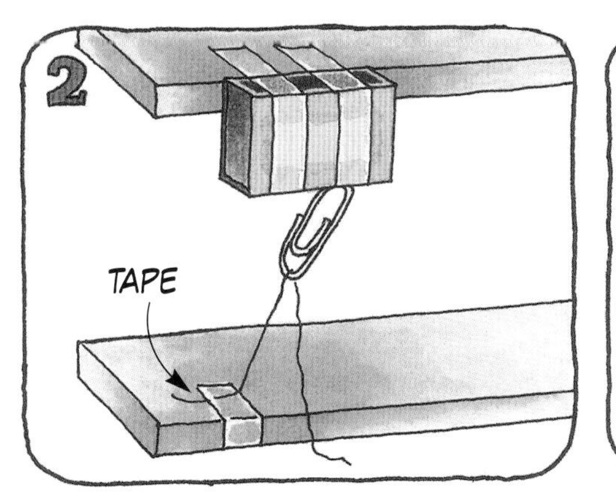

Stick the end of a long piece of thread to the shelf below with tape. Hook a paper clip on to the thread and hold it up to the matchbox. Let go when it sticks.

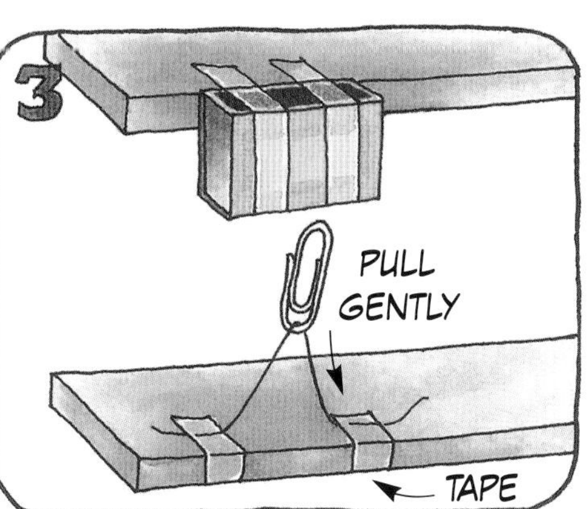

Pull the free end of the thread down very gently until the paper clip is floating just below the matchbox. Stick this end down with tape to the shelf below.

If anyone thinks the paper clip is held up by a thread or wire, pass a piece of cardboard between the clip and the matchbox.

MAKING A COMPASS

The Earth is a huge magnet. That is why a compass needle always points to the North Pole. Make your own compass and it will swing to the North.

YOU WILL NEED

- a horseshoe magnet
- 3 needles
- a small strip of paper
- some model clay
- sticky tape and scissors

Hold a needle by the eye and stroke it gently about six times with a magnet. Always move the magnet in the same direction.

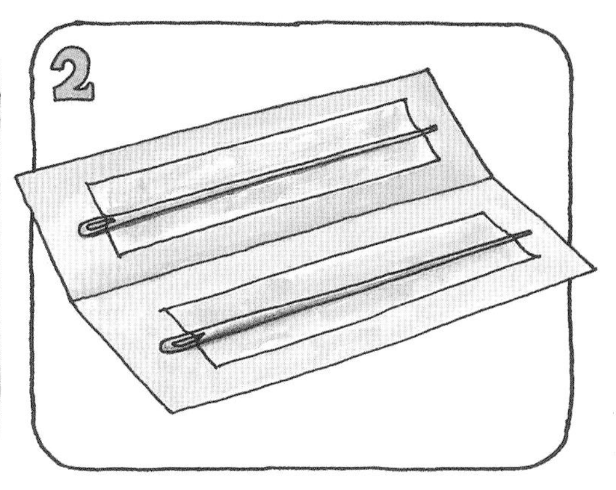

Stroke a second needle in the same way. Fold the strip of paper in half and stick the needles to it with tape, like this. Both needles must point the same way.

Take a paper clip out of a glass of water without getting your fingers wet. Hold a magnet to the outside of a glass and slide the clip up the glass.

Mark the needle eye end of the paper with an S and the point end with an N. Push a third needle into some model clay. Balance the paper on top so it can swing.

If you want to take the compass out of doors, hang the paper by a thread. Tie the thread to a pencil and drop the paper into a glass jar, like this.

Batteries and circuits

Shopping list

These are the things you will need to make the batteries and circuits here. You can buy most of them at a hardware store or an electrical store.

- Batteries – The strength of a battery is measured in volts. If you use a 4·5 volt battery, like one of these, it will last longer.
- Flex – This is wire covered with plastic. If you can't buy the single-strand flex, get the two-stranded sort and pull it apart. Or buy the flat kind and split it down the middle.
- Florists' wire – This is thin, bendy wire without any covering on it.
- Glazed copper wire – This is shiny copper wire coated with varnish. It is used to make electro-magnets.
- Bulbs – Buy 2·5 or 3·5 volt torch bulbs. A 2·5 volt bulb will give a brighter light, but a 3·5 volt bulb will last longer.
- Bulb holder
- Small screwdriver
- Horseshoe magnet
- Iron bolt or big iron nail for an electro-magnet
- Paper clips and fasteners

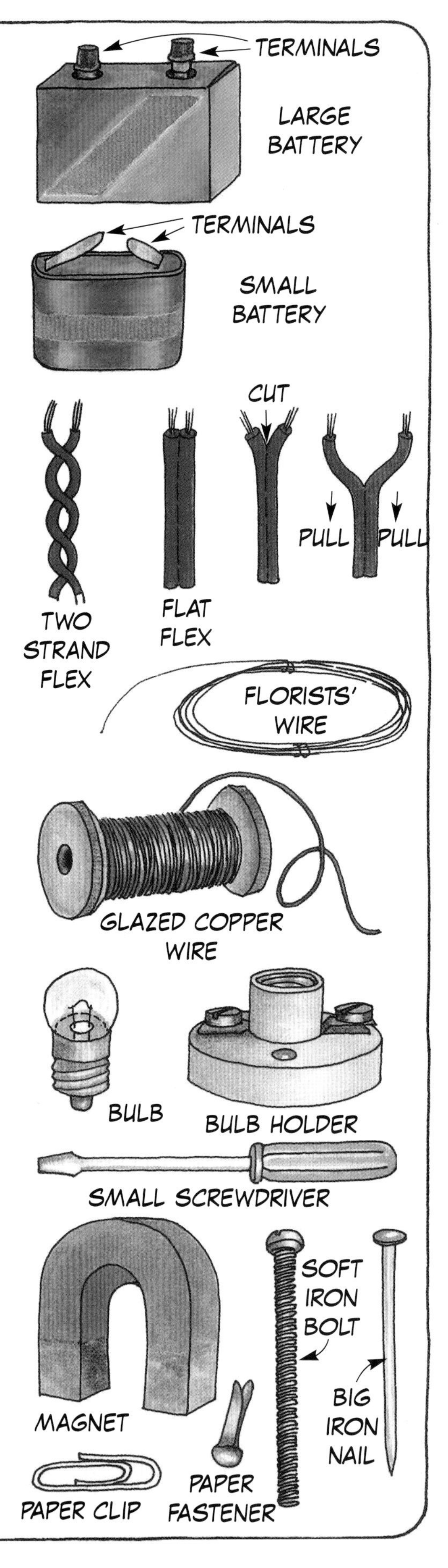

1 Preparing the flex

CUT ALL AROUND

PUSH OFF

Using pliers, strip about 3cm (1¼in) of plastic off the ends of each piece of flex. Be careful not to cut through the wires.

1 Wiring up a bulb holder

Put a screwdriver in the slot on one of the screws. Give it a few turns, in the direction shown, but don't take the screw out. Undo the other screw.

1 Battery and bulb holder

Bend one end of a piece of flex on the bulb holder into a hook. Undo a terminal on the battery and hook the flex on. Then do up the terminal tightly.

If your flex has bundles of little wires inside the plastic, twist them together to make a neat end, like this.

Unwind the two terminals on the battery, giving each one a few turns, like this. Bend the bare wires at the ends of two pieces of flex into small hooks.

Hook a piece of flex on to one terminal and tighten the terminal, turning it this way. Hook the other flex on to the second terminal and do it up in the same way.

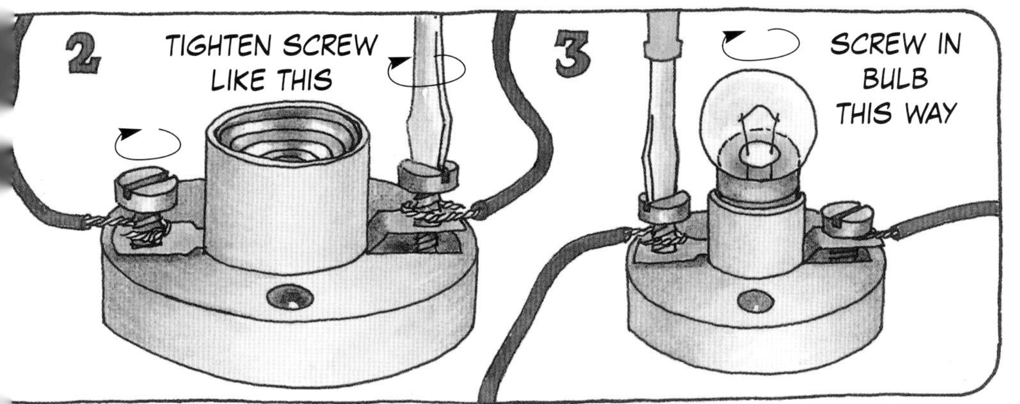

Make small loops at the ends of two pieces of flex. Hook a loop around each screw. Push the flex around with the screwdriver to make a small circle.

Do both screws up tightly, turning the screwdriver, like this. Screws always do up this way. Put in the bulb, turning it this way.

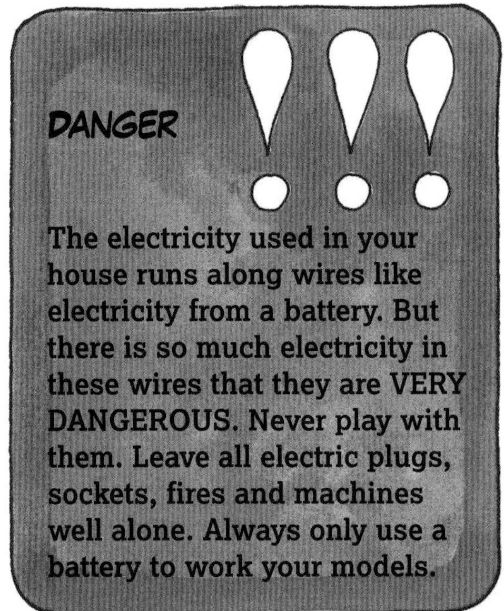

The electricity used in your house runs along wires like electricity from a battery. But there is so much electricity in these wires that they are VERY DANGEROUS. Never play with them. Leave all electric plugs, sockets, fires and machines well alone. Always only use a battery to work your models.

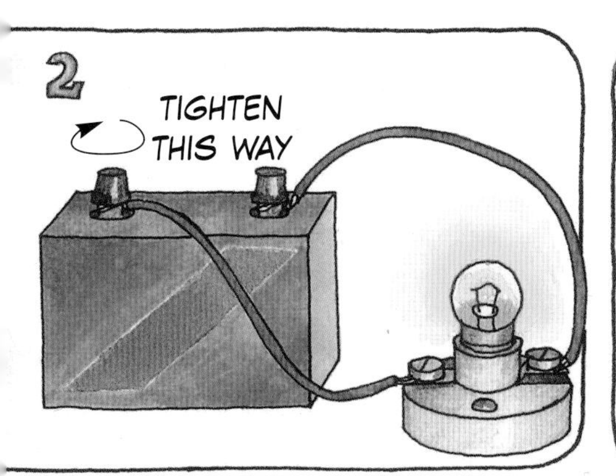

Make a hook on the end of the other flex and hook it on to the second terminal. The light will go on. To make it stay on, do up the terminal.

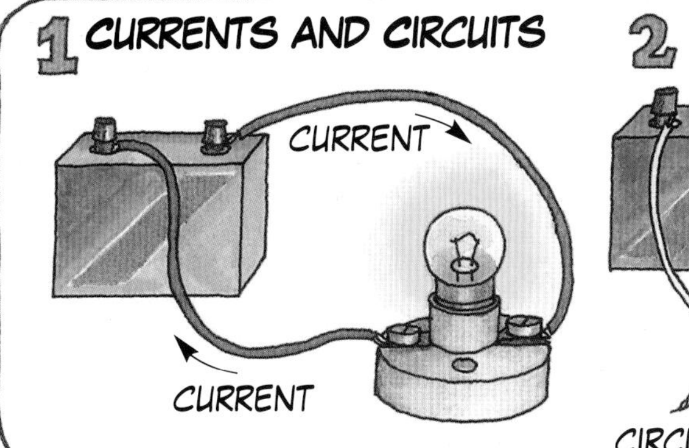

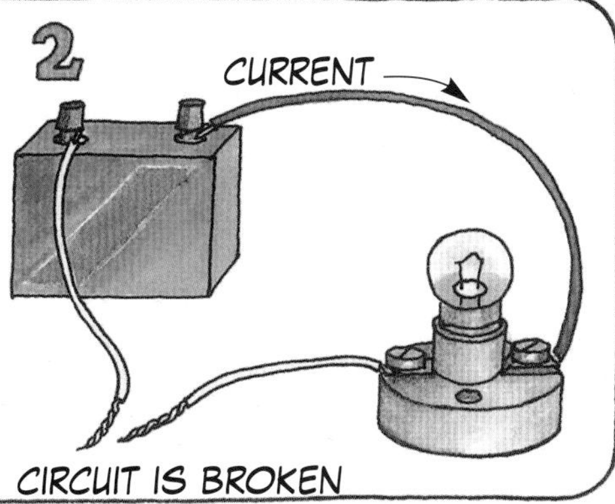

The light goes on when the electric current from the battery runs along the flex, through the bulb and back to the battery. Its path is called a circuit.

If the flex is cut, the circuit is broken and the light will not go on. If the cut wires touch, the circuit is complete and the bulb will light up.

Bulb holders and switches

MAKING THE KNOWHOW BULB HOLDER

Make this KnowHow bulb holder and use it for the models and games on the next few pages.

YOU WILL NEED

- a matchbox
- a large paper clip
- a piece of kitchen foil
- 2 paper fasteners
- 2 pieces of flex, with stripped ends (see page 98)
- a 3·5 volt bulb
- scissors

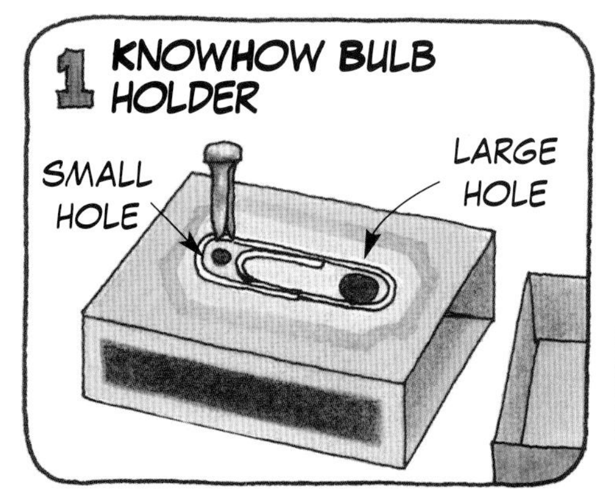

Take the tray out of the matchbox. Make a small hole in the top of the box. Put a paper clip over it and push a paper fastener through. Make a larger hole, as shown.

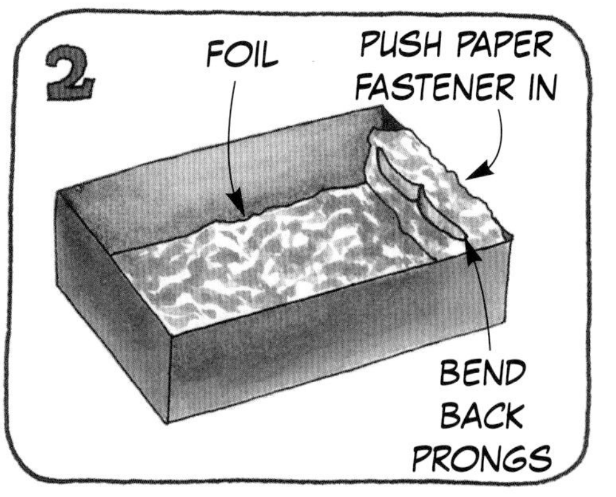

Line the bottom and one end of the tray with foil. Push a paper fastener through the lined end and bend back the prongs.

THE KNOWHOW SWITCH

This useful KnowHow switch is simple and easy to make.

YOU WILL NEED

- a small piece of cardboard about 5cm x 5cm (2in x 2in)
- 2 paper fasteners
- a large paper clip
- 3 pieces of flex with stripped ends (see page 98)
- a KnowHow bulb holder with a 3·5 volt bulb
- a 4·5 volt battery

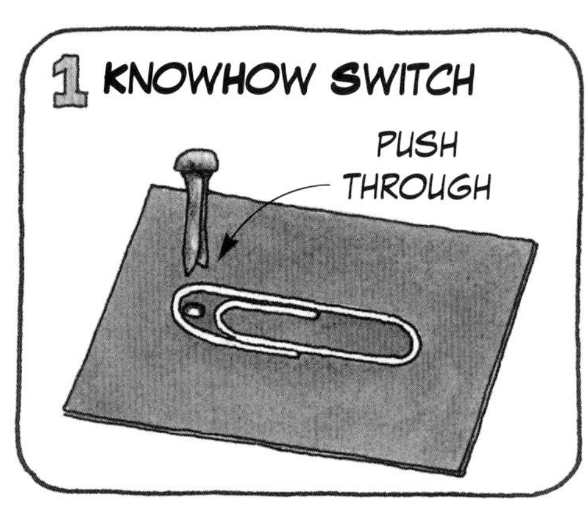

Make a small hole in a piece of cardboard. Hold one end of the paper clip over the hole and push a paper fastener through. Bend back the ends underneath.

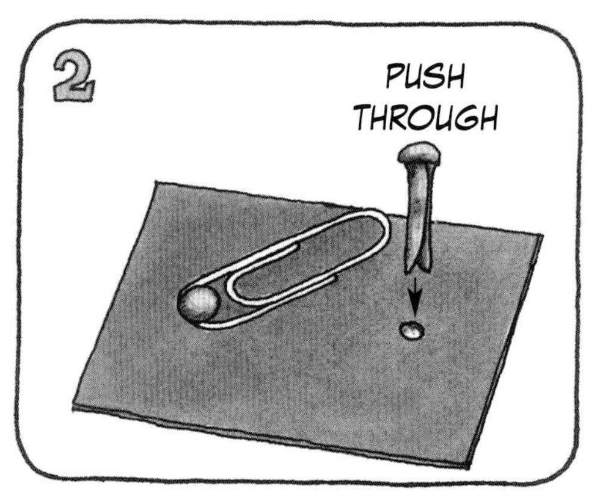

Make another hole at the other end of the paper clip and push a paper fastener through. Bend back the ends, but do not let them touch the other fastener.

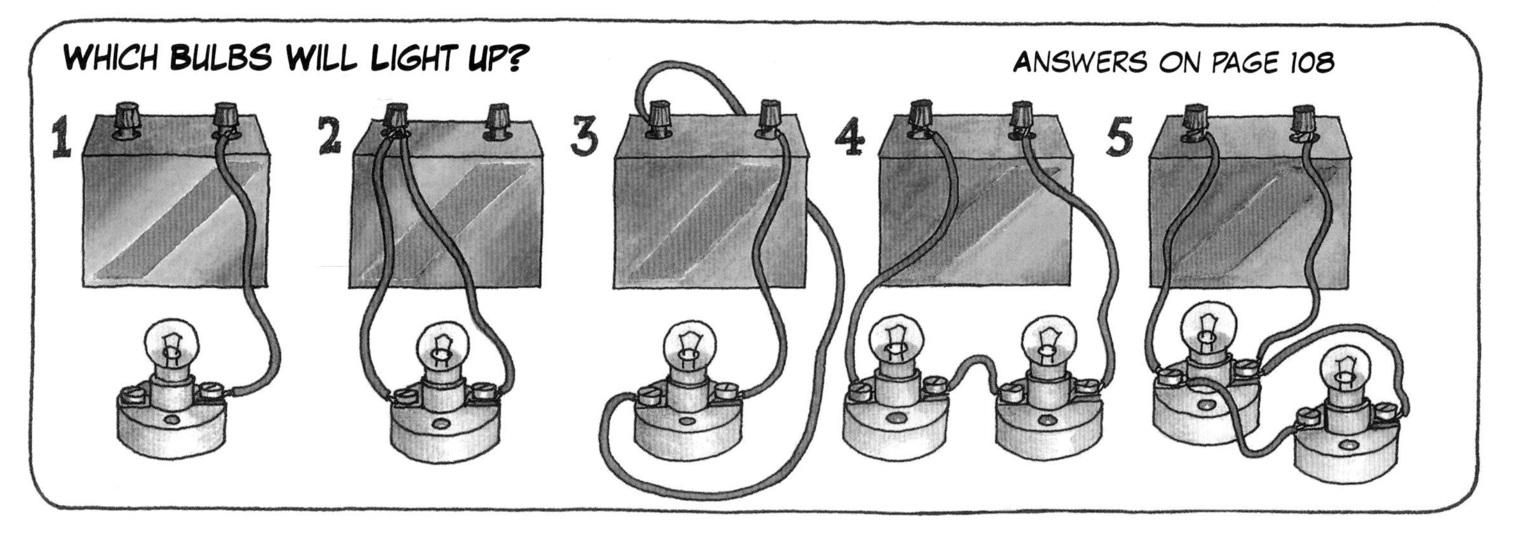

Push the tray into the matchbox. Screw the bulb through the paper clip into the large hole. The bottom of the bulb must touch the foil inside the box.

Wind the end of one piece of flex around the paper fastener on top of the box. Wind the other piece around the fastener on the end of the tray.

Join the end of each piece of flex from the bulb holder to a terminal on the battery. This will make the bulb light up.

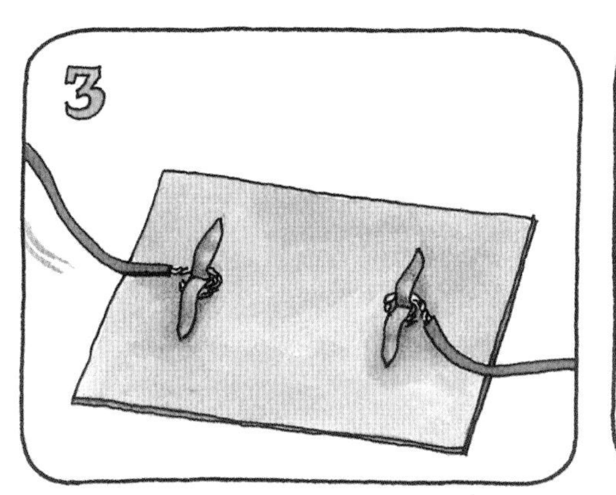

Turn the cardboard over. Wind an end of one piece of flex around one fastener, and one end of another flex around the second fastener.

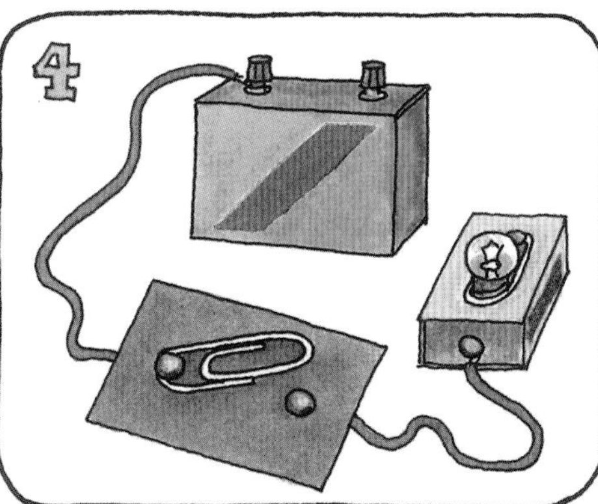

Join the free end of one flex to a battery terminal. Wind the end of the other flex around a fastener on the bulb holder.

Join one end of a third flex to the free battery terminal. Wind the other end around the free fastener on the bulb holder. Switch on.

QUICK SWITCH & HOLDER

Here is an easy way to make a quick switch. You can also tape the ends of the cardboard down and turn it into a bulb holder.

YOU WILL NEED

- a strip of cardboard about 15cm (6in) long and 5cm (2in) wide
- some foil 5cm (2in) square
- 2 pieces of flex with stripped ends (see page 98)
- a 3·5 volt bulb
- a 4·5 volt battery
- sticky tape and scissors

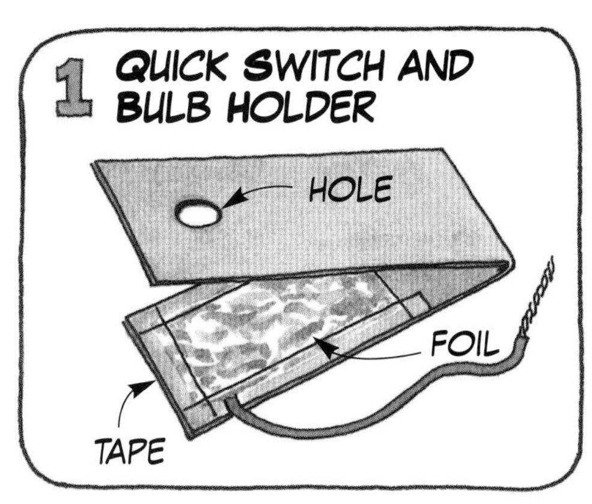

Make a hole in the cardboard at one end. Fold it in half. Put the flex on the cardboard, like this. Put the foil over it and stick down the edges with tape.

Push the bulb through the hole. Wind one end of the second piece of flex around the bulb. Join the free ends of the flex to the two battery terminals.

KnowHow night light

MAKING A NIGHT LIGHT

YOU WILL NEED

- a small cardboard box, a little bigger than the battery
- a KnowHow bulb holder with a 3·5 volt bulb
- a 4·5 volt battery
- 3 pieces of flex with stripped ends (see page 98)
- 2 paper fasteners
- 1 paper clip
- a sheet of paper
- sticky tape, glue and scissors

Make a hole in the box lid, big enough for the bulb to go through. Wind the end of a piece of flex around each of the fasteners on the KnowHow bulb holder.

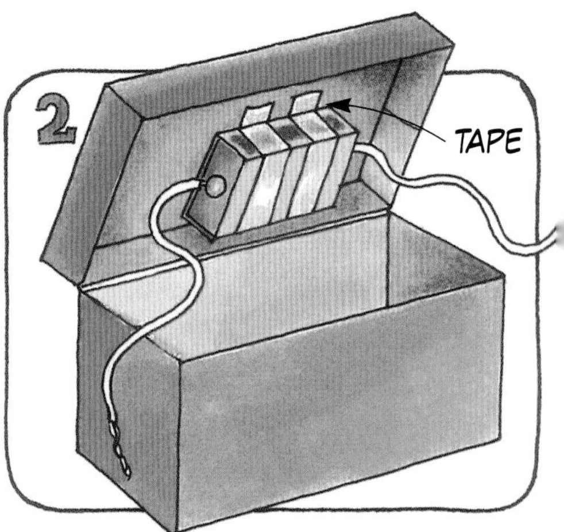

Put the bulb holder underneath the lid and push the bulb up through the hole. Fix the bulb holder to the inside of the lid with some sticky tape.

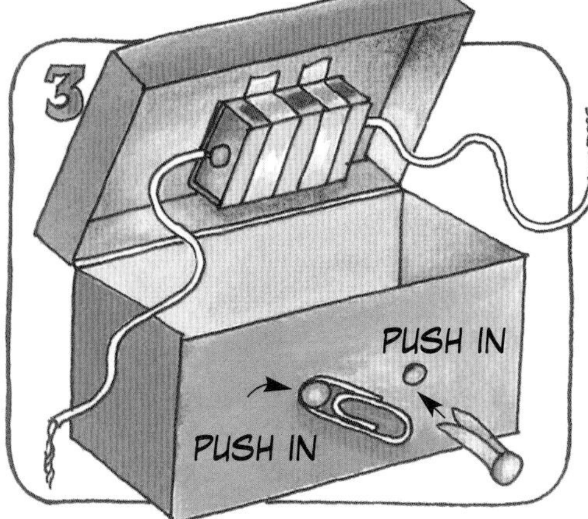

Make a small hole in the front of the box. Hold a paper clip over the hole and push a paper fastener through. Push a second fastener in near the clip.

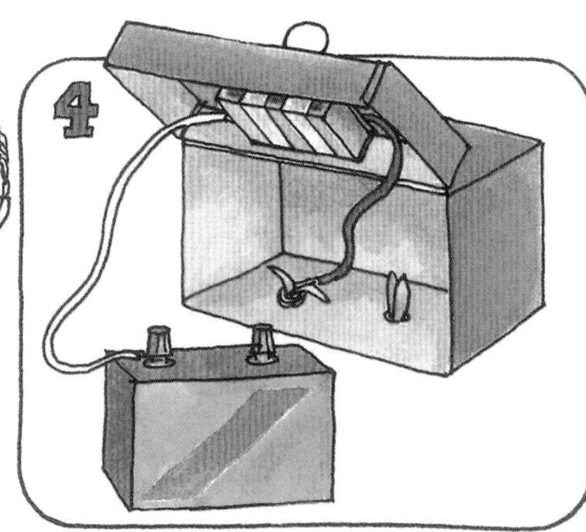

Lay the box on its front and wind the end of a bulb holder flex around one paper fastener. Join the other flex to a terminal on the battery.

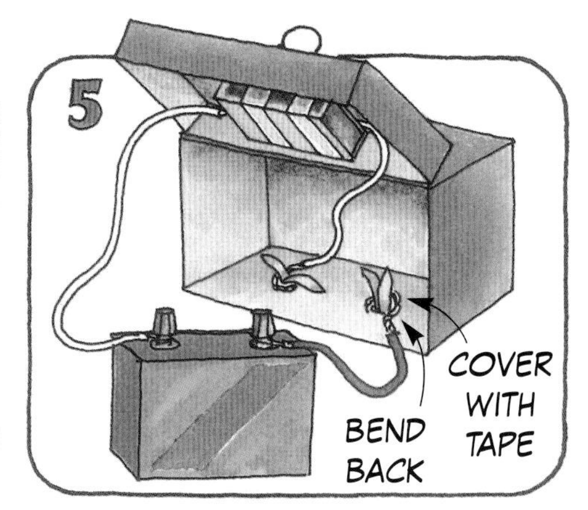

Wind one end of a third flex around the free fastener. Join the other end to the free battery terminal. Bend back the prongs of the fasteners and cover with tape.

Put the battery in the box. Tuck in all the flex and close the lid. Stick it down with tape.

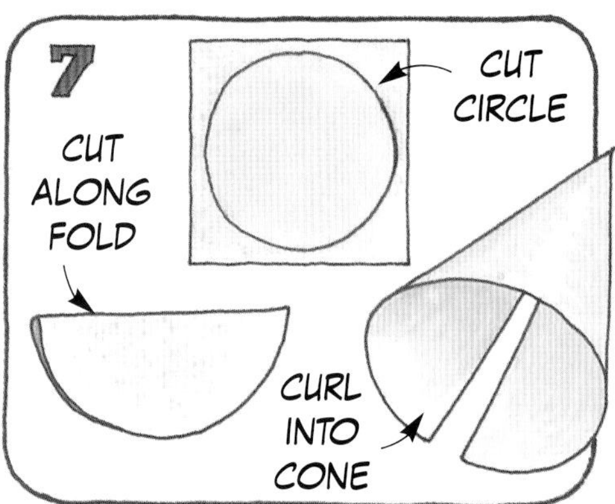

To make the shade, cut out a circle of paper. Fold it in half and cut all the way along the fold. Curl one half circle into a cone.

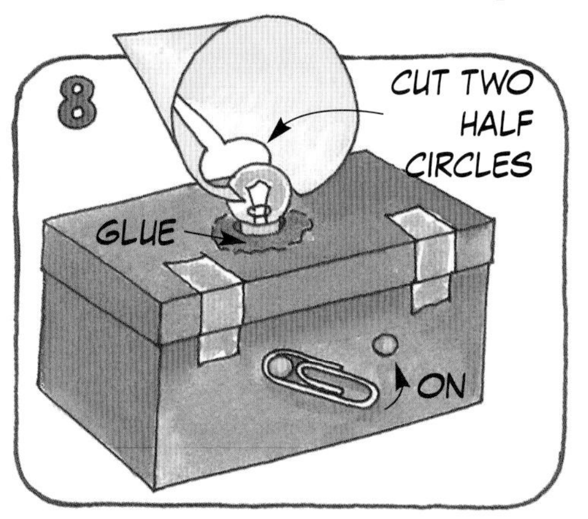

Hold the cone around the bulb in the box and mark where the bulb will be. Cut out two little half circles at the marks. Curl up the cone and glue it around the bulb.

Bright lights

Switch on and turn the handle on the box to make the light change shades. Try working it in the dark or use it for signals.

YOU WILL NEED

- a KnowHow night light, like the one opposite, but in a larger, tall cardboard box
- cardboard
- shaded cellophane
- a pencil and a paper clip
- paper and kitchen foil
- sticky tape, glue and scissors

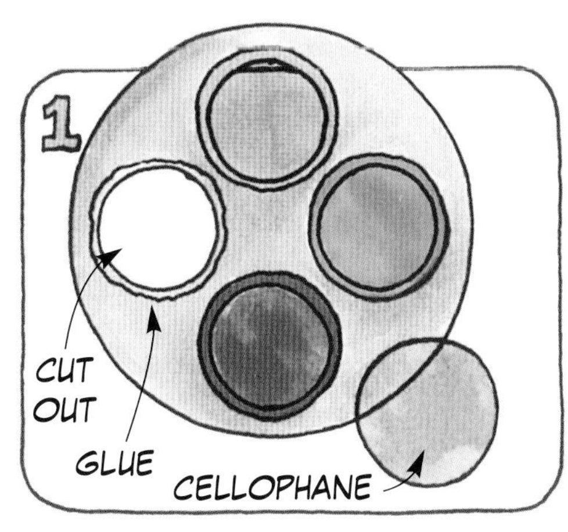

Cut out a circle of cardboard about one and a half times the height of the box. Cut out four circles and glue circles of different shaded cellophane over them.

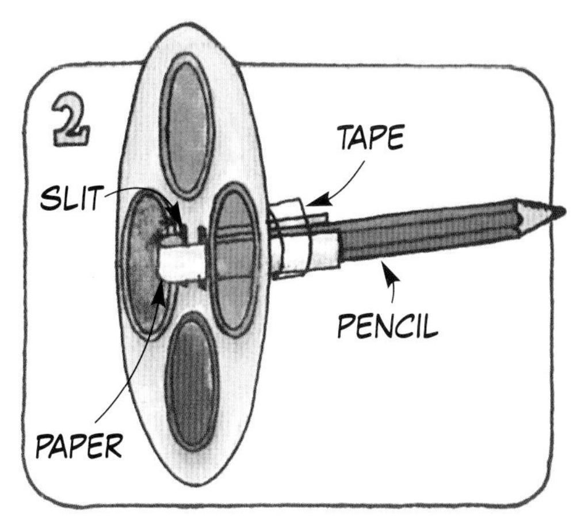

Make two slits in the middle of the cardboard circle. Thread a strip of cardboard through them and stick the ends to a pencil with tape, as shown here.

Make a hole through the box about 3cm (1¼in) from the top. Push a pencil through. Bend a paper clip to make a handle and tape it to the end of the pencil.

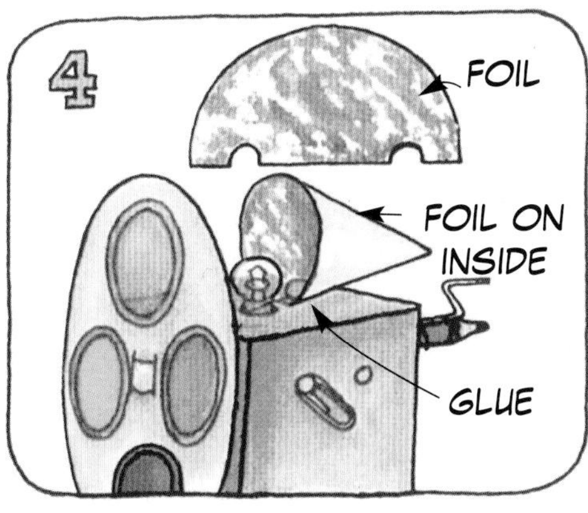

Cut out a half circle of paper and snip two little circles on the straight edge. Stick some foil on one side, roll it into a cone and then glue it around the bulb.

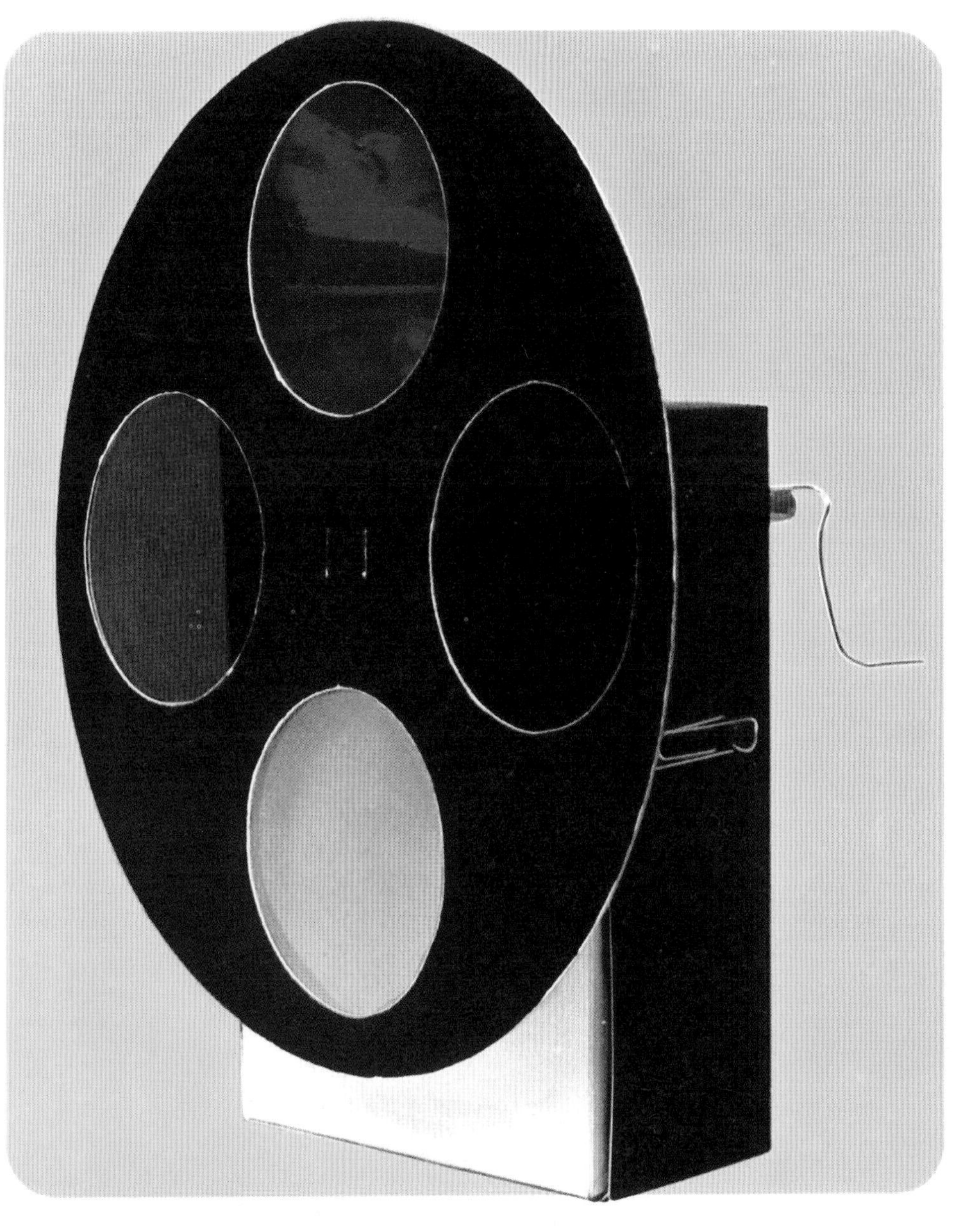

Making an electro-magnet

You can make an electro-magnet with an iron bolt or nail, some glazed copper wire and a battery.

When the electricity from the battery flows through the wire around the bolt, the bolt becomes a magnet. Break the circuit by switching off and the bolt is no longer a magnet.

The more times you wind the wire around the bolt, the stronger the magnet will be. Remember to switch off the electro-magnet when you're not using it or the battery will wear out quickly.

YOU WILL NEED

- an iron bolt about 5cm (2in) long or a big iron nail
- a piece of glazed copper wire, about 2m (6½ft) long
- 2 pieces of flex with stripped ends (see page 98)
- KnowHow switch (see page 100)
- a 4·5 volt battery
- sticky tape and scissors

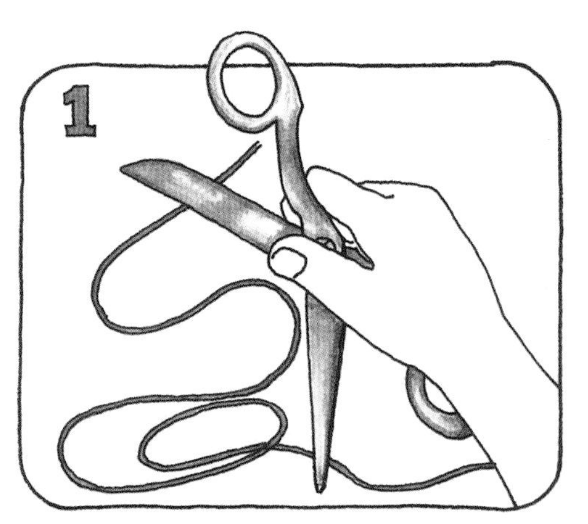

Use a blade of the scissors to scrape about 2cm (¾in) of varnish off both ends of the copper wire. Do this carefully or the electro-magnet will not work.

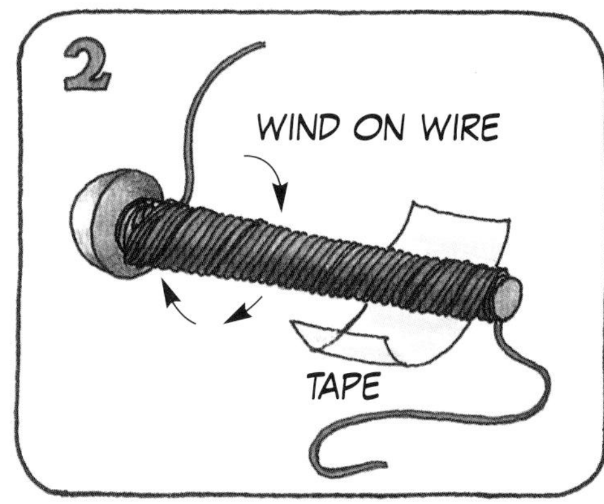

Hold one end of the wire against the bolt or nail and wind the wire tightly around. Keep the coils very close together.

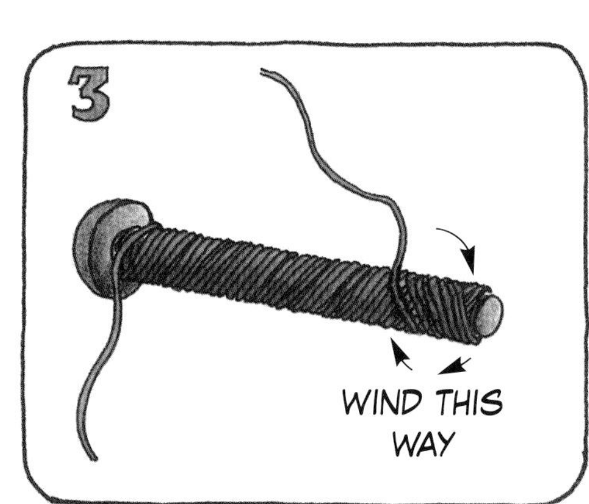

When you reach the end of the bolt or nail, put some tape on the wire. Wind the rest of the wire back along the bolt again. Keep the coils as close as you can.

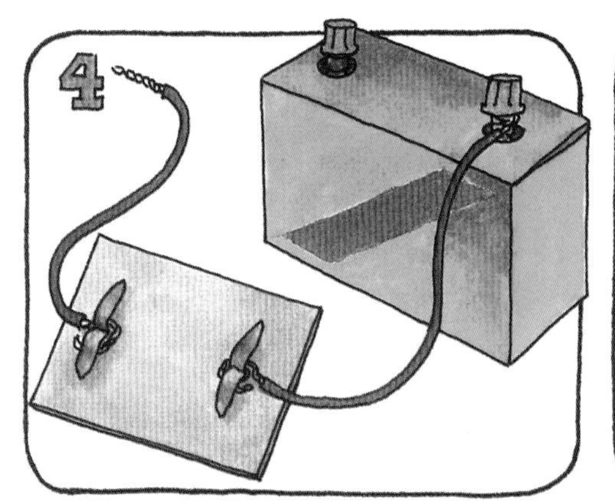

Join a piece of flex to each of the fasteners on the KnowHow switch. Wind the free end of one flex around a battery terminal.

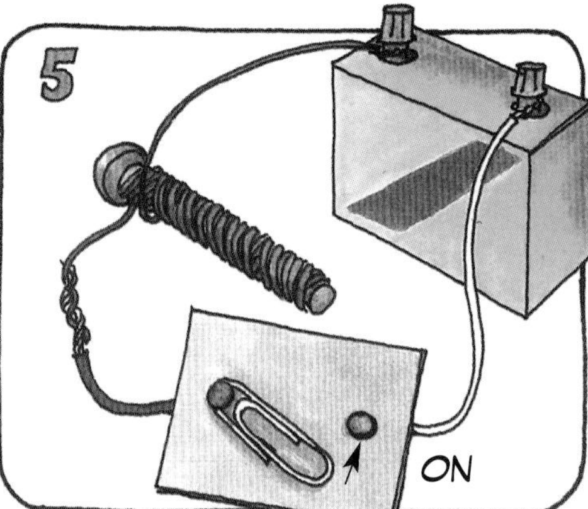

Twist the other flex around one wire on the electro-magnet. Join the end of the free wire on the bolt to the second battery terminal.

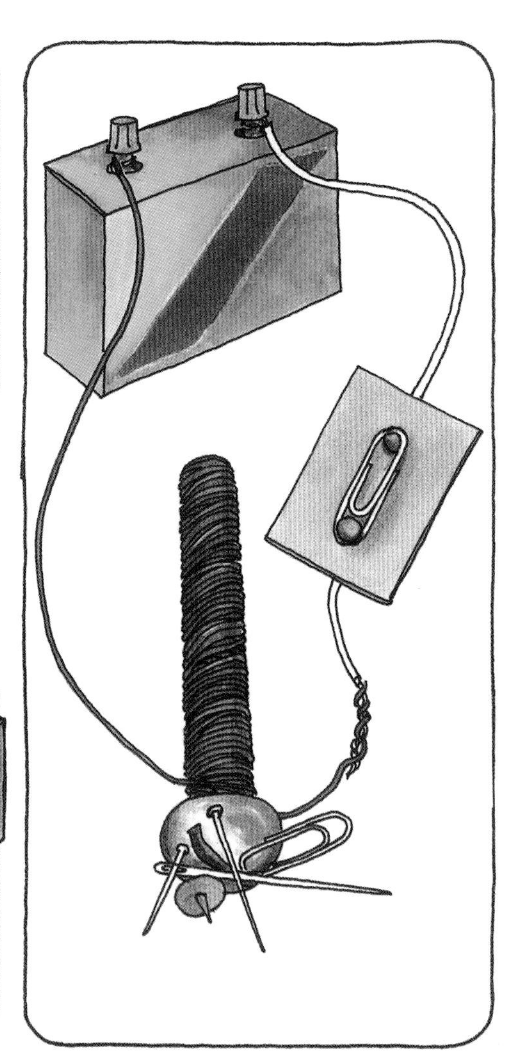

Switch on the electro-magnet by moving the paper clip to the on position, and pick up a few pins. Switch off, and they'll drop off.

Putting the shot

YOU WILL NEED

- an electro-magnet wired to a battery and a switch (see opposite)
- a large cereal box
- 2 strips of stiff cardboard 5cm (2in) wide, 25cm (10in) long
- a sheet of paper the same size as the box
- a pencil and ruler
- scissors and sticky tape

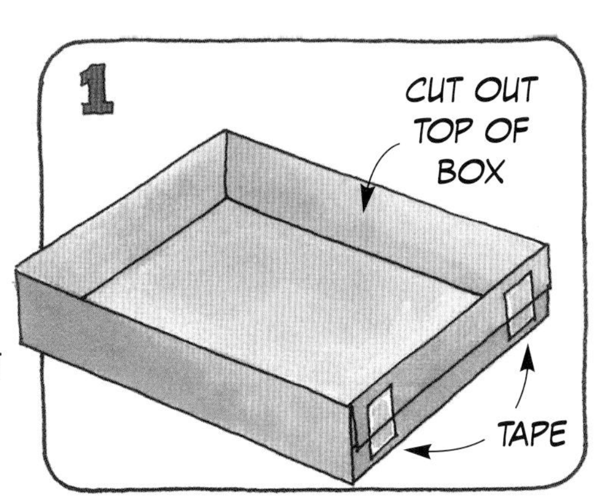

Close the end of the box and stick it down with tape. Cut out one side and lie the box down flat.

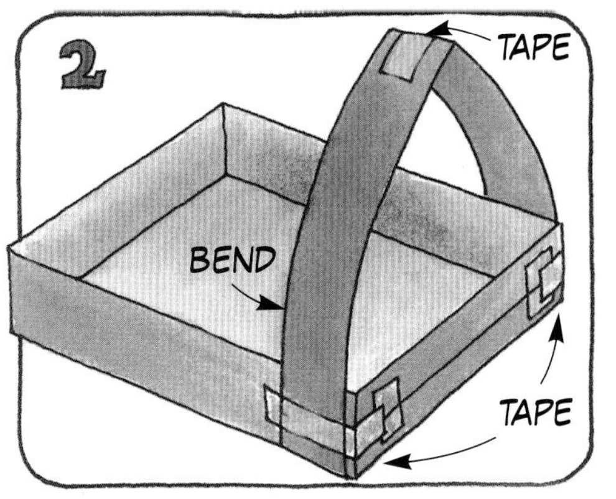

Stick the strips of cardboard one either side of the box, at one end, like this. Bend the tops until they meet and stick them together with tape.

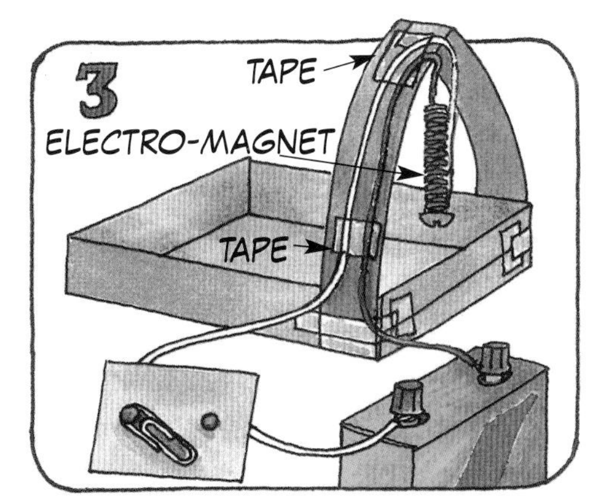

Hang the electro-magnet over the arch, so it can swing easily, and stick the flex to the top of the arch with tape. Tape the flex down one of the strips of cardboard.

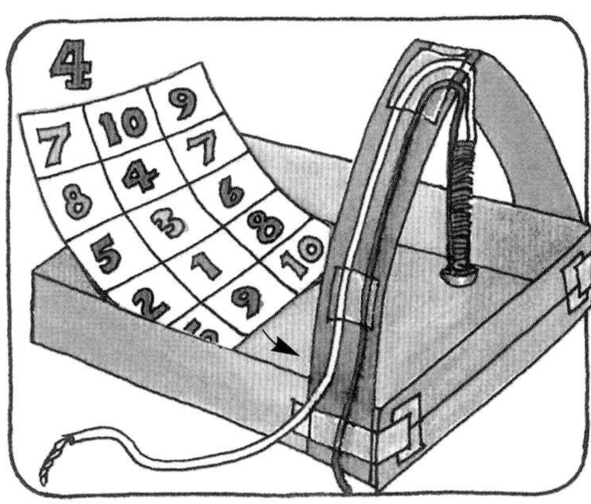

Draw lines across and down the piece of paper. Write a number in each section, putting the higher numbers at the sides. Lay the paper inside the box, as shown.

HOW TO PLAY

Switch on the electro-magnet and stick a small nail or paper clip to it. Pull the electro-magnet back and let it swing. Then switch off and see which number the nail or paper clip drops on.

Keep the score for each player. If the nail or clip goes out of the box, the player loses a point. The player with the highest score wins.

Magnetic pick-up truck

This electro-magnet truck will pick up pins and nails, or tow a small metal car. Just wind down the electro-magnet, switch it on and pick something up. Winch it up and push the truck away to the dumping ground. Switch off and drop the load.

Remember to switch off when you are not using the truck, or the battery will wear out quickly.

YOU WILL NEED

- a strong cardboard box, 20cm (8in) long, 12cm (4¾in) wide
- stiff cardboard
- 8 paper fasteners
- a cotton reel
- a pencil
- a piece of string about 30cm (1ft) long
- a 4·5 volt battery
- an electro-magnet (page 104)
- 3 paper clips
- 2 pieces of flex about 20cm (8in) long, with stripped ends (see page 98)
- sticky tape and scissors

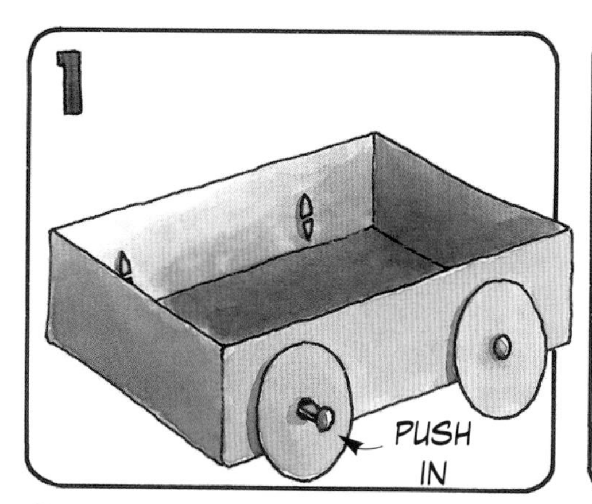

Cut out the side of the box. Cut out four cardboard circles for wheels. Push a fastener through the middle of each wheel and then through the sides of the box.

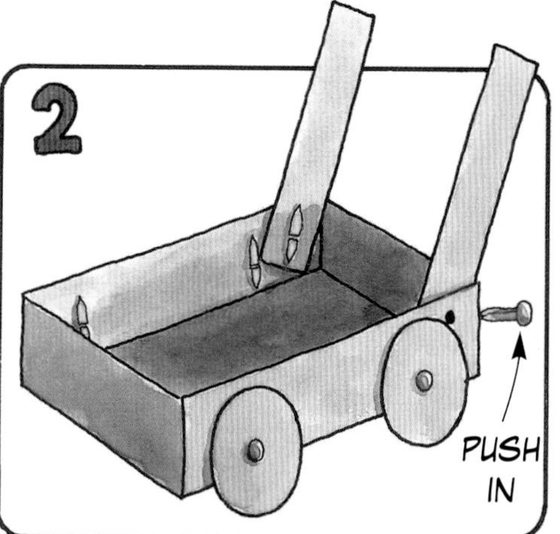

Cut two strips of cardboard the same length. Join them, like this, to the sides of the box with paper fasteners.

Make a hole in the end of each cardboard strip. Put a cotton reel between them and push a straightened paper clip through the holes. Bend over the ends.

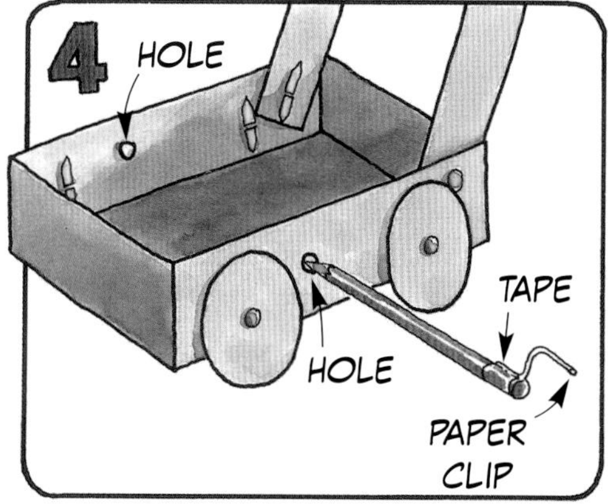

Bend another paper clip to make a handle. Stick it to the end of a pencil with tape. Make two holes in the sides of the box and push the pencil through.

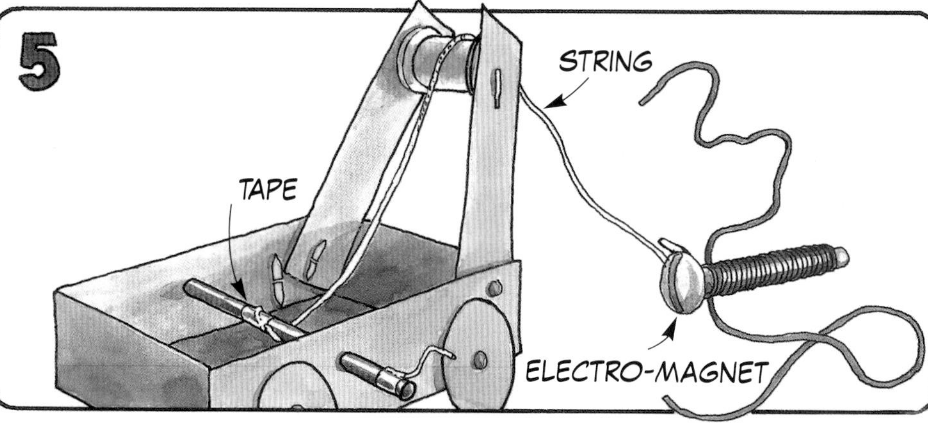

Fix one end of a piece of string to the middle of the pencil and hold it in place with sticky tape.

Run the string over the cotton reel and tie the other end to an electro-magnet.

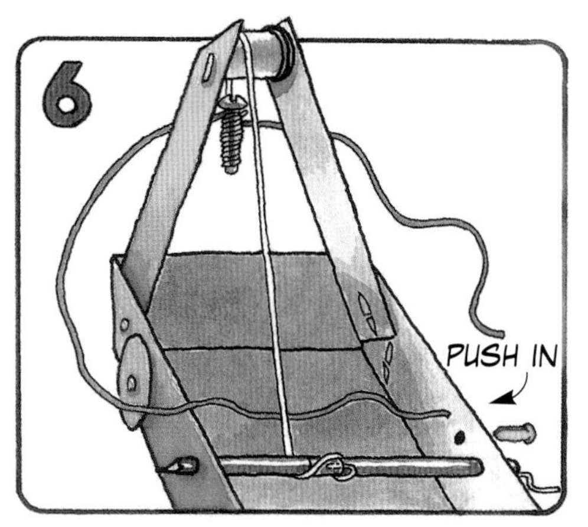

To make a switch, push a paper fastener through the box side. Wind one electro-magnet wire around it and bend back the ends.

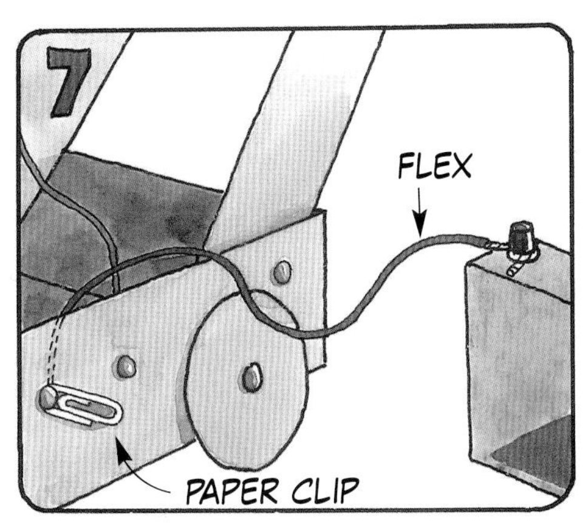

Push a second fastener through a paper clip and through the box, near the first fastener. Join one end of a new piece of flex to it and the other end to the battery.

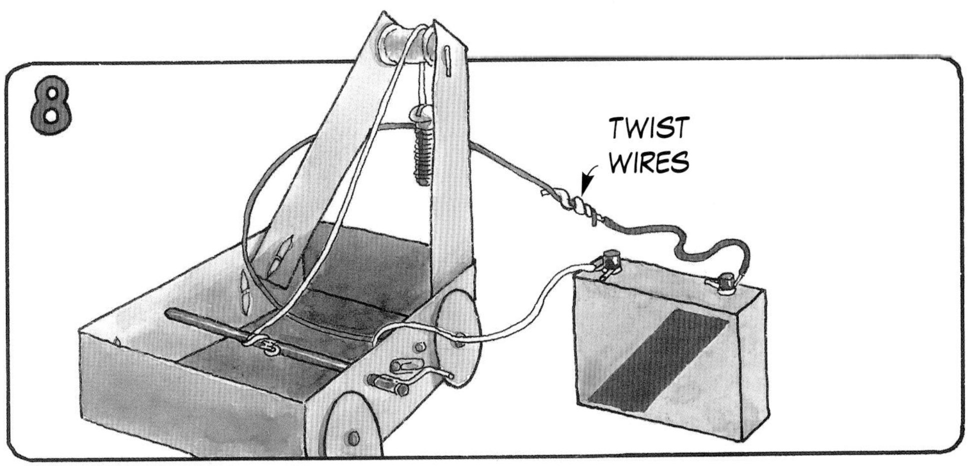

Twist one end of another piece of flex around the end of the second wire from the electro-magnet.

Join the other end of the flex to the second battery terminal. Put the battery inside the box.

You could make a driver's cab out of a small cardboard box.

Cut out or paint on doors and windows. Then glue or tape the box to the front of the truck.

Making a lighthouse

YOU WILL NEED

- a round bulb holder and a 3·5 volt bulb
- Some thin cardboard, 20cm (8in) long, 10cm (4in) wide
- 3 pieces of flex about 30cm (1ft) long, with stripped ends (see page 98)
- a KnowHow switch (see page 100), model clay and bright paper, a small glass or plastic jar, sticky tape, glue, scissors

Join the end of a piece of flex to each of the two screws on the bulb holder.

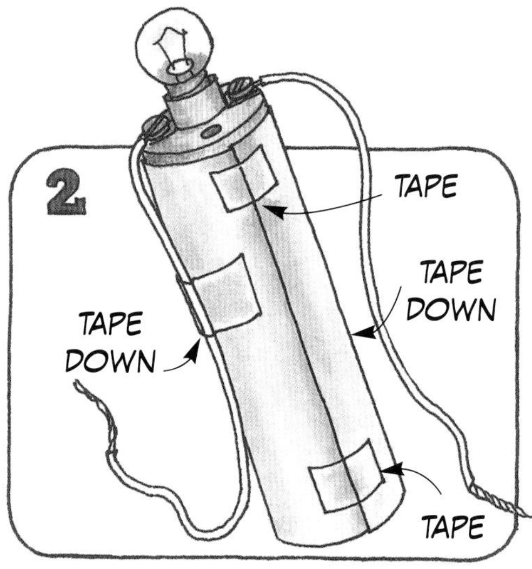

Roll the piece of cardboard around the bulb holder, with the flex on the outside, like this. Stick the roll with the tape and then tape the flex to the tube.

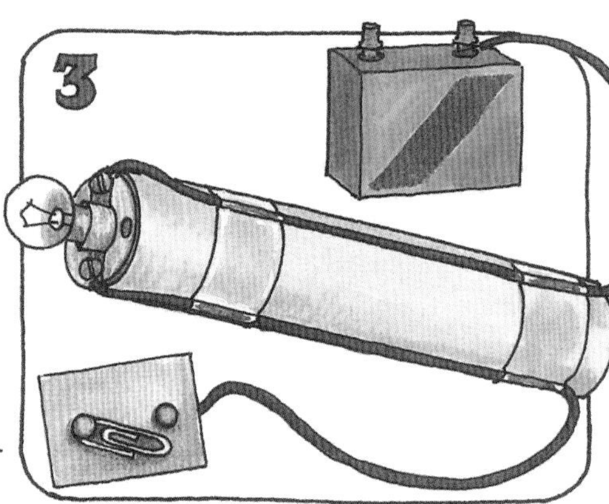

Wind the end of one flex from the bulb holder around one of the fasteners on the KnowHow switch. Join the other bulb holder flex to a battery terminal.

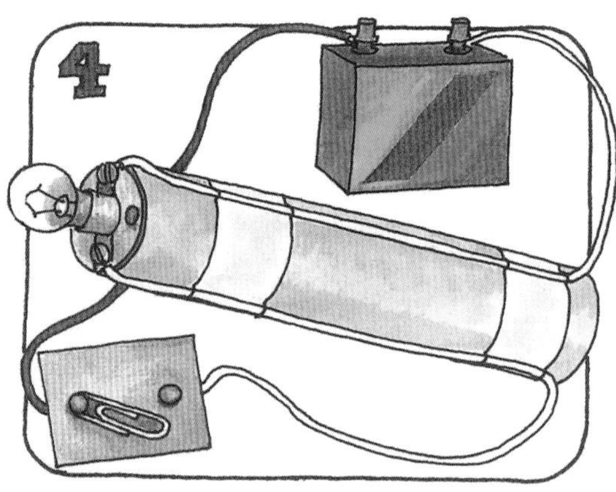

Wind a new piece of flex around the other fastener on the switch. Join the other end of the flex to the second battery terminal.

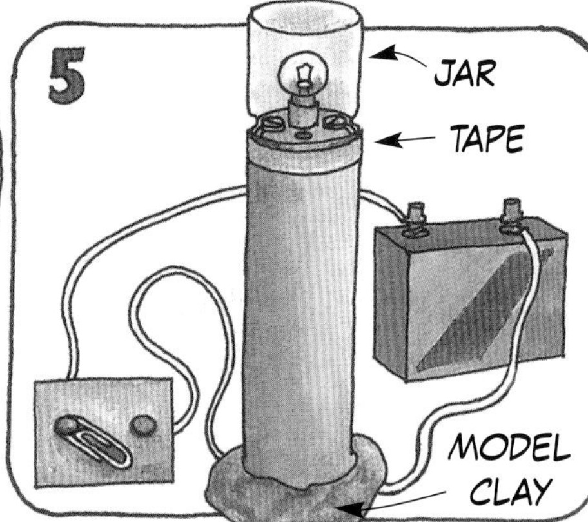

Cover the cardboard with paper and glue it down. Press model clay around the tube base. Put a jar over the bulb and stick with tape.

Check the flex is tight around the battery terminals, that you have made a proper circuit, and that no bare wires touch each other.

ANSWERS TO PAGE 100

1. No. This is not a complete circuit with one flex. 2. No. There are two wires on one terminal. 3. Yes. This is a complete circuit. 4. Yes. This is a complete circuit with two bulb holders. 5. Yes. This is a complete circuit with two bulb holders.

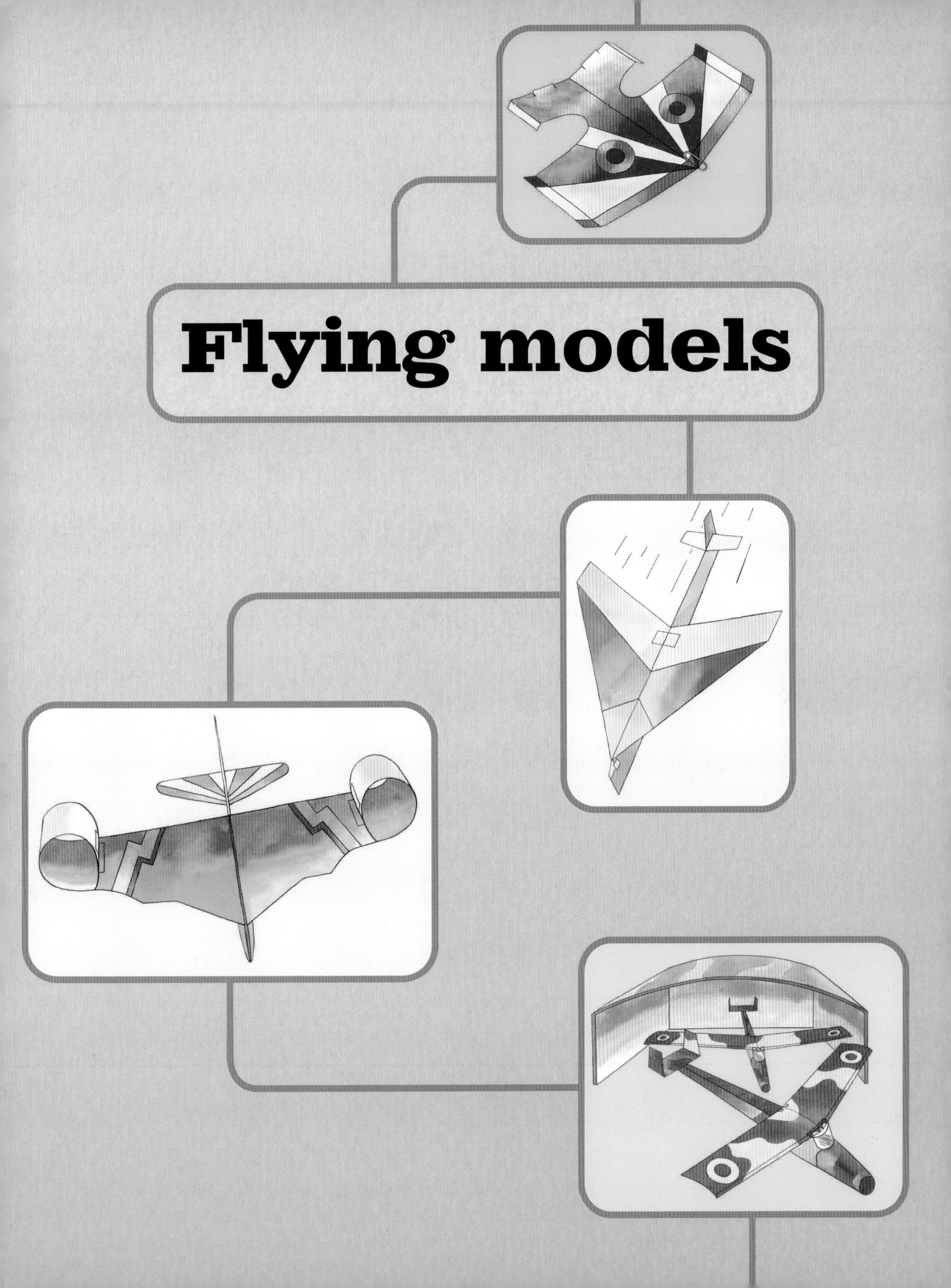

Flying models

KH01 Prototype

The KH01 Prototype is a very easy plane to make. All you need is a sheet of paper 21 x 29cm (8¼ x 11½in), which is sometimes known as A4 paper.

If you can't make it fly properly, look at the flying tips in the middle of this page. On page 113 you can find out how to launch it.

Fold a piece of paper exactly down the middle. Unfold it. Now fold it exactly down the middle in the other direction. These folds are your guide lines.

Score a line 1cm (½in) from the long edge of the paper. Then fold up the paper along this line, as shown above.

THE KH01 PROTOTYPE

Planes can fly badly in lots of ways. Sometimes they stall. A stalling plane goes up and down like this. It stalls because its nose is not heavy enough.

Fix a paper clip on its front like this. Launch it. If it still stalls, add another one, or try putting a piece of tape along the folded edge.

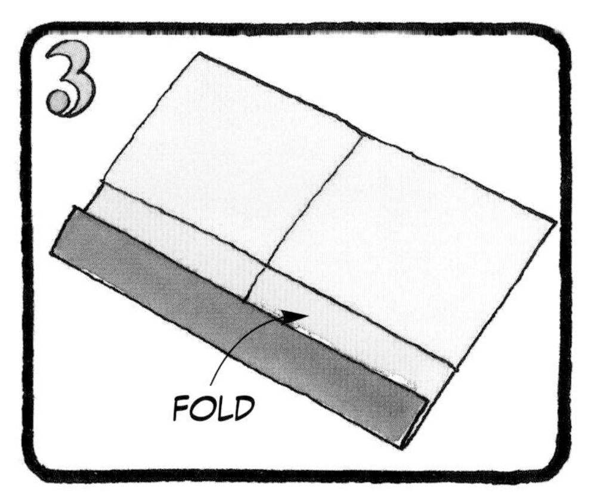

Fold the paper again and again until your folded edge reaches the middle guide line.

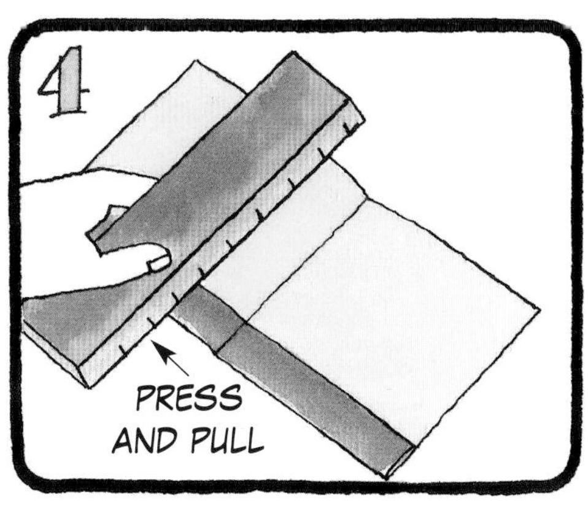

The last fold has to be really tight, so press your ruler down hard on the paper and run it all the way along the edge.

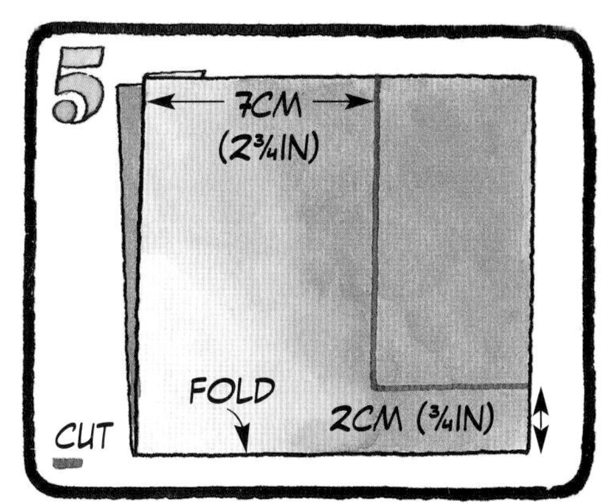

Now fold the paper in half with the folds on the inside. Draw and cut out the shape, and then decorate it (see page 122).

Your plane may dive nose first to the ground. This may mean that the nose is too heavy, or that the tail isn't working properly.

Make a small cut each side of the tail and bend the paper up as shown. Launch it again. If it still dives, bend the paper up a bit more. Keep doing this until the plane glides smoothly.

Planes have lots of different parts. Each part has its own special job to do.

Look at the plane shown here and see where the parts are and what they do.

For paper planes, paper folds must be really accurate. The best way is to hold the edges together with your fingers while you smooth the fold with your thumbs.

Lay the paper on something hard and flat. Put your ruler along the line you want to score. Rule a line with a ballpoint pen. Press the pen down hard all the time.

The Free Flyer

The Free Flyer flies through the air in a very smooth, slow glide. You can make it from a sheet of A4 paper, 21 x 29cm (8¼ x 11½in).

On these pages you will find out how to launch it properly and how to make it turn left and right. All flattish planes like the Free Flyer are launched in this way.

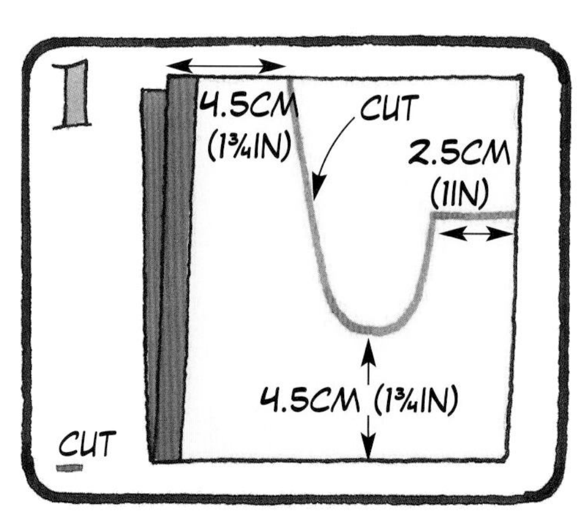

Follow boxes one to four on pages 110-111. Then fold the paper in half with the folded edge on the outside. Draw and cut out the Free Flyer shape as shown.

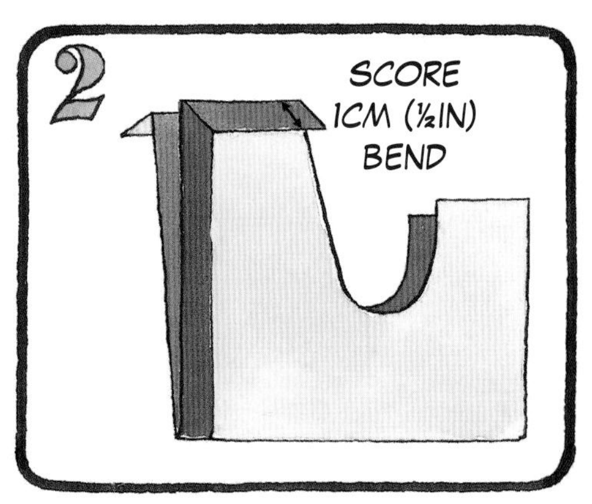

Score a line 1cm (½in) from the tips of the wings. Bend the top wing edge over the score line and bend the bottom one over in the opposite direction as shown.

THE FREE FLYER

Fold the plane the other way. Score a line 1cm (½in) from the tip of the tail as shown. Bend the tail tips over the score line in opposite directions to each other.

Bend the back wing edges down by running them between your thumb and fingers. This will curve the wing edge and the plane will fly better. It is called cambering.

Fold the plane and make two snips in the tail as shown. Unfold the plane. The ends are called tail elevators. Bend them up until the plane flies smoothly.

Put your fore-finger on top of the plane like this, with your thumb and other fingers underneath. Point the plane in the direction you want it to go.

Move your hand forward at the speed you think it will fly at and just let it go. Do not jerk or push it forward. Just let it glide from your hand.

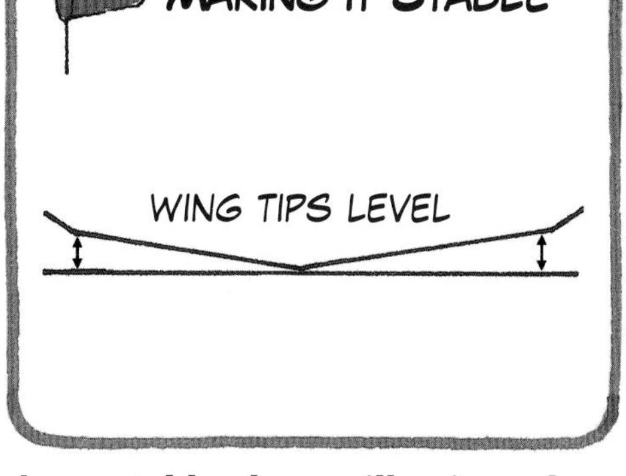

An unstable plane will spin and somersault to the ground. Hold it up, making sure that the wing tips are level as shown. If not, push them up or down to level them.

If you want to, you can make the Free Flyer fly in different directions. Make two little cuts in the back of the wings as shown, to make ailerons.

To make the plane go left, bend the left aileron up and the right aileron down. To make it go right, bend the right aileron up and the left one down.

The Free Flyer will fly better if you put a paper clip on its nose and bend the tail elevators so they stand up a little.

The Air Scorpion

The Air Scorpion is a racing plane. It has swept-back wings and it flies very fast and straight.

YOU WILL NEED

THE PATTERN FOR THE TAIL FIN ON PAGE 126

- a sheet of paper 21 x 29cm (8¼ x 11½in) – A4 paper
- a ballpoint pen for scoring
- scissors
- a ruler, pencil
- sticky tape

Fold the paper in half like this. Put it along the line you can see at the top of this page. Mark A and B on both edges of the paper.

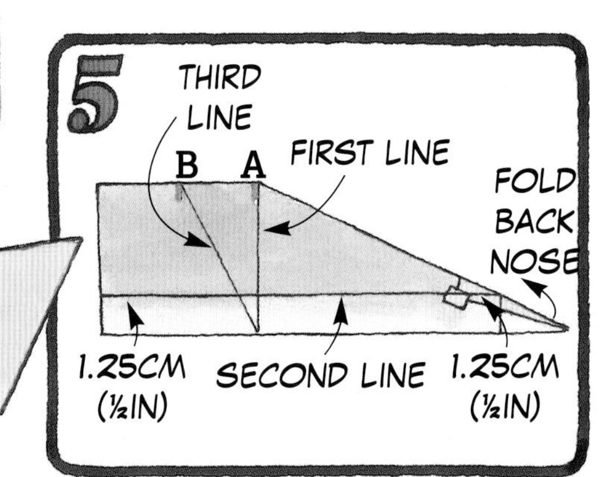

Fold the paper down the middle and fold the nose in. Draw three lines, one from A down to the fold, another across the bottom of the paper and the last from B, as above.

Hold the plane by its keel. Point it down a little and let it go gently.

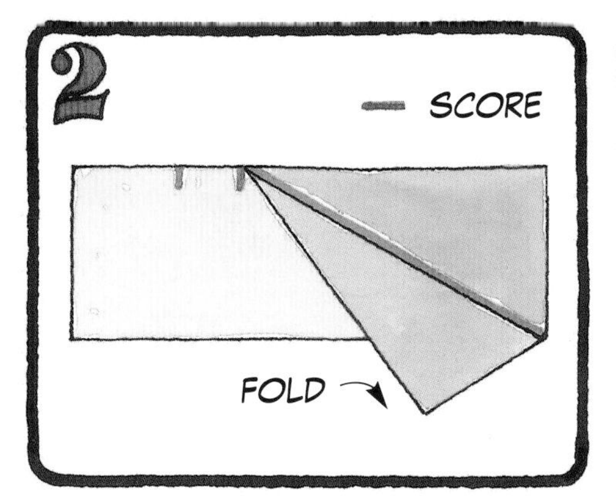

Score a line from A to the top of the fold. Fold one of the corners over along this line.

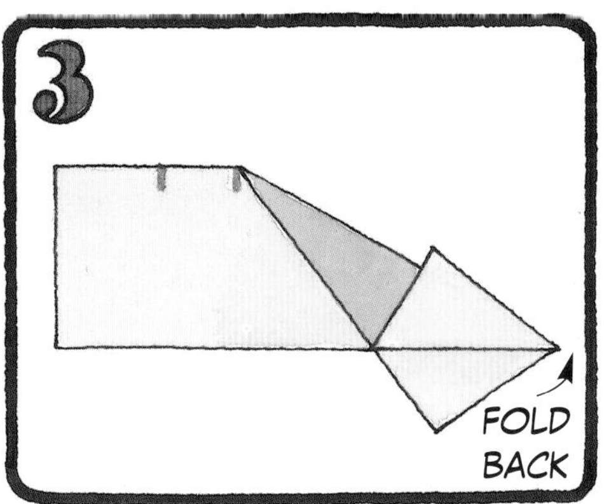

Then fold the other corner back the other way. Now fold both the corners back, as shown here.

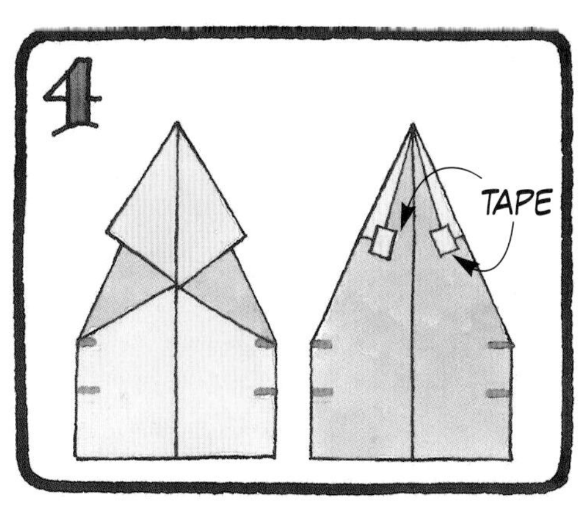

Open the paper. It should look like this from the front (left). Turn it and fold both corners over tightly, and then tape them down (right).

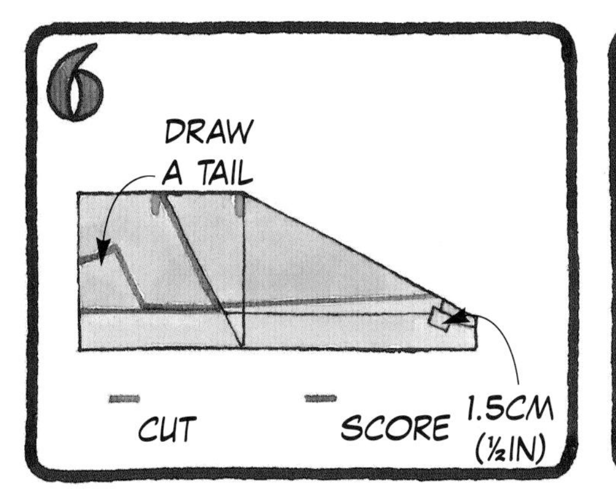

Draw a tail shape and cut the plane out as shown. Score a line across the wings as shown. Score another across the tail.

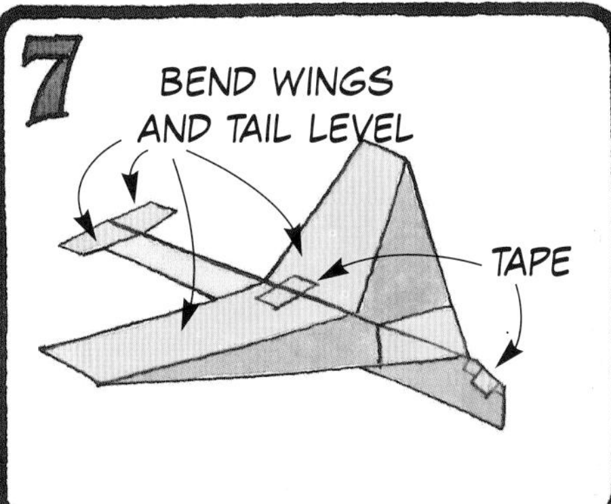

Bend the tail and wings along the score line so that they are level. Keep the wings in place with tape and tape the front of the nose.

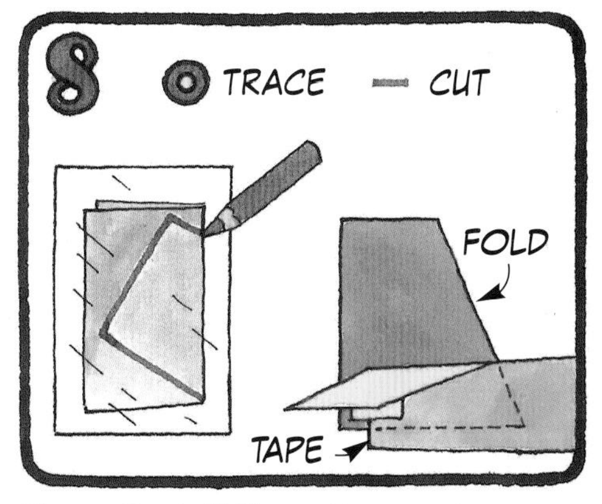

Trace the tail fin pattern onto a folded piece of paper. Cut it out. Tape it inside the body of the plane, fold first, so that it sticks out a little, like this.

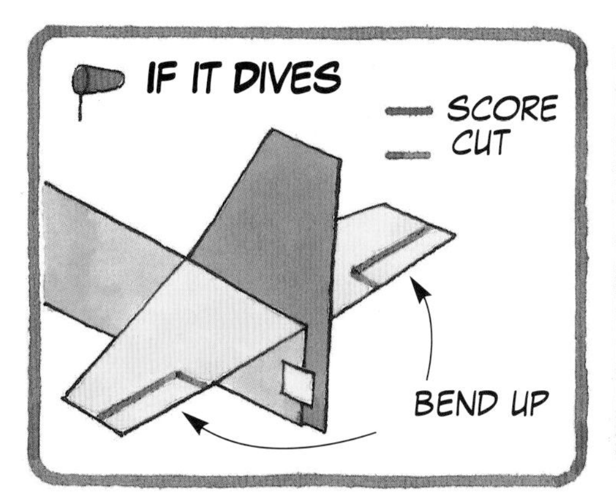

You can stop it diving by giving it tail elevators. Make a cut each side of the tail fin as shown. Bend the tail elevators up a little. (See page 113.)

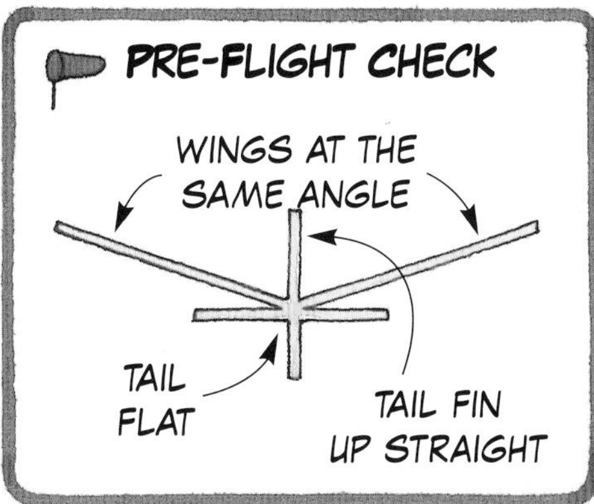

Hold your plane up and see if it looks like this from the back. The wings must be at the same angle. The tail should be flat and the tail fin should point straight up.

Draw the outline on tracing paper. Turn it over and scribble over it in pencil. Put the tracing, right side up, on paper and draw around the outline.

The Range Moth

YOU WILL NEED

THE PATTERN ON PAGE 126

- a big sheet of paper, at least 30 x 44cm (1ft x 17½in)
- tracing paper and a pencil
- a ballpoint pen cap, pieces of card or model clay
- scissors, sticky tape and glue

See page 115 for how to make a tracing.

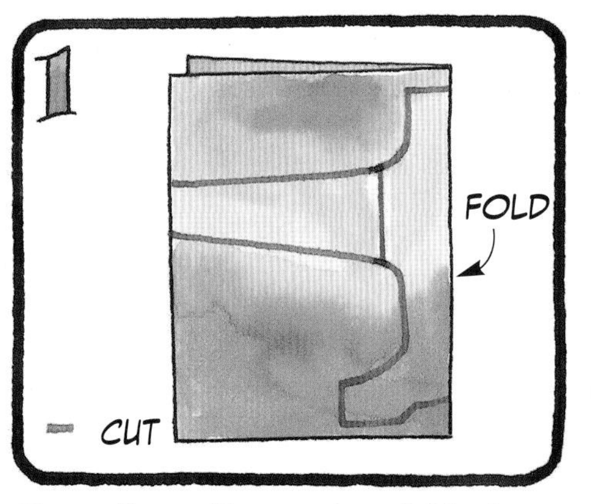

Trace the pattern onto a folded piece of paper. Remember to trace the score line too. Cut the plane out, but don't cut along the fold.

Put a ruler exactly onto the score lines. Score one line across the wing, and score another line across the tail, as shown.

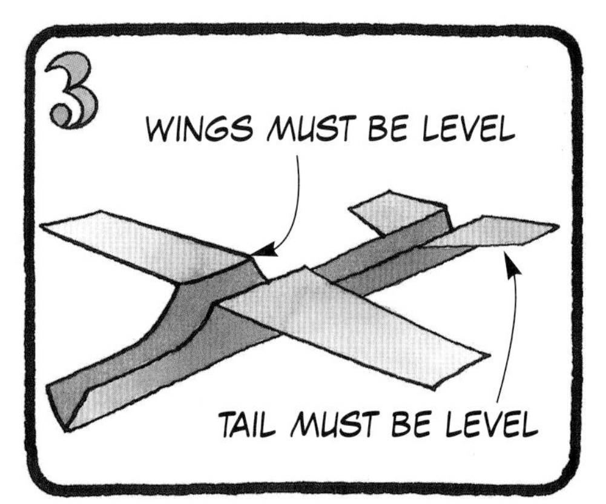

Now carefully bend down the wings and tail along the score lines, as shown above.

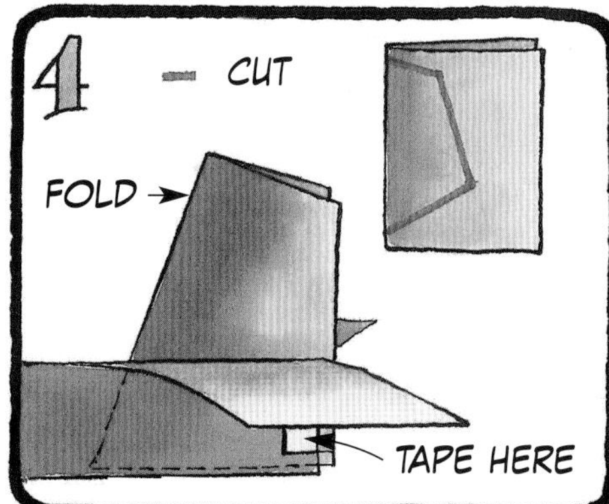

Trace the tail fin onto a folded piece of paper. Cut it out, but not along the fold. Tape the tail fin, fold first into the inside back of the plane, as shown.

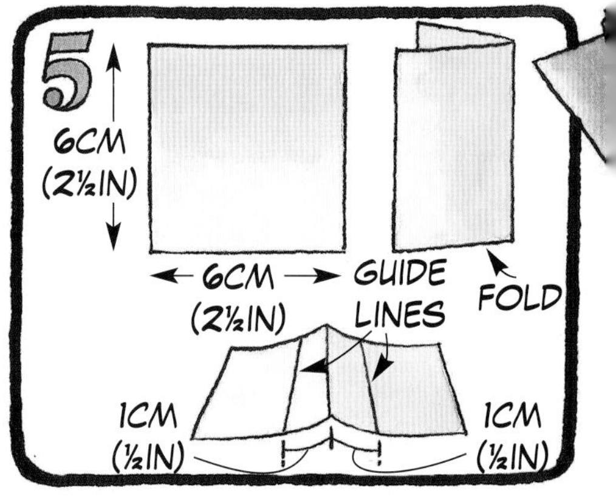

Cut out a piece of paper 6 x 6cm (2½ x 2½in) and fold it in half. Then open it out and draw two guide lines 1cm (½in) from the fold, as shown.

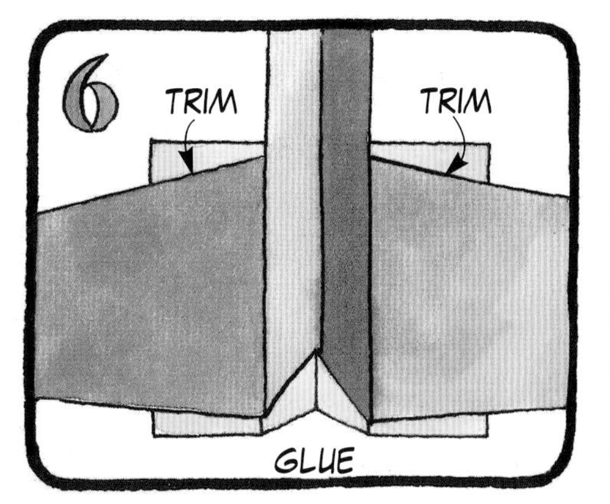

Glue the plane down onto this piece of paper. The wings are following the guide lines you drew on the piece of paper. Trim any paper that overlaps.

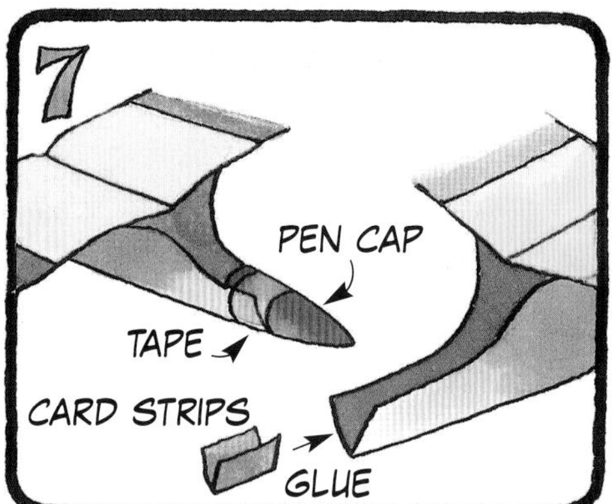

Tape the plastic cap of a felt or ballpoint pen into the nose. If you want to, you can cut out small strips of card and glue them into the nose instead.

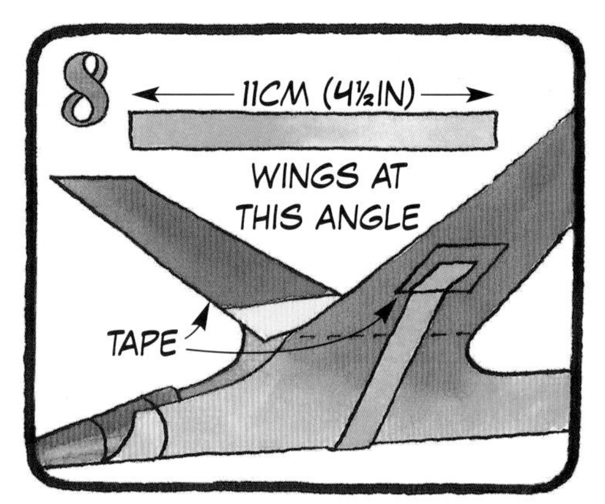

Cut out a strip of paper 11cm (4½in) long. Fold it in half. Hold it under the plane. Tape it to each side of the wings so that the wings tilt up at the same angle.

THE RANGE MOTH

If you want to, you can make a parachute as well.

YOU WILL NEED

- a square sheet of polythene 20 x 20cm (8 x 8in)
- a big paper clip
- scissors and thread

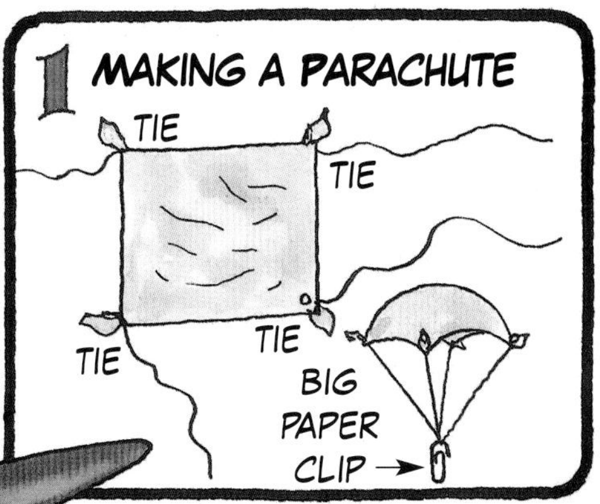

Cut some thread into four equal lengths about 18cm (7in) long. Tie each thread to a corner of a square of polythene. Tie the other ends of the threads to a big paper clip.

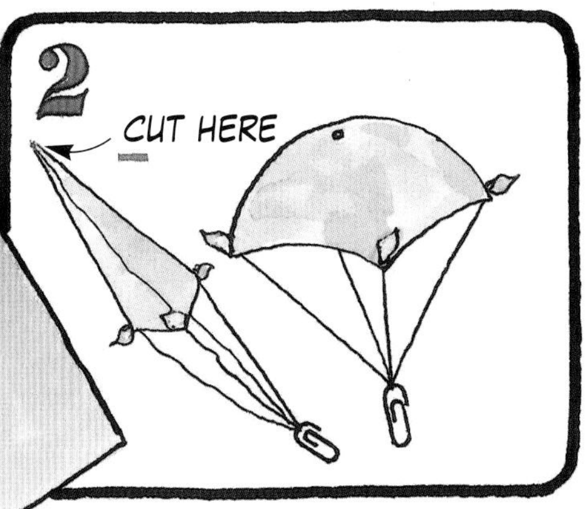

Launch the parachute from somewhere nice and high. If it sways too much on its way down, make a tiny cut in the middle, as shown above.

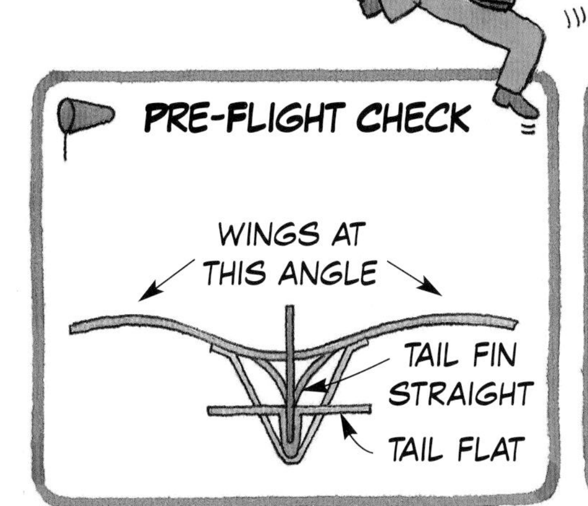

The plane should look like this if you hold it up in front of you. The tail fin must point straight up with the tail pieces flat. Wings must be at an angle.

Weight the top of the nose with model clay until the plane glides smoothly. Then push the same model clay into the pen cap with a pencil, as shown.

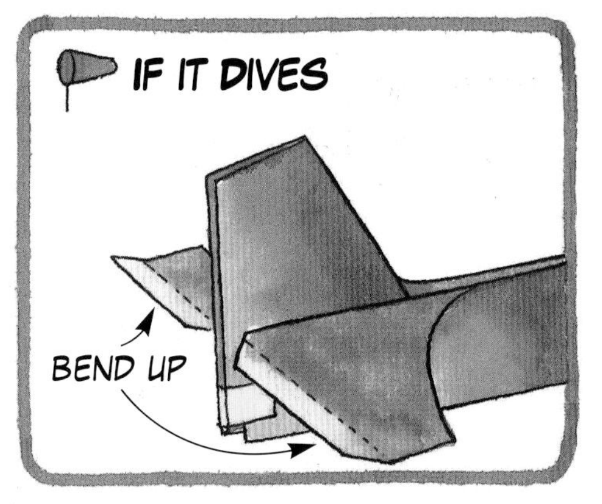

You could try giving it tail elevators (see page 113), and bend them up as shown here.

The Moon Explorer

You will find that the Moon Explorer is an easy plane to make.

See page 115 for how to make a tracing.

YOU WILL NEED

THE MOON EXPLORER PATTERN YOU CAN FIND ON PAGE 126

- a sheet of paper 21 x 29cm (8¼ x 11½in) – A4 paper
- tracing paper and a pencil
- scissors and sticky tape
- a ruler
- a ballpoint pen for scoring

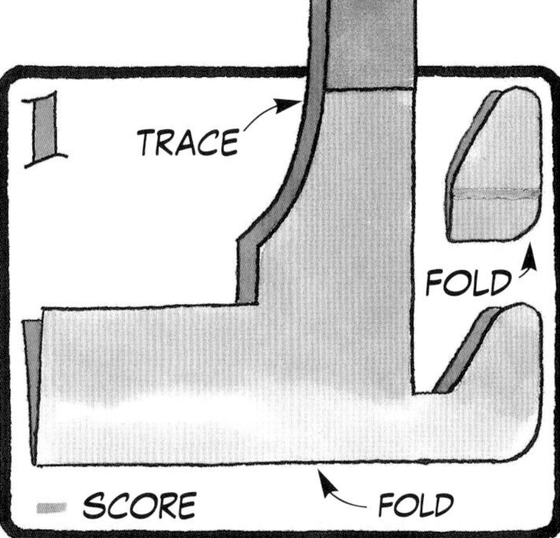

Fold the paper and trace the plane and tail pattern onto it. Cut it out, but don't cut along the fold. Trace the lines on the wings and tail. Score the tail as shown.

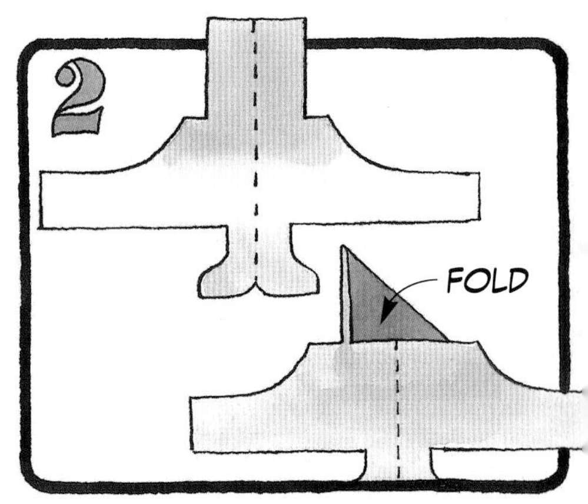

To make the nose of this plane, you will have to make guide lines. Start with the paper opened out. Then fold one of the corners over, as shown here.

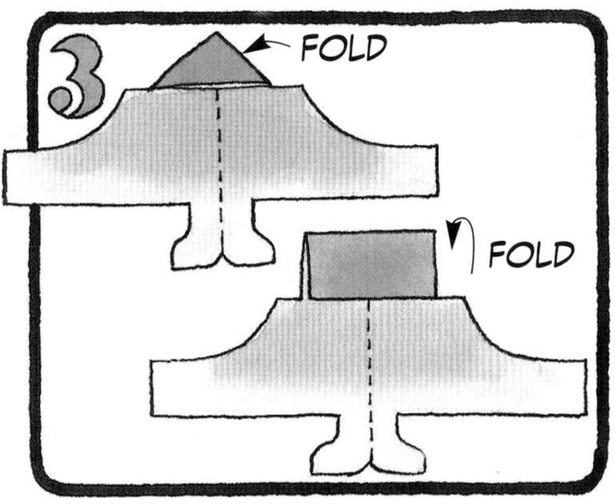

Fold the other corner over to make a triangle, like this. Open out the paper and make a third fold. Open the paper out once more and you have your guide lines.

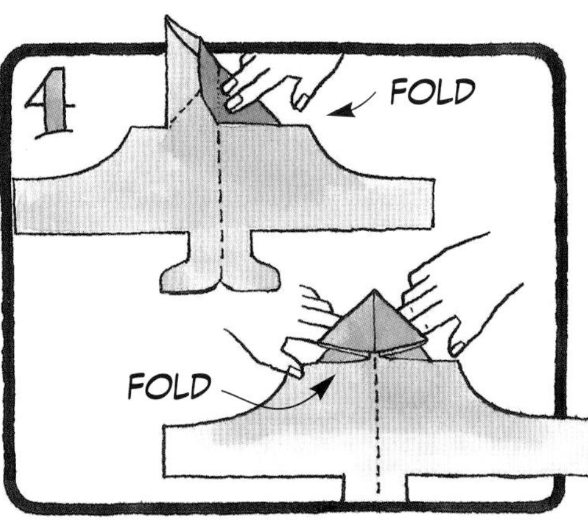

Make a fold like this on one side of the paper. Then hold this fold down and fold the other side down in the same way.

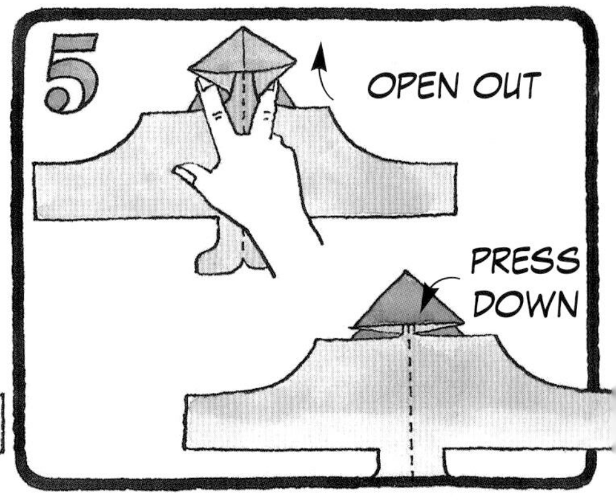

Hold the paper folds in place with one hand and with the other open the paper above them out. Then press all the paper down.

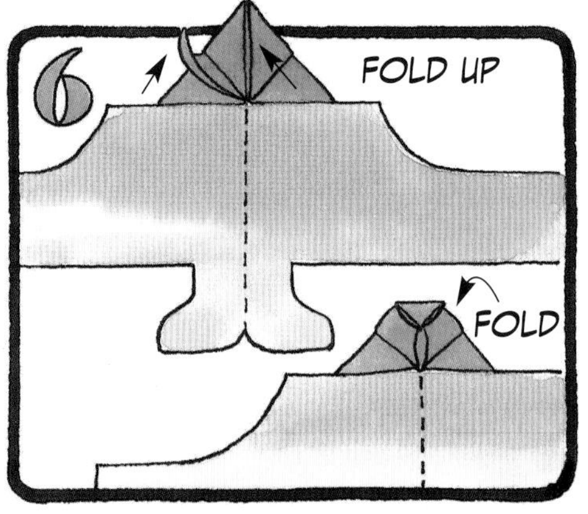

Fold the two bottom corners up as shown above. Then fold the pointed end down.

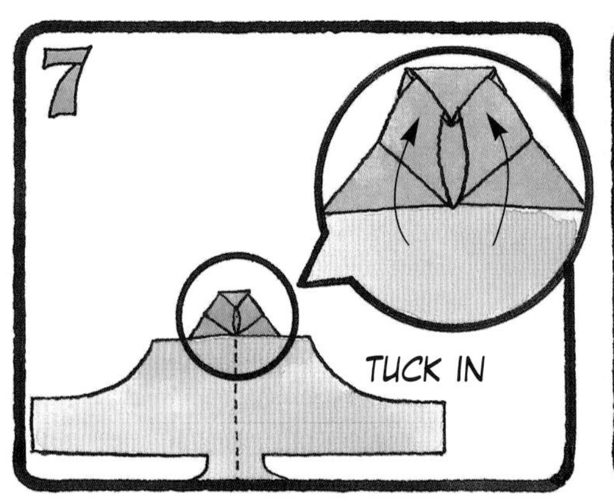

When you folded the pointed end down, you made pockets at the top of the paper. Tuck the two free corners into the pockets.

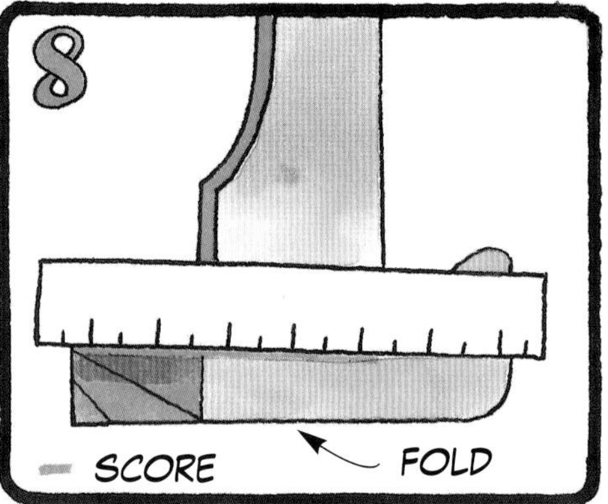

Fold the paper in half. Put your ruler along the top of the fuselage and score a line across the wings.

Bend the wings back along the score lines so that they are level.

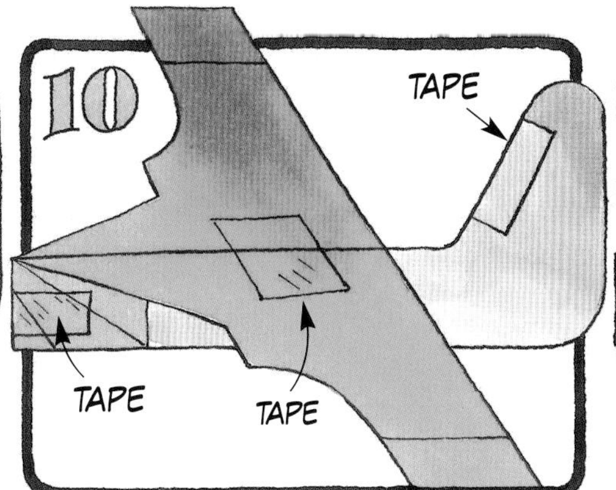

Tape the plane together at the nose and across the top of the wings. Tape the tail fin together, as shown above.

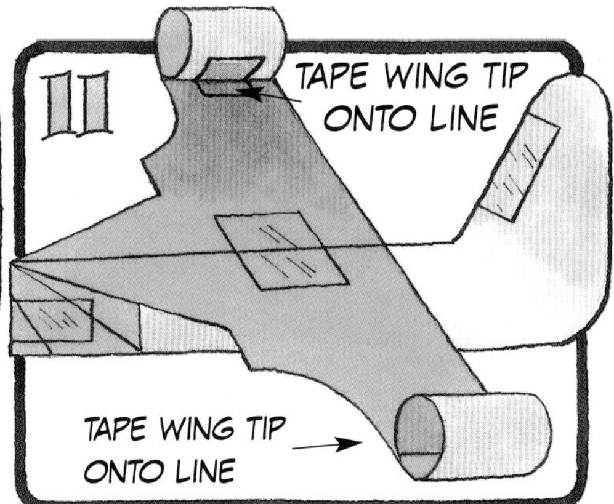

Curl the wing tips over and tape them onto the wings at the traced lines as shown.

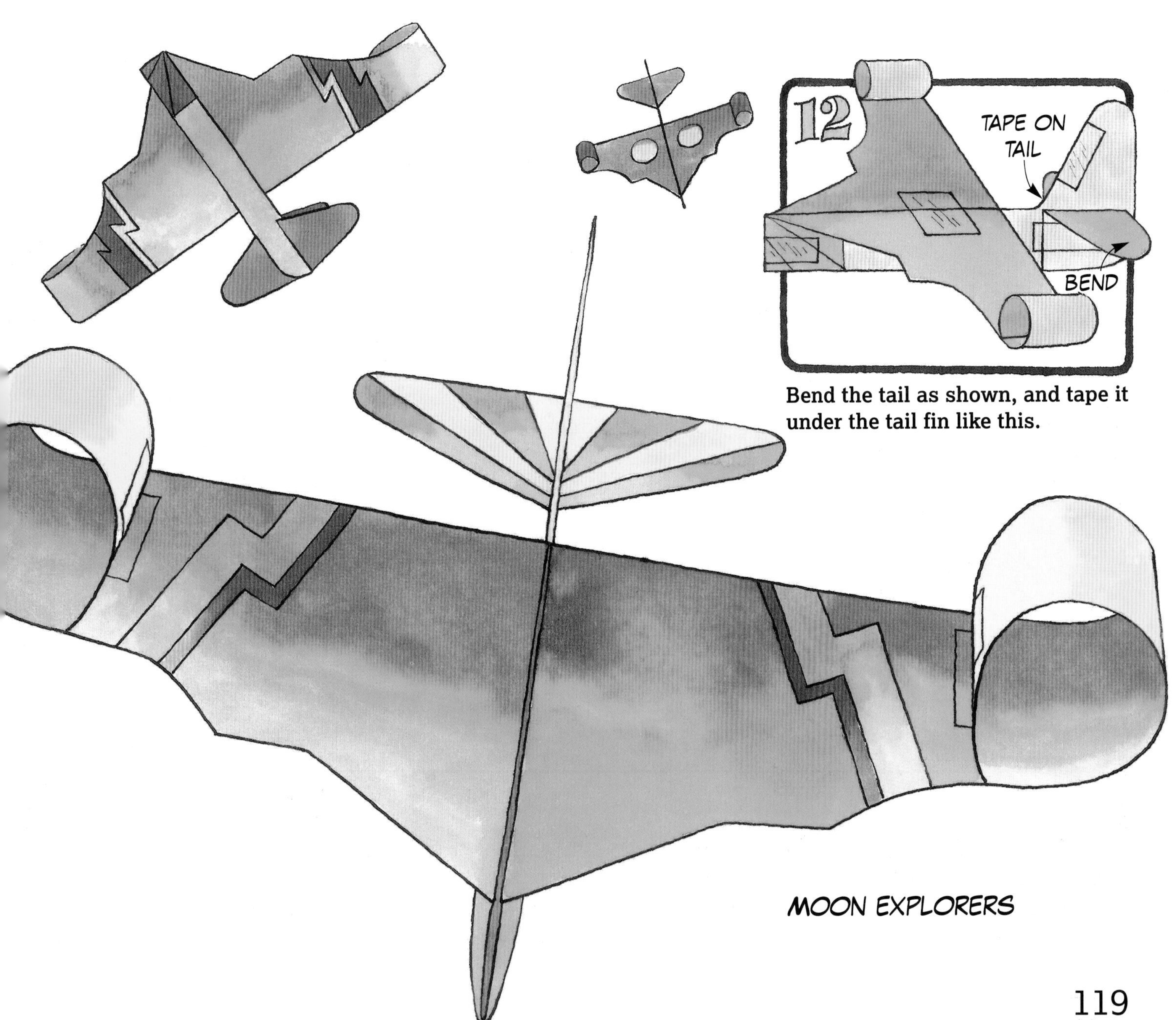

Bend the tail as shown, and tape it under the tail fin like this.

Drinking Straw Glider

The Drinking Straw Glider has a special kind of curved wing. It is called a cambered wing. The camber gives the plane a little more lift. See page 115 for how to trace.

YOU WILL NEED

THE PATTERN ON PAGE 127

- paper for the wings and tail
- card from a document folder
- 2 drinking straws
- tracing paper and a pencil
- scissors and a ruler
- model clay or silver foil
- strong glue and sticky tape

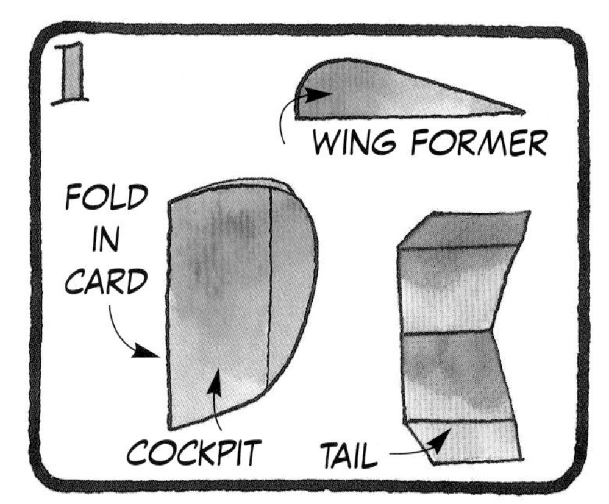

Trace and cut out a card cockpit, two card wing formers and a paper tail. Remember to trace all the lines on the patterns.

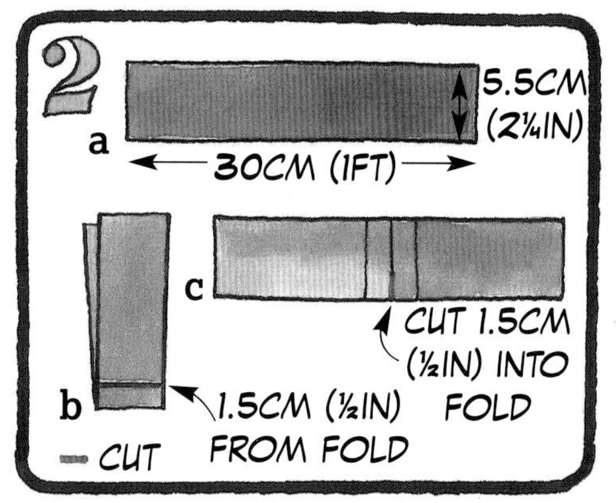

(a) Cut out a paper wing as shown. (b) Fold the paper in half and draw a line 1.5cm (½in) from the fold. (c) Open the wings out and cut a notch into the fold.

Put glue on the curved edge of the wing formers. Glue them onto the wings along the lines you drew each side of the notch.

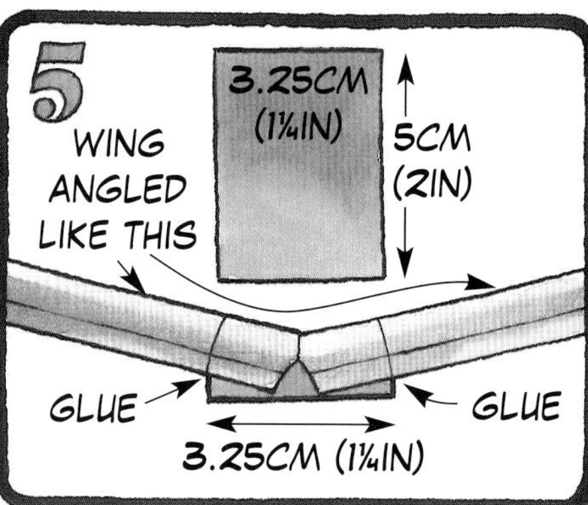

Cut out some card 5 x 3.25cm (2 x 1¼in). Glue its long edges to the bottom edges of the wing formers so that the wings become angled, as shown here.

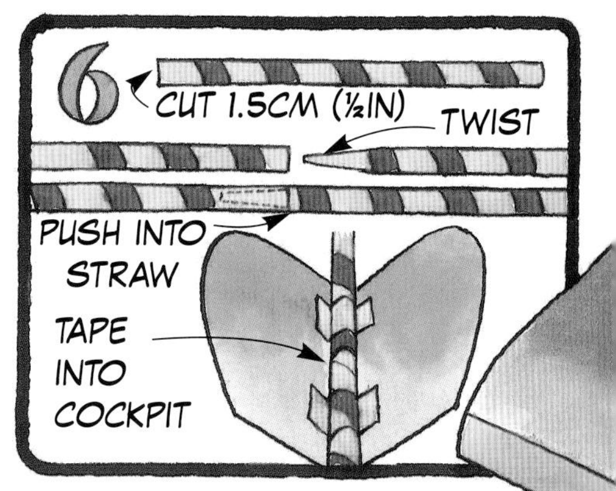

Slit the end of a straw, and twist it into a point. Push it into another straw to make one long straw. Tape the middle of this straw into the cockpit.

Score the cockpit along the lines you traced. Bend the cockpit along the score lines as shown.

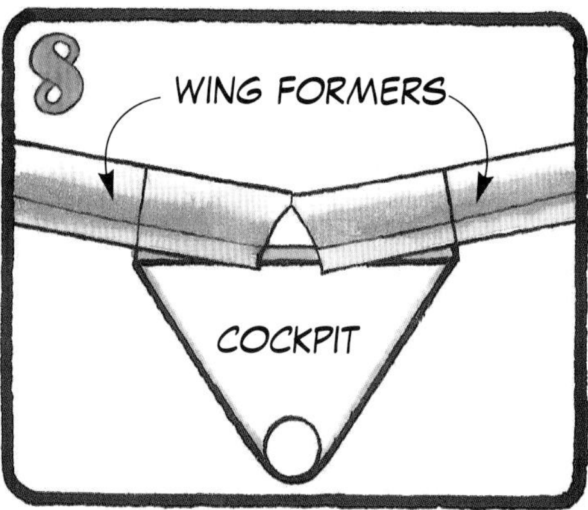

Glue together the wings and cockpit, with the cockpit outside the wing formers as shown.

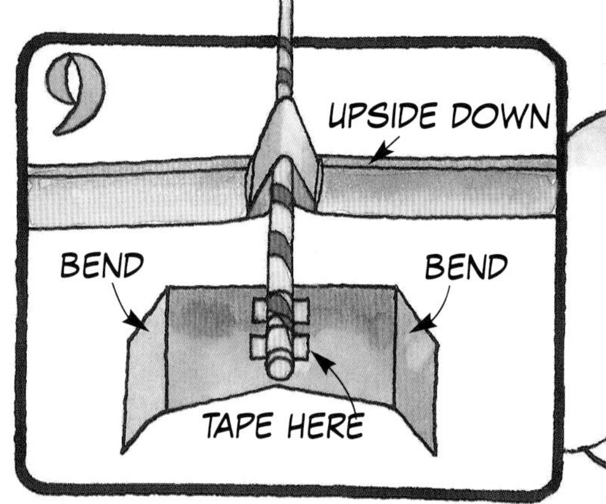

Put the plane upside down and tape the tail onto it, with the straw lying along the line down the middle of the tail. Bend the sides of the tail, as shown.

Half stick some tape along the notched edge of one wing as shown (left). Then put a ROUND pencil onto the unstuck half of the tape, in line with the front wing edge (right).

Roll the pencil up the wing as far as the end of the notch. Then unroll the pencil and take the tape off it very carefully. Do it again on the other wing.

Then fold the free edge of the tape up over the wing edge, like this (bottom). The curve you have just made is called a camber.

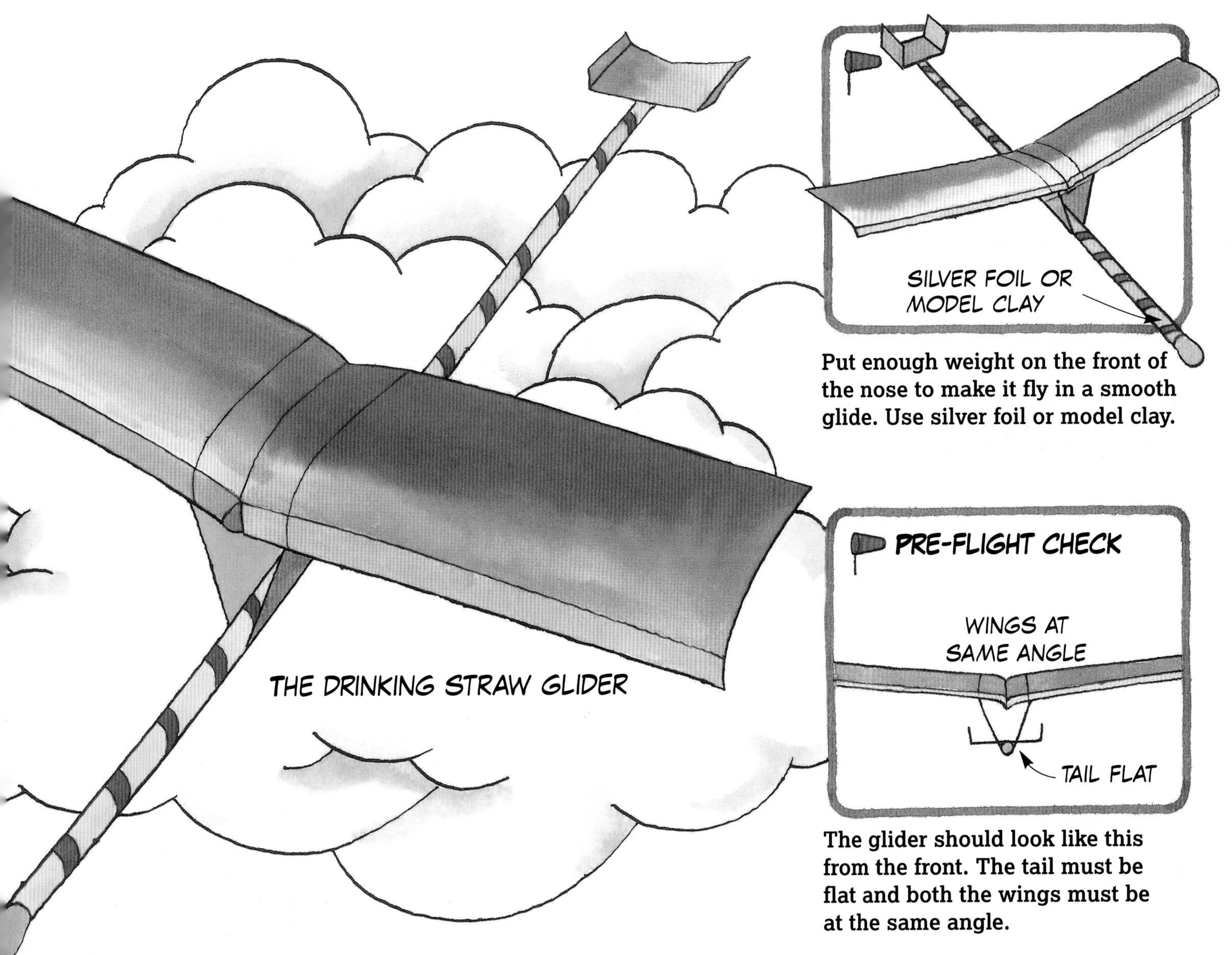

Put enough weight on the front of the nose to make it fly in a smooth glide. Use silver foil or model clay.

The glider should look like this from the front. The tail must be flat and both the wings must be at the same angle.

Jungle Fighter KH20

Make the Jungle Fighter KH20 difficult to spot by camouflaging it. See page 115 for how to trace.

JUNGLE FIGHTERS

YOU WILL NEED

THE PATTERN ON PAGE 127

- card from a document folder
- a sheet of paper
- a large cardboard box
- a large sheet of stiff paper
- a small piece of thick card
- tracing paper and a pencil
- scissors and strong glue
- sticky tape and a ruler
- a ballpoint pen for scoring
- felt tip pens for camouflage

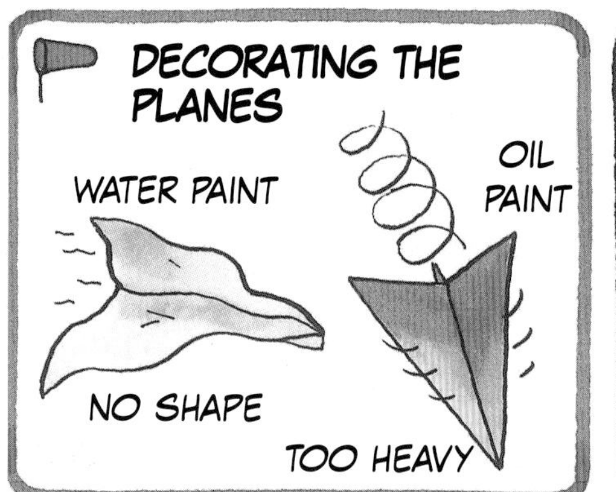

Use felt tip pens to decorate your planes. Don't use water-based paints on them. The paper will crumple up and lose its shape. Oil paints are too heavy.

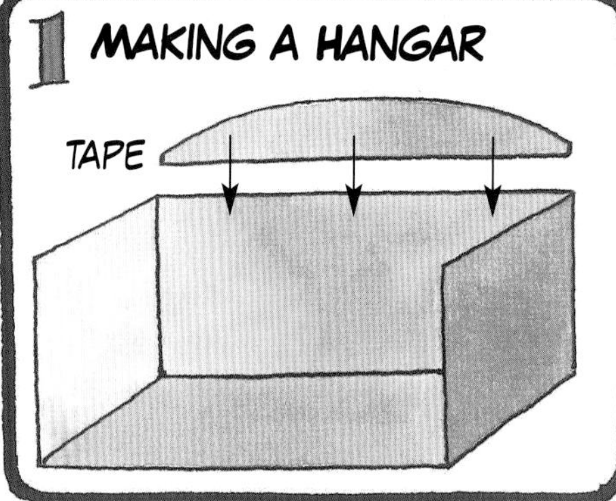

Put a large cardboard box on its side. Cut off the top side. Cut out a curved shape from the extra cardboard as shown. Tape the shape onto the back of the box.

Make a roof by laying some stiff paper over the curved shape and taping it to the sides of the box. Camouflage it by painting it the same shade as its surroundings.

Trace and cut out a card cockpit and cockpit top. Score and bend the cockpit top as shown, and glue it into the top of the cockpit.

(a) Trace and cut out a paper nose. (b) Bend the nose around, dab glue on its tab and join it up. (c) Glue it to the front of the cockpit.

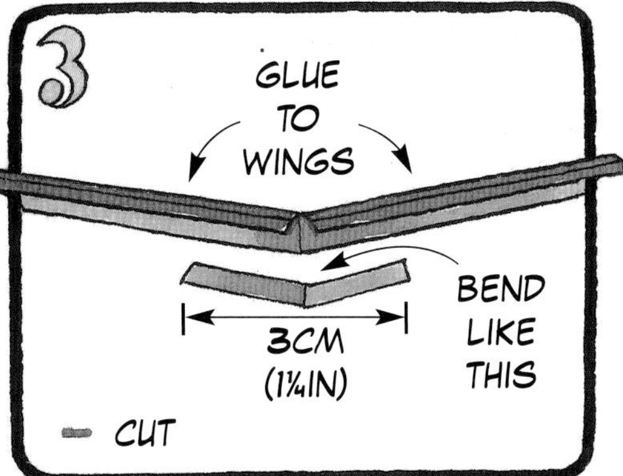

Trace and cut out its wings. Make a small snip as shown and camber them (see page 121). Cut out a strip of thick card. Bend it, and glue the wings onto it as shown.

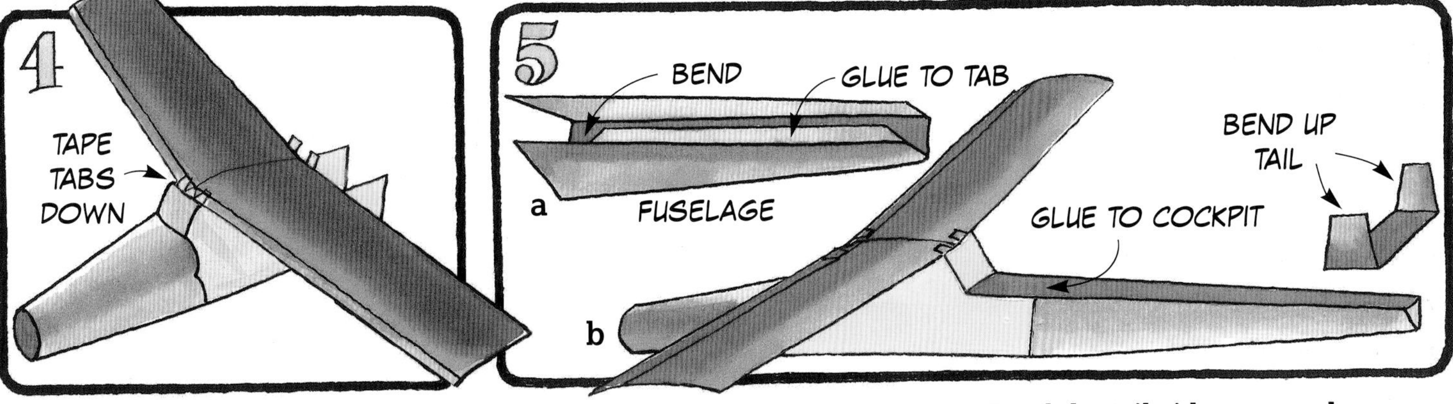

Put the wings on top of the cockpit. Bend the front and back cockpit top tabs over the wings and tape as shown.

Trace and cut out a paper fuselage, and bend it as shown. (a) Put glue on its tab and glue it together. Then trace and cut out a paper tail.

Bend the tail sides up as shown. (b) Glue the fuselage into the back of the cockpit, like this. Now glue the tail on top of the end of the fuselage as shown.

Put some sticky tape over the front of the cockpit. Trace and cut out a card cockpit back. Score it and glue into the back of the cockpit.

If it stalls, the nose is not heavy enough. Make the nose heavier by squeezing model clay into it or crunching silver foil around it.

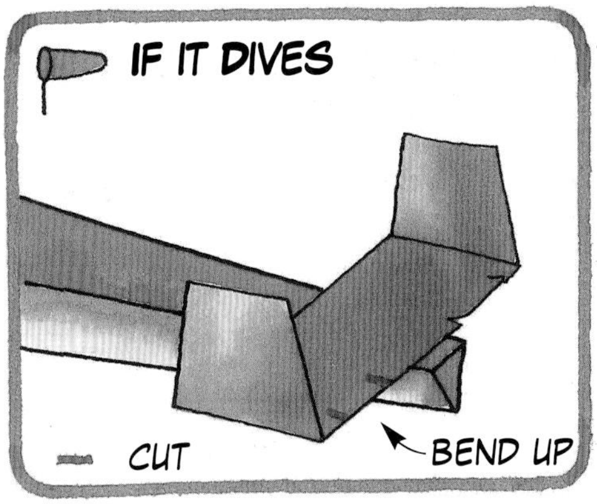

If it dives, it means that the nose is too heavy. Take some weight off the nose or make tail elevators (see page 113). Bend them up as shown.

Flying tips

If you have managed to make your planes glide smoothly in a straight line, you might like to try making them fly in other ways.

On these pages you can find out how to make the different controls on a plane that make it fly in different directions and perform flying tricks.

Some of these, like looping-the-loop and S-bends, take a lot of skill and rehearsal.

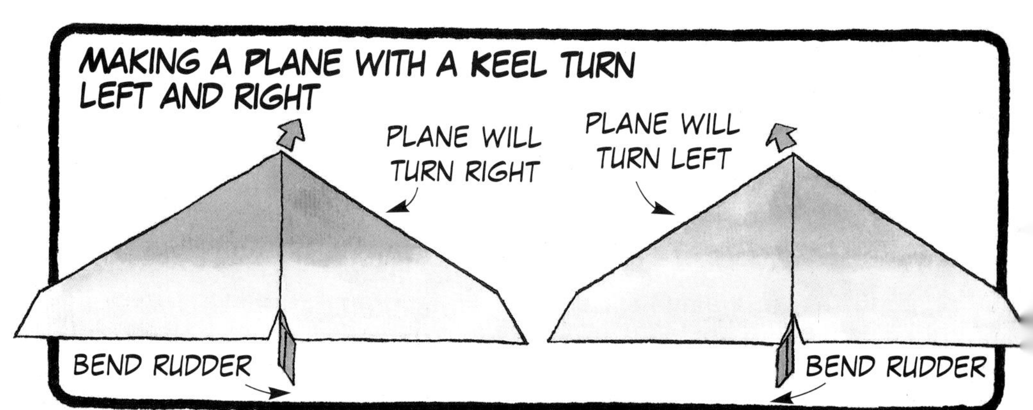

Planes with a keel, like Air Scorpions, can be made to turn left and right just like darts. To do this, make a short snip in the keel at the back under the wings.

Then stick the two sides together with tape. This makes a rudder. Bend the rudder left to make the plane turn left, bend it right to make the plane turn right.

To make these planes turn, you can give their wings ailerons. Make two cuts on each wing as shown. To make a plane fly left, bend the left aileron up and bend the right aileron down. To make it fly to the right, bend the right aileron up and the left one down.

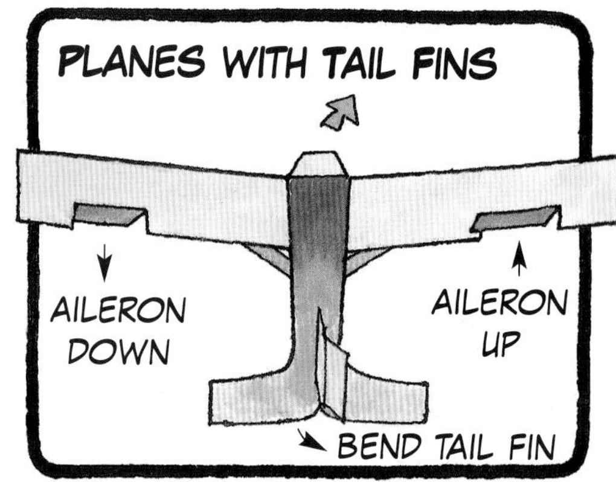

If your plane has ailerons and a tail fin, bend the ailerons in the usual way and bend the end of the tail fin to point in the direction you want the plane to fly.

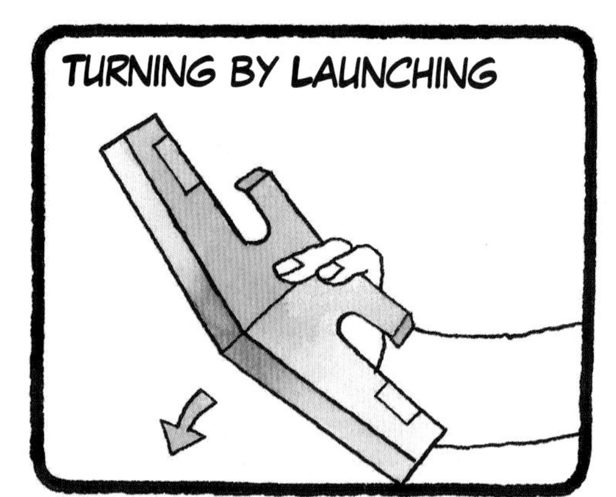

A plane set to fly straight can be made to fly left by launching it at this angle. Tilt it in the other direction to make it turn right. This is launching it in a bank.

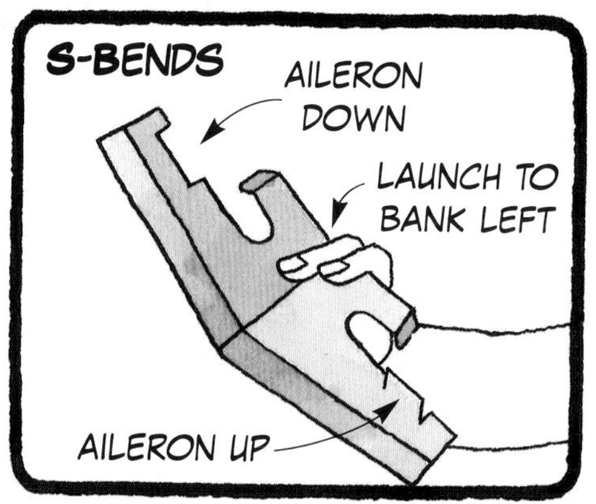

If you find it easy to launch your plane in a bank, try making it do an S-Bend. Set the controls to make it fly one way then launch it in a bank in the opposite direction.

Some people can make their planes loop-the-loop. Bend the tail elevators up, point the plane down and launch it very hard. This takes a lot of skill and rehearsal.

There are air currents outside which make it more difficult for a paper plane to fly. Try making your plane heavier by weighting the nose. Bend the elevators up.

Planes can do strange things in a wind. If you launch a plane so that it flies in the same direction as the wind, it will fly much faster than it would inside.

If you launch a plane in the opposite direction to the way the wind is blowing, it may fly backwards like this.

If you want, you could make an obstacle course by tying brooms to chairs and flying your planes through and around them.

FLING GLIDING

Heavier planes can be exciting to fly by fling gliding. Tie one end of a piece of string to the edge of a wing, tie the other end to a strong stick or ruler.

Bend the tail elevators up a bit. Hold the stick and swing it around and around, facing the stick all the time. See how long you can make the string without losing control.

Patterns for tracing

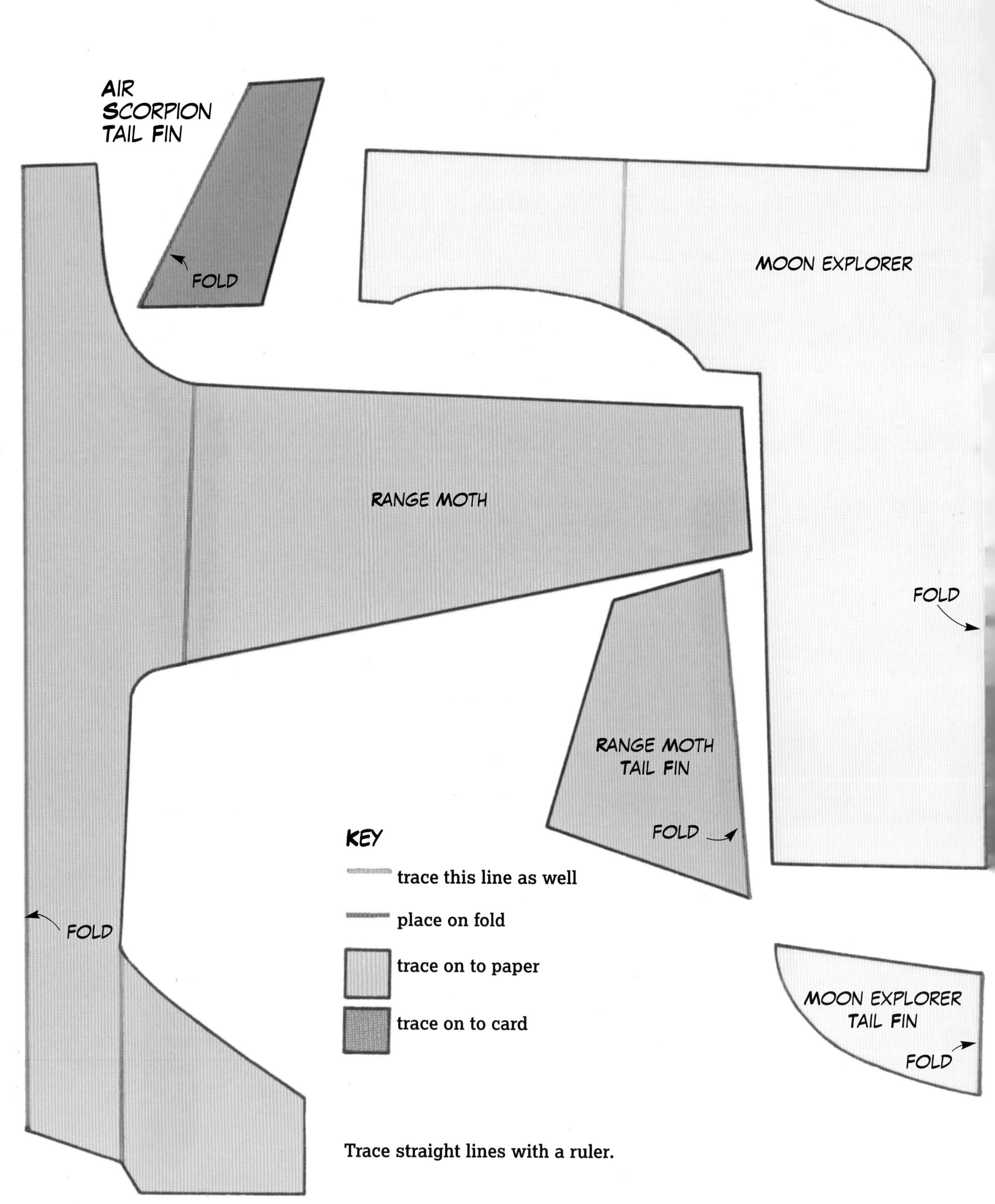

Trace straight lines with a ruler.

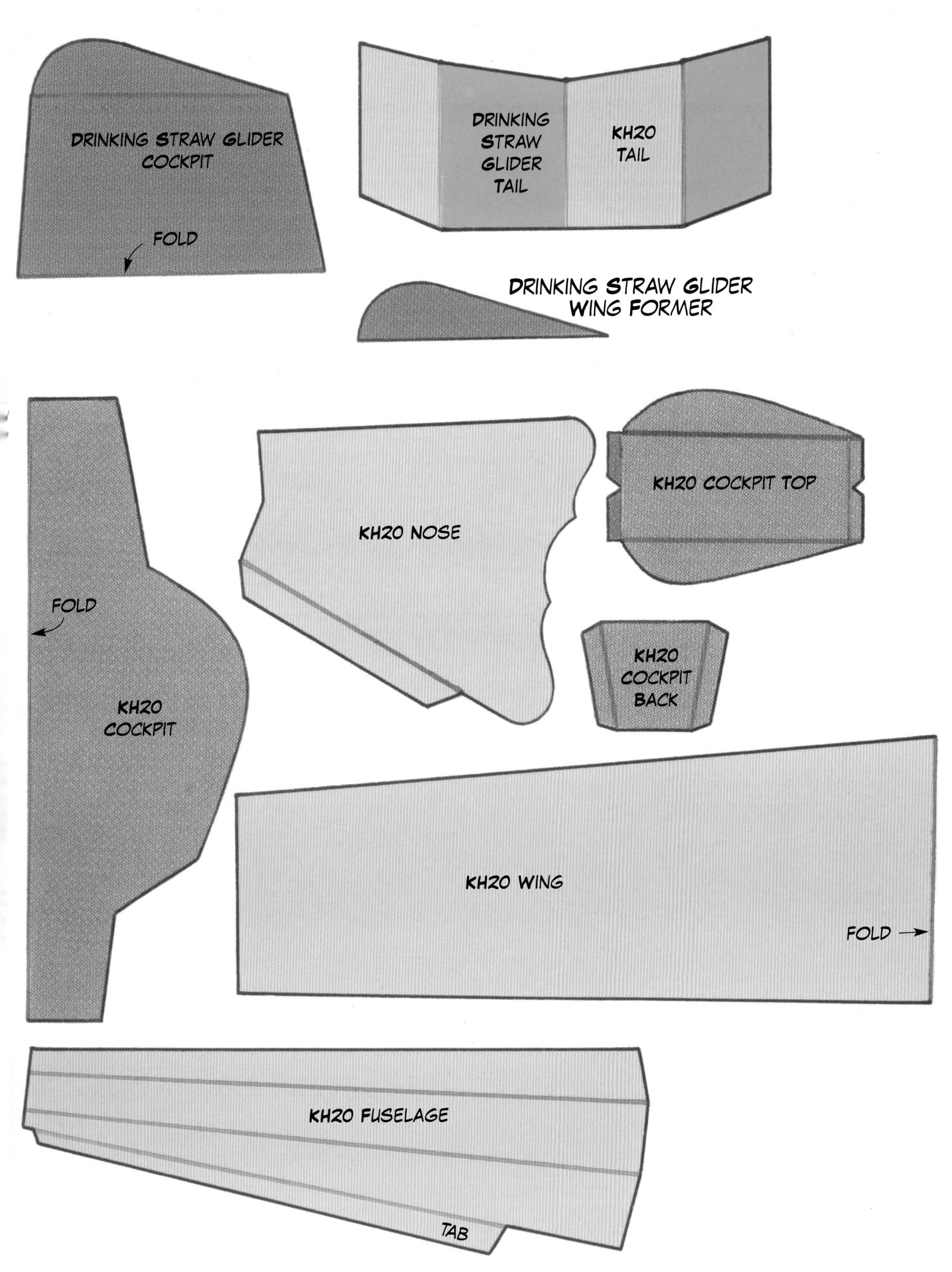
DRINKING STRAW GLIDER COCKPIT
FOLD
DRINKING STRAW GLIDER TAIL
KH2O TAIL
DRINKING STRAW GLIDER WING FORMER
KH2O NOSE
KH2O COCKPIT TOP
FOLD
KH2O COCKPIT
KH2O COCKPIT BACK
KH2O WING
FOLD
KH2O FUSELAGE
TAB

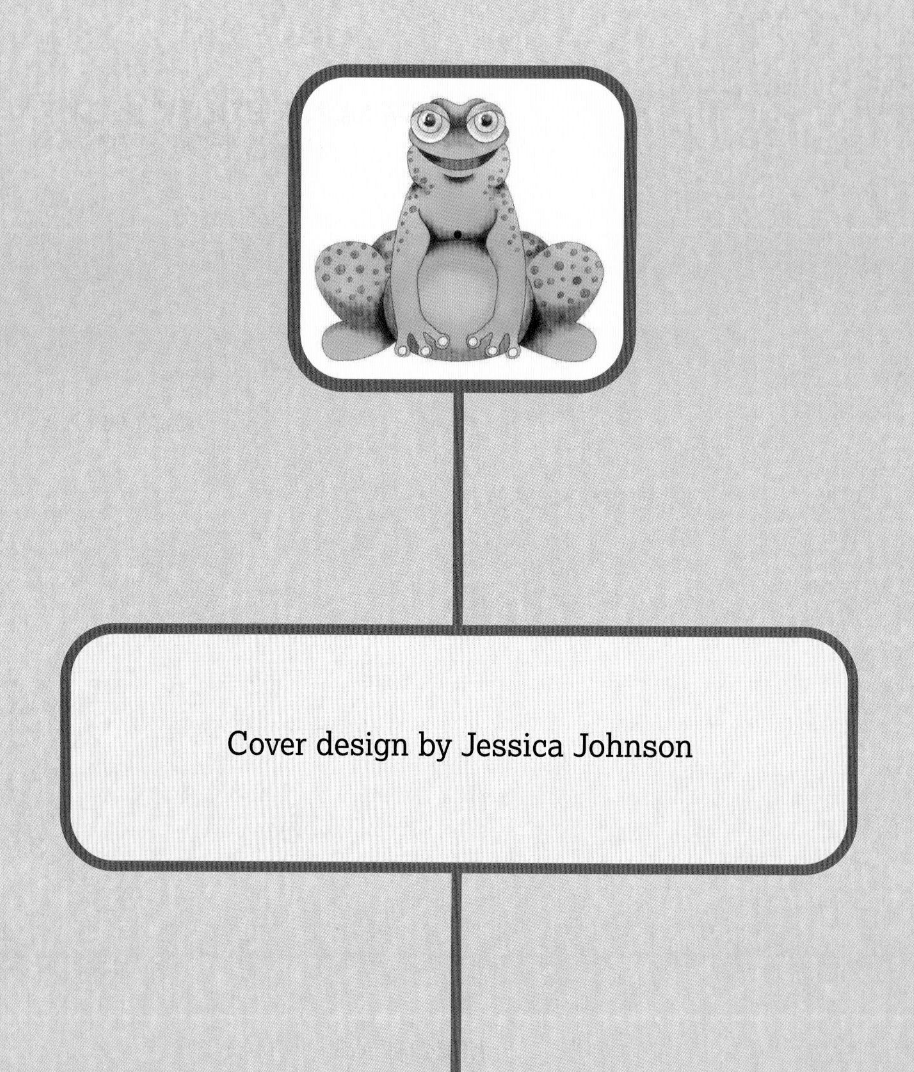

Cover design by Jessica Johnson

This edition published in 2009 by Usborne Publishing Ltd., 83-85 Saffron Hill, London EC1N 8RT, England. www.usborne.com
Printed in Dubai.